The Open University

MST209 Math

C000225613

Block 3

Contents

The Open University, Walton Hall, Milton Keynes, MK7 6AA.

First published 2005. Second edition 2008.

Copyright © 2005, 2008 The Open University

Edited, designed and typeset by The Open University, using the Open University TeX System.

Printed and bound in the United Kingdom by Charlesworth Press, Wakefield.

ISBN 978 0 7492 5283 0

1.1

UNIT 9 Matrices and determinants

Study guide for Unit 9

This is the first of four units devoted to the study of mathematical methods involving matrices. Much of the material in this unit and the next will provide you with the necessary background for solving systems of linear differential equations in *Unit 11* and systems of non-linear differential equations in *Unit 13*.

You may have met matrices before; in this unit we review most of their basic properties and show you how they can be applied to solving systems of linear equations.

Sections 1 and 2 are independent and could be interchanged if you wish. You may find it helpful to read Section 2 before Section 1 if you have not met matrices before.

Section 5 is a computer session where you will use the computer algebra package for the course. This section contains computer activities that are associated with Sections 1, 2, 3 and 4.

Introduction

In this unit we shall examine some of the properties and applications of matrices, where an $m \times n$ *matrix* is a rectangular array of elements with m rows and n columns. For example, $\begin{bmatrix} 1 & 2 & 3 \\ 4 & 5 & 6 \end{bmatrix}$ is a 2×3 matrix.

In this course the elements of matrices are real numbers. Other words for *element* are *component* and *entry*.

Among their many applications, matrices are useful in describing electrical circuits, in the analysis of forces and in writing down the equations of motion for a system of particles; and they form an essential component of an engineer's or scientist's toolkit. Matrices have a role to play whenever we need to manipulate arrays of numbers; in applications, m and n may be very large, so do not be misled by the fact that the discussion concentrates on small matrices.

In applied mathematics, one common problem is to solve a system of equations involving unknown constants, i.e. to determine values of the constants that satisfy the equations. Matrices can be used to store details of such a problem. For example, a system of equations such as

$$\begin{cases} 2x + 3y = 8, \\ 4x - 5y = -6, \end{cases} \tag{0.1}$$

contains three relevant pieces of information:

The use of the curly bracket here emphasizes that we are dealing with a *system* of equations.

- the numbers on the left-hand sides of the equations, which can be stored in the 2×2 matrix

$$\begin{bmatrix} 2 & 3 \\ 4 & -5 \end{bmatrix};$$

- the constants to be determined, which can be stored in the 2×1 matrix

$$\begin{bmatrix} x \\ y \end{bmatrix};$$

A matrix with one column is often referred to as a *vector*, or sometimes as a *column vector*. You met vectors in *Unit 4*.

- the numbers on the right-hand sides of the equations, which can be stored in the 2×1 matrix

$$\begin{bmatrix} 8 \\ -6 \end{bmatrix}.$$

With this notation, the essential information in these equations can be written in the form

$$\begin{bmatrix} 2 & 3 \\ 4 & -5 \end{bmatrix} \begin{bmatrix} x \\ y \end{bmatrix} = \begin{bmatrix} 8 \\ -6 \end{bmatrix}. \tag{0.2}$$

If we put

$$\mathbf{A} = \begin{bmatrix} 2 & 3 \\ 4 & -5 \end{bmatrix}, \quad \mathbf{x} = \begin{bmatrix} x \\ y \end{bmatrix}, \quad \mathbf{b} = \begin{bmatrix} 8 \\ -6 \end{bmatrix},$$

then Equation (0.2) can be written as

$$\mathbf{A}\mathbf{x} = \mathbf{b}. \tag{0.3}$$

For the moment you may regard Equation (0.2) as merely a convenient shorthand for the original system of equations, but later we shall see that it is compatible with matrix multiplication. Generally the matrix $\mathbf{A}$ will be an $n \times n$ matrix, while $\mathbf{x}$ and $\mathbf{b}$ are vectors containing n elements, where n may be large. In this unit we shall be concerned with the solutions of such systems, which are known as systems of *linear* equations, and the problem of finding a solution can be expressed as one of finding the vector $\mathbf{x}$ that satisfies Equation (0.3).

The term *linear* comes from the fact that each of the equations can be represented graphically by a straight line.

There is a graphical interpretation of the system of equations (0.1). Each equation represents a straight line, as you can see by rearranging the equations as $y = -\frac{2}{3}x + \frac{8}{3}$ and $y = \frac{4}{5}x + \frac{6}{5}$. The solution of this system of equations thus lies at the point of intersection of the graphs of the straight lines, as illustrated in Figure 0.1. For this pair of equations, there is just one solution, i.e. $x = 1$, $y = 2$.

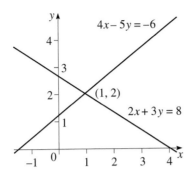

Figure 0.1

For two equations in two unknowns it is easy to draw graphs or to manipulate the equations to determine the solution. It would be much more difficult if we were faced with a problem involving 100 equations in 100 unknowns. Then we would need a systematic method of working with matrices to obtain the solution, because this would enable us to program a computer to solve systems of linear equations.

You may already have met a matrix method of solving a system of two linear equations in two unknowns using the inverse of a matrix. Although this method works well for 2×2 matrices, it is not very efficient for large systems of equations compared with other methods.

Matrices and matrix operations are revised in Section 2.

In Section 1 you will be introduced to a matrix method of solving large systems of linear equations, called the Gaussian elimination method, and you will see the conditions required for the method to work. In Section 2 we review some of the properties of matrices that make them so useful, and introduce the determinant of a matrix (a concept that is important for the discussion of eigenvalues in the next unit). In Section 3 we introduce two applications. In the first we investigate the problem of determining a polynomial of degree n that passes through $n + 1$ data points. The second application is the least squares method, which allows us to find the 'best' polynomial of degree n when there are more than $n + 1$ data points. Section 4 shows that in certain situations numerical errors can accumulate and render a solution unreliable. Section 5 is a computer session where you can explore the ideas and methods of Sections 1, 2, 3 and 4.

What is meant by 'best' will be explained in Section 3.

1   Simultaneous linear equations

The purpose of this section is to outline an efficient systematic method of obtaining the solution of a system of linear equations, known as *Gaussian elimination*. In Subsection 1.1 we introduce the method by manipulating equations, then in Subsection 1.2 we do the same calculations using matrices. To complete this section we look at the types of solution that can arise when solving such systems of linear equations. We illustrate the method by solving systems of three equations in three unknowns.

1.1 Manipulating equations

We begin with an example where the solution of a system of three equations in three unknowns can be found fairly easily.

For ease of reference, we label the equations E_1, E_2 and E_3. The unknowns in our equations will always be written in the order x_1, x_2, x_3.

Example 1.1

Find the solution of the system of equations

$$\begin{cases} x_1 - 4x_2 + 2x_3 = -9, & E_1 \\ \qquad 10x_2 - 3x_3 = 34, & E_2 \\ \qquad\qquad 2x_3 = 4. & E_3 \end{cases}$$

Solution

We can find the values of x_1, x_2 and x_3 from E_1, E_2 and E_3. Starting with E_3, we obtain $x_3 = 2$. Substituting this value into E_2, we obtain $10x_2 - (3 \times 2) = 34$, so $x_2 = 4$. Substituting the values for x_2 and x_3 into E_1, we obtain $x_1 - (4 \times 4) + (2 \times 2) = -9$, so $x_1 = 3$. Hence the solution is $x_1 = 3$, $x_2 = 4$, $x_3 = 2$. ∎

The system of equations in the above example is easy to solve because the equations are in **upper triangular form**, i.e. the first non-zero coefficient in E_i is the coefficient of x_i. For a system of equations of the form

$$\begin{cases} x_1 - 4x_2 + 2x_3 = -9, & E_1 \\ 3x_1 - 2x_2 + 3x_3 = 7, & E_2 \\ 8x_1 - 2x_2 + 9x_3 = 34, & E_3 \end{cases}$$

the objective of the first stage of the Gaussian elimination process is to manipulate the equations so that they are in upper triangular form. The second stage of the process is to solve the system of equations in upper triangular form using **back substitution**, where, starting with the last equation, we work *back* to the first equation, *substituting* the known values, in order to determine the next value, as demonstrated in Example 1.1.

Stage 1: elimination

Stage 2: back substitution

The key property of the equations that we shall use is that we may add and subtract multiples of them without affecting the desired solution. For example, $x_1 = 3$, $x_2 = 4$, $x_3 = 2$ satisfies both of the equations

$$x_1 - 4x_2 + 2x_3 = -9, \qquad\qquad E_1$$
$$3x_1 - 2x_2 + 3x_3 = 7. \qquad\qquad E_2$$

Suppose that we form E_{2a} by subtracting 3 times E_1 from E_2, so that $E_{2a} = E_2 - 3E_1$, i.e.

$$3x_1 - 2x_2 + 3x_3 - 3(x_1 - 4x_2 + 2x_3) = 7 - 3(-9),$$

giving

$$10x_2 - 3x_3 = 34. \qquad\qquad E_{2a}$$

Then $x_1 = 3$, $x_2 = 4$, $x_3 = 2$ also satisfies E_{2a}.

More generally, we could form an equation E_{2a} by writing $E_{2a} = pE_1 + qE_2$, for any numbers p and q. Then E_{2a} is said to be a *linear combination* of E_1 and E_2, and again $x_1 = 3$, $x_2 = 4$, $x_3 = 2$ satisfies E_{2a}. Our strategy in the elimination stage is to form linear combinations of equations to reduce the system to upper triangular form. The Gaussian elimination method uses a particular algorithm in which linear combinations of the form $E_{2a} = E_2 - mE_1$ are used, as we shall see in the following discussion and examples.

*An *algorithm* is a procedure or set of rules to be used in a calculation.*

Example 1.2

Use the Gaussian elimination method to reduce the following simultaneous equations (see above) to upper triangular form. Hence deduce the solution.

$$\begin{cases} x_1 - 4x_2 + 2x_3 = -9 & E_1 \\ 3x_1 - 2x_2 + 3x_3 = 7 & E_2 \\ 8x_1 - 2x_2 + 9x_3 = 34 & E_3 \end{cases}$$

Solution

Stage 1: elimination

We begin with the elimination stage, where we eliminate x_1 (in Stage 1(a)) and then x_2 (in Stage 1(b)).

Stage 1(a)   To eliminate x_1, first we subtract a multiple of E_1 from E_2 to obtain a new equation with no term in x_1. Subtracting 3 times E_1 from E_2 gives

$$10x_2 - 3x_3 = 34. \qquad\qquad E_{2a}$$

Each step of the Gaussian elimination algorithm is indicated in the margin below.

$E_{2a} = E_2 - 3E_1$

Now we subtract a multiple of E_1 from E_3 to obtain a new equation with no term in x_1. Subtracting 8 times E_1 from E_3 gives

$$30x_2 - 7x_3 = 106. \qquad\qquad E_{3a}$$

$E_{3a} = E_3 - 8E_1$

So, on completion of Stage 1(a), the equations have been reduced to

$$\begin{cases} x_1 - 4x_2 + 2x_3 = -9, & E_1 \\ 10x_2 - 3x_3 = 34, & E_{2a} \\ 30x_2 - 7x_3 = 106. & E_{3a} \end{cases}$$

Stage 1(b)   Next we eliminate x_2. We see that E_{2a} and E_{3a} are two equations in two unknowns. So we subtract a multiple of E_{2a} from E_{3a} to obtain an equation E_{3b} with no term in x_2. Subtracting 3 times E_{2a} from E_{3a} gives

$$2x_3 = 4. \qquad\qquad E_{3b}$$

$E_{3b} = E_{3a} - 3E_{2a}$

At this point, the elimination process is finished. We have brought our equations into upper triangular form as

$$\begin{cases} x_1 - 4x_2 + 2x_3 = -9, & E_1 \\ 10x_2 - 3x_3 = 34, & E_{2a} \\ 2x_3 = 4. & E_{3b} \end{cases}$$

Stage 2: back substitution

We now solve this system of equations in the back substitution stage.

This system was solved in Example 1.1, using back substitution, to give the solution $x_1 = 3$, $x_2 = 4$, $x_3 = 2$. Checking that the solution satisfies the original system of equations, we have

LHS of $E_1 = x_1 - 4x_2 + 2x_3 = (1 \times 3) - (4 \times 4) + (2 \times 2) = -9 = \text{RHS}$,
LHS of $E_2 = 3x_1 - 2x_2 + 3x_3 = (3 \times 3) - (2 \times 4) + (3 \times 2) = 7 = \text{RHS}$,
LHS of $E_3 = 8x_1 - 2x_2 + 9x_3 = (8 \times 3) - (2 \times 4) + (9 \times 2) = 34 = \text{RHS}$.   ∎

The process of solving simultaneous equations described in Examples 1.1 and 1.2 is called the **Gaussian elimination method**. The method provides a systematic approach to the problem of solving simultaneous equations that should cope with the rather larger sets of equations that can occur in real-life applications. In practice, hand calculation will almost certainly involve fractions, and computer calculations will involve numeric approximations to these fractions and so will introduce rounding errors. We have avoided such problems in Example 1.2 and in the next exercise.

We do not give a formal procedure for the Gaussian elimination method at this point, since we give a matrix formulation shortly.

*Exercise 1.1 ────────────────────────────

Solve the following simultaneous equations using the Gaussian elimination method.

$$\begin{cases} x_1 + x_2 - x_3 = 2 & E_1 \\ 5x_1 + 2x_2 + 2x_3 = 20 & E_2 \\ 4x_1 - 2x_2 - 3x_3 = 15 & E_3 \end{cases}$$

1.2 Manipulating matrices

The Gaussian elimination method relies on manipulating equations. In this subsection we shall see that it can be formulated efficiently in terms of matrices.

When we use the Gaussian elimination method to solve the equations in Example 1.2, the new equation E_{2a} is obtained by subtracting a multiple of E_1 from E_2. The actions are performed on the numbers multiplying x_1, x_2 and x_3 (the coefficients of x_1, x_2 and x_3). For instance, the operation on the coefficients of x_2 in the equation $E_{2a} = E_2 - 3E_1$, $-2x_2 - 3 \times (-4x_2) = 10x_2$, could be recorded as $-2 - 3 \times (-4) = 10$, provided that we remember that the operation is associated with x_2.

Thus, during the elimination stage, we need to record just the coefficients of x_1, x_2 and x_3, and the right-hand side of each equation, rather than the whole system of equations each time. We record the coefficients in E_1, E_2 and E_3 in a **coefficient matrix A**, the unknown constants in a vector **x**, and the right-hand sides in a **right-hand-side vector b** as

$$\mathbf{A} = \begin{bmatrix} 1 & -4 & 2 \\ 3 & -2 & 3 \\ 8 & -2 & 9 \end{bmatrix}, \quad \mathbf{x} = \begin{bmatrix} x_1 \\ x_2 \\ x_3 \end{bmatrix}, \quad \mathbf{b} = \begin{bmatrix} -9 \\ 7 \\ 34 \end{bmatrix}.$$

The problem, in terms of matrices, is to determine the vector **x** that satisfies the equation $\mathbf{Ax} = \mathbf{b}$, which can be written as

$$\underbrace{\begin{bmatrix} 1 & -4 & 2 \\ 3 & -2 & 3 \\ 8 & -2 & 9 \end{bmatrix}}_{\mathbf{A}} \underbrace{\begin{bmatrix} x_1 \\ x_2 \\ x_3 \end{bmatrix}}_{\mathbf{x}} = \underbrace{\begin{bmatrix} -9 \\ 7 \\ 34 \end{bmatrix}}_{\mathbf{b}}.$$

For computing purposes it is sufficient just to record the information in the **augmented matrix**

$$\mathbf{A}|\mathbf{b} = \begin{bmatrix} 1 & -4 & 2 & | & -9 \\ 3 & -2 & 3 & | & 7 \\ 8 & -2 & 9 & | & 34 \end{bmatrix}.$$

The first row of $\mathbf{A}|\mathbf{b}$ contains the coefficients of x_1, x_2 and x_3 and the right-hand side of E_1, the second row contains similar information about E_2, and the third row contains similar information about E_3.

An alternative description of $\mathbf{A}|\mathbf{b}$ is to say that the first three columns of $\mathbf{A}|\mathbf{b}$ represent, respectively, the coefficients of x_1, x_2 and x_3, and the column after the bar represents the right-hand sides of the equations.

*Exercise 1.2 ────────────────────────────

Write the following systems of equations in augmented matrix form.

(a) $\begin{cases} 3x_1 - 5x_2 = 8 \\ 4x_1 + 7x_2 = 11 \end{cases}$ (b) $\begin{cases} x_1 + 2x_2 \quad\quad = 3 \\ 2x_1 - x_2 + x_3 = 1 \\ \quad\quad x_2 - x_3 = -1 \end{cases}$

Once the information has been written in augmented matrix form, the stages in the Gaussian elimination process are equivalent to manipulating the rows of the matrix, as we demonstrate in the next example.

Example 1.3

Solve the simultaneous equations of Example 1.2 using the matrix form of the Gaussian elimination method, where

$$\mathbf{A}|\mathbf{b} = \begin{bmatrix} 1 & -4 & 2 & -9 \\ 3 & -2 & 3 & 7 \\ 8 & -2 & 9 & 34 \end{bmatrix}.$$

Solution

We use the matrix representing these equations throughout the elimination procedure. For brevity, we denote the first row of the matrix, namely $\begin{bmatrix} 1 & -4 & 2 & | & -9 \end{bmatrix}$, by $\mathbf{R}_1$, and so on.

$$\begin{bmatrix} 1 & -4 & 2 & -9 \\ 3 & -2 & 3 & 7 \\ 8 & -2 & 9 & 34 \end{bmatrix} \begin{matrix} \mathbf{R}_1 \\ \mathbf{R}_2 \\ \mathbf{R}_3 \end{matrix}$$

Notice that $\mathbf{R}_i$ encapsulates all the information about the equation E_i.

Stage 1: elimination

Each part of the elimination stage in Example 1.2 has an equivalent part in matrix form.

Stage 1(a)   First we eliminate x_1 as before. Equation E_{2a} in Example 1.2 was found by subtracting $3E_1$ from E_2. Arithmetically, this is the same operation as subtracting $3\mathbf{R}_1$ from $\mathbf{R}_2$, and it is useful to record this operation. The way in which the new rows are formed is recorded on the left of the matrix.

Adding or subtracting a multiple of one row to/from another is called a **row operation**.

$$\begin{matrix} \\ \mathbf{R}_2 - 3\mathbf{R}_1 \\ \mathbf{R}_3 - 8\mathbf{R}_1 \end{matrix} \begin{bmatrix} 1 & -4 & 2 & -9 \\ 0 & 10 & -3 & 34 \\ 0 & 30 & -7 & 106 \end{bmatrix} \begin{matrix} \mathbf{R}_1 \\ \mathbf{R}_{2a} \\ \mathbf{R}_{3a} \end{matrix}$$

It is essential to keep a record of the derivation of each row if you wish to check your working.

Stage 1(b)   Now we eliminate x_2, as before.

$$\begin{matrix} \\ \\ \mathbf{R}_{3a} - 3\mathbf{R}_{2a} \end{matrix} \begin{bmatrix} 1 & -4 & 2 & -9 \\ 0 & 10 & -3 & 34 \\ 0 & 0 & 2 & 4 \end{bmatrix} \begin{matrix} \mathbf{R}_1 \\ \mathbf{R}_{2a} \\ \mathbf{R}_{3b} \end{matrix}$$

A triangle of zeros appears in the matrix at the end of the elimination stage. This shows us that each equation has one fewer unknown than the previous one, which is what we need in order to do the back substitution.

The final coefficient matrix is known as an **upper triangular matrix**, since the only non-zero elements it contains are on or above the **leading diagonal**, i.e. the diagonal from top-left to bottom-right, here containing the numbers 1, 10 and 2.

The leading diagonal is sometimes called the *main diagonal*.

Stage 2: back substitution

Before carrying out the back substitution stage, we write the final matrix as a system of equations:

$$\begin{cases} x_1 - 4x_2 + 2x_3 = -9, & E_1 \\ \quad\quad 10x_2 - 3x_3 = 34, & E_2 \\ \quad\quad\quad\quad 2x_3 = 4. & E_3 \end{cases}$$

This is exactly the same as in Example 1.1. The solution $x_1 = 3$, $x_2 = 4$, $x_3 = 2$ is then found using back substitution as before. ∎

The objective of Stage 1 of the Gaussian elimination method is to reduce the matrix $\mathbf{A}$ to an upper triangular matrix, $\mathbf{U}$ say. At the same time, the right-hand-side vector $\mathbf{b}$ is transformed into a new right-hand-side vector, $\mathbf{c}$ say, where, in this example,

$$\mathbf{U} = \begin{bmatrix} 1 & -4 & 2 \\ 0 & 10 & -3 \\ 0 & 0 & 2 \end{bmatrix}, \quad \mathbf{c} = \begin{bmatrix} -9 \\ 34 \\ 4 \end{bmatrix}.$$

The Gaussian elimination method in Procedure 1.1 underpins the algorithm used by the computer algebra package for the course.

Procedure 1.1   Gaussian elimination method

To solve a system of n linear equations in n unknowns, with coefficient matrix $\mathbf{A}$ and right-hand-side vector $\mathbf{b}$, carry out the following steps.

(a) Write down the augmented matrix $\mathbf{A}|\mathbf{b}$ with rows $\mathbf{R}_1, \ldots, \mathbf{R}_n$.

(b) Subtract multiples of $\mathbf{R}_1$ from $\mathbf{R}_2, \mathbf{R}_3, \ldots, \mathbf{R}_n$ to reduce the elements below the leading diagonal in the first column to zero.

   In the new matrix obtained, subtract multiples of $\mathbf{R}_2$ from $\mathbf{R}_3, \mathbf{R}_4, \ldots, \mathbf{R}_n$ to reduce the elements below the leading diagonal in the second column to zero.

   Continue this process until $\mathbf{A}|\mathbf{b}$ is reduced to $\mathbf{U}|\mathbf{c}$, where $\mathbf{U}$ is an upper triangular matrix.

(c) Solve the system of equations with coefficient matrix $\mathbf{U}$ and right-hand-side vector $\mathbf{c}$ by back substitution.

This procedure does not always work. We examine cases where it breaks down in the next subsection.

Stage 1: elimination

Stage 1(a)

Stage 1(b)

Stage 1(c), ...

Stage 2: back substitution

The steps of the elimination stage of Example 1.3 are

$$\mathbf{R}_{2\mathrm{a}} = \mathbf{R}_2 - 3\mathbf{R}_1,$$
$$\mathbf{R}_{3\mathrm{a}} = \mathbf{R}_3 - 8\mathbf{R}_1,$$
$$\mathbf{R}_{3\mathrm{b}} = \mathbf{R}_{3\mathrm{a}} - 3\mathbf{R}_{2\mathrm{a}}.$$

The numbers 3, 8 and 3 are called *multipliers*. In general, to obtain, for example, an equation $E_{2\mathrm{a}}$ without a term in x_1 from

$$a_{11}x_1 + a_{12}x_2 + \cdots = d_1, \qquad\qquad E_1$$
$$a_{21}x_1 + a_{22}x_2 + \cdots = d_2, \qquad\qquad E_2$$
$$a_{31}x_1 + a_{32}x_2 + \cdots = d_3, \qquad\qquad E_3$$

where $a_{11} \neq 0$, we subtract $(a_{21}/a_{11})E_1$ from E_2. The number a_{21}/a_{11} is the **multiplier**.

In forming a multiplier, we divide by a number, a_{11} in the above generalization. The number by which we divide is referred to as a **pivot** or **pivot element**, and the row in which it lies is the **pivot row**. Looking again at Example 1.3: in Stage 1(a) the multipliers are $3 = 3/1 = a_{21}/a_{11}$ and $8 = 8/1 = a_{31}/a_{11}$, and the pivot is $a_{11} = 1$; in Stage 1(b) the multiplier is $3 = 30/10 = a_{32}/a_{22}$ and the pivot is $a_{22} = 10$. In general, the kth pivot is the number in the denominator of the multipliers in Stage 1(k) of the elimination stage. At the end of the elimination stage, the pivots comprise the elements of the leading diagonal of $\mathbf{U}$.

Example 1.4

Use the matrix form of the Gaussian elimination method to solve the following simultaneous equations.

$$\begin{cases} 3x_1 + x_2 - x_3 = 1 & \qquad E_1 \\ 5x_1 + x_2 + 2x_3 = 6 & \qquad E_2 \\ 4x_1 - 2x_2 - 3x_3 = 3 & \qquad E_3 \end{cases}$$

Solution

The augmented matrix representing these equations is as follows.

$$\begin{bmatrix} 3 & 1 & -1 & | & 1 \\ 5 & 1 & 2 & | & 6 \\ 4 & -2 & -3 & | & 3 \end{bmatrix} \begin{matrix} \mathbf{R}_1 \\ \mathbf{R}_2 \\ \mathbf{R}_3 \end{matrix}$$

The row operations used to solve this example are highlighted in the margin below.

Stage 1(a)   We reduce the elements below the leading diagonal in column 1 to zero.

The pivot is a_{11}.

$$\begin{matrix} \\ \mathbf{R}_2 - \frac{5}{3}\mathbf{R}_1 \\ \mathbf{R}_3 - \frac{4}{3}\mathbf{R}_1 \end{matrix} \begin{bmatrix} 3 & 1 & -1 & | & 1 \\ 0 & -\frac{2}{3} & \frac{11}{3} & | & \frac{13}{3} \\ 0 & -\frac{10}{3} & -\frac{5}{3} & | & \frac{5}{3} \end{bmatrix} \begin{matrix} \mathbf{R}_1 \\ \mathbf{R}_{2a} \\ \mathbf{R}_{3a} \end{matrix}$$

$$\mathbf{R}_{2a} = \mathbf{R}_2 - \frac{a_{21}}{a_{11}}\mathbf{R}_1$$
$$\mathbf{R}_{3a} = \mathbf{R}_3 - \frac{a_{31}}{a_{11}}\mathbf{R}_1$$

Stage 1(b)   We reduce the element below the leading diagonal in column 2 to zero.

The pivot is a_{22}.

$$\begin{matrix} \\ \\ \mathbf{R}_{3a} - \frac{(-10/3)}{(-2/3)}\mathbf{R}_{2a} \end{matrix} \begin{bmatrix} 3 & 1 & -1 & | & 1 \\ 0 & -\frac{2}{3} & \frac{11}{3} & | & \frac{13}{3} \\ 0 & 0 & -20 & | & -20 \end{bmatrix} \begin{matrix} \mathbf{R}_1 \\ \mathbf{R}_{2a} \\ \mathbf{R}_{3b} \end{matrix}$$

$$\mathbf{R}_{3b} = \mathbf{R}_{3a} - \frac{a_{32}}{a_{22}}\mathbf{R}_{2a}$$

Stage 2   The equations represented by the new matrix are

$$\begin{cases} 3x_1 + x_2 - x_3 = 1, & E_1 \\ -\frac{2}{3}x_2 + \frac{11}{3}x_3 = \frac{13}{3}, & E_{2a} \\ -20x_3 = -20. & E_{3b} \end{cases}$$

From E_{3b}, we have $x_3 = 1$. From E_{2a}, we have $-\frac{2}{3}x_2 + \frac{11}{3} = \frac{13}{3}$, so $x_2 = -1$. From E_1, we have $3x_1 - 1 - 1 = 1$, so $x_1 = 1$. Hence the solution is

$$x_1 = 1, \quad x_2 = -1, \quad x_3 = 1. \quad \blacksquare$$

Exercise 1.3

Use the matrix form of the Gaussian elimination method to solve the following simultaneous equations.

$$\begin{cases} x_1 + 2x_2 = 4 & E_1 \\ 3x_1 - x_2 = 5 & E_2 \end{cases}$$

*Exercise 1.4

Use the matrix form of the Gaussian elimination method to solve the following simultaneous equations.

$$\begin{cases} x_1 + x_2 - x_3 = 2 & E_1 \\ 5x_1 + 2x_2 + 2x_3 = 20 & E_2 \\ 4x_1 - 2x_2 - 3x_3 = 15 & E_3 \end{cases}$$

1.3 Special cases

The previous examples and exercises may have led you to believe that Procedure 1.1 will always be successful, but this is not the case. The procedure will fail if at any stage of the calculation a pivot is zero. We shall see that sometimes it is possible to overcome this difficulty, but this is not so in every case. In the following example we point out some difficulties, and indicate whether they can be overcome.

Example 1.5

Consider the following four systems of linear equations. Try to solve them using the matrix form of the Gaussian elimination method as given in Procedure 1.1. In each case the method breaks down. Suggest, if possible, a method of overcoming the difficulty, and hence determine the solution if one exists.

(a) $\begin{cases} 10x_2 - 3x_3 = 34 \\ x_1 - 4x_2 + 2x_3 = -9 \\ 2x_3 = 4 \end{cases}$

(b) $\begin{cases} x_1 + 10x_2 - 3x_3 = 8 \\ x_1 + 10x_2 + 2x_3 = 13 \\ x_1 + 4x_2 + 2x_3 = 7 \end{cases}$

(c) $\begin{cases} x_1 + 4x_2 - 3x_3 = 2 \\ x_1 + 2x_2 + 2x_3 = 5 \\ 2x_1 + 2x_2 + 9x_3 = 7 \end{cases}$

(d) $\begin{cases} x_1 + 4x_2 - 3x_3 = 2 \\ x_1 + 2x_2 + 2x_3 = 5 \\ 2x_1 + 2x_2 + 9x_3 = 13 \end{cases}$

Solution

(a) Since the first pivot a_{11} is zero, there is no multiple of the first row that we can subtract from the second row to eliminate the term in x_1. However, interchanging two equations does not change the solution of a system of equations. Hence, interchanging the first two equations gives a system of equations in upper triangular form, from which we can determine the solution $x_1 = 3$, $x_2 = 4$, $x_3 = 2$.

> This may appear to be a trivial difficulty, but if we hope to devise a procedure that could be implemented on a computer, the process must allow for every contingency.

(b) We begin by writing down the augmented matrix.

$$\mathbf{A}|\mathbf{b} = \begin{bmatrix} 1 & 10 & -3 & | & 8 \\ 1 & 10 & 2 & | & 13 \\ 1 & 4 & 2 & | & 7 \end{bmatrix} \begin{matrix} \mathbf{R}_1 \\ \mathbf{R}_2 \\ \mathbf{R}_3 \end{matrix}$$

Stage 1(a)   We reduce the elements below the leading diagonal to zero, starting with column 1.

$$\begin{matrix} \\ \mathbf{R}_2 - \mathbf{R}_1 \\ \mathbf{R}_3 - \mathbf{R}_1 \end{matrix} \begin{bmatrix} 1 & 10 & -3 & | & 8 \\ 0 & 0 & 5 & | & 5 \\ 0 & -6 & 5 & | & -1 \end{bmatrix} \begin{matrix} \mathbf{R}_1 \\ \mathbf{R}_{2a} \\ \mathbf{R}_{3a} \end{matrix}$$

Stage 1(b)   We now want to reduce the element in column 2 that is below the leading diagonal to zero. The difficulty here is that we cannot subtract a multiple of $\mathbf{R}_{2a}$ from $\mathbf{R}_{3a}$ to eliminate the coefficient of x_2, since the pivot a_{22} is zero. We can overcome this difficulty by interchanging $\mathbf{R}_{2a}$ and $\mathbf{R}_{3a}$.

$$\begin{matrix} \\ \\ \mathbf{R}_{2a} \leftrightarrow \mathbf{R}_{3a} \end{matrix} \begin{bmatrix} 1 & 10 & -3 & | & 8 \\ 0 & -6 & 5 & | & -1 \\ 0 & 0 & 5 & | & 5 \end{bmatrix} \begin{matrix} \mathbf{R}_1 \\ \mathbf{R}_{2b} \\ \mathbf{R}_{3b} \end{matrix}$$

This is now in upper triangular form, and we can proceed to Stage 2 to determine the solution using back substitution. We find that the solution is $x_1 = x_2 = x_3 = 1$.

> The notation $\mathbf{R}_{2a} \leftrightarrow \mathbf{R}_{3a}$ indicates that we have interchanged $\mathbf{R}_{2a}$ with $\mathbf{R}_{3a}$. Such interchanges are also called row operations.

(c) We begin by writing down the augmented matrix.

$$\mathbf{A}|\mathbf{b} = \begin{bmatrix} 1 & 4 & -3 & | & 2 \\ 1 & 2 & 2 & | & 5 \\ 2 & 2 & 9 & | & 7 \end{bmatrix} \begin{matrix} \mathbf{R}_1 \\ \mathbf{R}_2 \\ \mathbf{R}_3 \end{matrix}$$

Stage 1(a)   We reduce the elements below the leading diagonal to zero, starting with column 1.

$$\begin{matrix} \\ \mathbf{R}_2 - \mathbf{R}_1 \\ \mathbf{R}_3 - 2\mathbf{R}_1 \end{matrix} \begin{bmatrix} 1 & 4 & -3 & | & 2 \\ 0 & -2 & 5 & | & 3 \\ 0 & -6 & 15 & | & 3 \end{bmatrix} \begin{matrix} \mathbf{R}_1 \\ \mathbf{R}_{2a} \\ \mathbf{R}_{3a} \end{matrix}$$

Stage 1(b)   We reduce the element below the leading diagonal in column 2 to zero.

$$\mathbf{R}_{3a} - 3\mathbf{R}_{2a} \quad \begin{bmatrix} 1 & 4 & -3 & 2 \\ 0 & -2 & 5 & 3 \\ 0 & 0 & 0 & -6 \end{bmatrix} \begin{matrix} \mathbf{R}_1 \\ \mathbf{R}_{2a} \\ \mathbf{R}_{3b} \end{matrix}$$

Stage 2   We now try to solve the system of equations represented by the above matrix by back substitution. The coefficient matrix is in upper triangular form, but if we write out the system of equations as

$$\begin{cases} x_1 + 4x_2 - 3x_3 = 2, \\ \quad -2x_2 + 5x_3 = 3, \\ \quad\quad\quad\quad 0x_3 = -6, \end{cases}$$

we see that the last equation has no solution since no value of x_3 can give $0x_3 = -6$. Hence the system of equations has no solution.

(d) We begin by writing down the augmented matrix.

$$\mathbf{A}|\mathbf{b} = \begin{bmatrix} 1 & 4 & -3 & 2 \\ 1 & 2 & 2 & 5 \\ 2 & 2 & 9 & 13 \end{bmatrix} \begin{matrix} \mathbf{R}_1 \\ \mathbf{R}_2 \\ \mathbf{R}_3 \end{matrix}$$

Stage 1(a)   We reduce the elements below the leading diagonal to zero, starting with column 1.

$$\begin{matrix} \\ \mathbf{R}_2 - \mathbf{R}_1 \\ \mathbf{R}_3 - 2\mathbf{R}_1 \end{matrix} \begin{bmatrix} 1 & 4 & -3 & 2 \\ 0 & -2 & 5 & 3 \\ 0 & -6 & 15 & 9 \end{bmatrix} \begin{matrix} \mathbf{R}_1 \\ \mathbf{R}_{2a} \\ \mathbf{R}_{3a} \end{matrix}$$

We shall refer back to these steps in *Example 1.6.*

Stage 1(b)   We reduce the element below the leading diagonal in column 2 to zero.

$$\mathbf{R}_{3a} - 3\mathbf{R}_{2a} \quad \begin{bmatrix} 1 & 4 & -3 & 2 \\ 0 & -2 & 5 & 3 \\ 0 & 0 & 0 & 0 \end{bmatrix} \begin{matrix} \mathbf{R}_1 \\ \mathbf{R}_{2a} \\ \mathbf{R}_{3b} \end{matrix}$$

Stage 2   We now try to solve the system of equations represented by the above matrix by back substitution. The coefficient matrix is in upper triangular form, but if we write out the system of equations as

$$\begin{cases} x_1 + 4x_2 - 3x_3 = 2, \\ \quad -2x_2 + 5x_3 = 3, \\ \quad\quad\quad\quad 0x_3 = 0, \end{cases}$$

Systems of equations of this kind occur in *Unit 10*, and you should take careful note of the method of solution used in this example.

we see that *any* value of x_3 gives $0x_3 = 0$. If we let $x_3 = k$, where k is an arbitrary number, then, proceeding with the back substitution, we have $-2x_2 + 5k = 3$, giving $x_2 = -\frac{3}{2} + \frac{5}{2}k$. The first equation gives $x_1 + (-6 + 10k) - 3k = 2$, so $x_1 = 8 - 7k$. So there is an infinite number of solutions of the form $x_1 = 8 - 7k$, $x_2 = \frac{5}{2}k - \frac{3}{2}$, $x_3 = k$. The *general solution* can be written as $[8 - 7k \quad \frac{5}{2}k - \frac{3}{2} \quad k]^T$ where k is an arbitrary number. ∎

In Example 1.5 parts (a) and (b), we were able to overcome the difficulty of a zero pivot by making an **essential row interchange**. In general, whenever one of the pivots is zero, we interchange that row of the augmented matrix with the first available row below it that would lead to a non-zero pivot, effectively reordering the original system of equations. The difficulties in (a) and (b) are thus easily overcome, but those occurring in (c) and (d) are more fundamental. In (c) there was a zero pivot that could not be avoided by interchanging rows, and we were left with an **inconsistent system of equations** for which there is no solution. The final example (d) illustrates the case where a pivot is zero and the system of equations has an **infinite number of solutions**. It is these last two cases in particular that we explore in the next subsection.

1.4   No solutions and an infinite number of solutions

We begin by looking at the general system of two linear equations in two unknowns, given by

$$\begin{cases} ax + by = e, & E_1 \\ cx + dy = f. & E_2 \end{cases}$$

All the points satisfying E_1 lie on one straight line, while all the points satisfying E_2 lie on another. The solution of the system of linear equations can be described graphically as the coordinates of the point of intersection of these two lines. However, if we draw two lines at random in a plane, there are three situations that can arise, as illustrated in Figure 1.1.

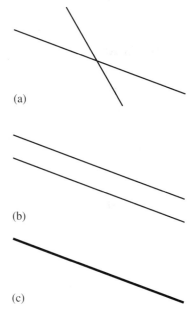

(a)

(b)

(c)

Figure 1.1

(a) This is the typical case, where the two lines are not parallel and there is a *unique solution* to the system of linear equations, corresponding to the point of intersection of the two lines (see Figure 1.1(a)).

(b) This is the special case where the two lines are parallel (and so do not intersect) and the corresponding system of linear equations has *no solution* (see Figure 1.1(b)).

(c) This is the very special case where the two lines coincide, so any point on the line satisfies both equations and we have an *infinite number of solutions* (see Figure 1.1(c)).

Exercise 1.5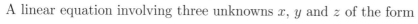

For each of the following pairs of linear equations, sketch their graphs and hence determine the number of solutions.

(a) $\begin{cases} x + y = 4 \\ 2x + 2y = 5 \end{cases}$ (b) $\begin{cases} x + y = 4 \\ 2x - 3y = 8 \end{cases}$

(c) $\begin{cases} x + y = 4 \\ 2x + 2y = 8 \end{cases}$ (d) $\begin{cases} y = 4 \\ 2x + 2y = 5 \end{cases}$

Exercise 1.6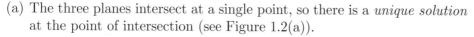

For the system of equations

$$\begin{cases} ax + by = e, \\ cx + dy = f, \end{cases}$$

what is the condition for the two lines to be parallel?

A linear equation involving three unknowns x, y and z of the form

$$ax + by + cz = d,$$

where a, b, c and d are constants, can be represented graphically as a plane in three-dimensional space. For a system of three equations in three unknowns, a graphical interpretation gives rise to three types of solution, as illustrated in Figure 1.2.

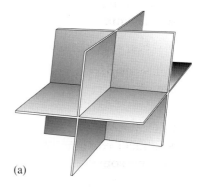

(a)

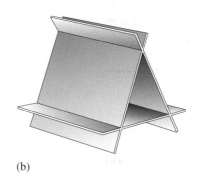

(b)

(a) The three planes intersect at a single point, so there is a *unique solution* at the point of intersection (see Figure 1.2(a)).

(b) The three planes form a tent shape, having no point of intersection and hence *no solution* (see Figure 1.2(b): the three lines where a pair of planes meet are parallel). A variant of this case occurs when two (or even all three) of the planes are parallel, and so cannot meet at all.

(c) The three planes have (at least) a common line of intersection and hence an *infinite number of solutions* (see Figure 1.2(c)).

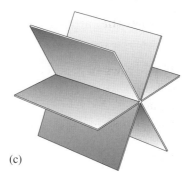

(c)

Figure 1.2

The next example gives an algebraic interpretation of one of these three types of solution. For this example, the following definition is required.

Definition

A **linear combination** of rows $\mathbf{R}_1, \mathbf{R}_2, \ldots, \mathbf{R}_n$ is a row $\mathbf{R}$ such that $\mathbf{R} = q_1\mathbf{R}_1 + q_2\mathbf{R}_2 + \cdots + q_n\mathbf{R}_n$, where the q_i ($i = 1, 2, \ldots, n$) are numbers. A **non-trivial linear combination** is one where at least one q_i is non-zero.

Example 1.6

Consider the system of linear equations in Example 1.5(d), where the corresponding augmented matrix is as follows.

$$\mathbf{A}|\mathbf{b} = \begin{bmatrix} 1 & 4 & -3 & 2 \\ 1 & 2 & 2 & 5 \\ 2 & 2 & 9 & 13 \end{bmatrix} \begin{matrix} \mathbf{R}_1 \\ \mathbf{R}_2 \\ \mathbf{R}_3 \end{matrix}$$

Show that there is a non-trivial linear combination of the rows of this matrix that is equal to a row of zeros.

Solution

We use the results of the elimination process in Example 1.5(d), noting that $\mathbf{R}_{3b}$ is equal to a row of zeros. From this, we see that

$$\mathbf{R}_{3b} = \mathbf{R}_{3a} - 3\mathbf{R}_{2a} = (\mathbf{R}_3 - 2\mathbf{R}_1) - 3(\mathbf{R}_2 - \mathbf{R}_1) = \mathbf{R}_1 - 3\mathbf{R}_2 + \mathbf{R}_3 = \mathbf{0}.$$

Hence there is a non-trivial linear combination of the rows that is equal to the zero row. ∎

In Example 1.6 we saw that $\mathbf{R}_{3b} = \mathbf{R}_1 - 3\mathbf{R}_2 + \mathbf{R}_3$, which means that $\mathbf{R}_{3b}$ is a linear combination of the rows of $\mathbf{A}|\mathbf{b}$. However, in the above example, we have something more: such a linear combination produces a row of zeros (and the corresponding equations have an infinite number of solutions, as we found in Example 1.5(d)). When such a relationship exists between the rows of a matrix, we say that the rows are *linearly dependent*.

This is the case where the three planes, corresponding to the three equations, meet in a line (see Figure 1.2(c)).

Definition

The rows $\mathbf{R}_1, \mathbf{R}_2, \ldots, \mathbf{R}_n$ of a matrix are **linearly dependent** if a non-trivial linear combination of these rows is equal to the zero row, i.e.

$$q_1\mathbf{R}_1 + q_2\mathbf{R}_2 + \cdots + q_n\mathbf{R}_n = \mathbf{0},$$

where the numbers $q_1, q_2, \ldots, q_n$ are not all zero.

Rows that are not linearly dependent are **linearly independent**.

If the rows of the matrix $\mathbf{A}$ are linearly independent, then the Gaussian elimination method works and produces a unique solution to the system of equations $\mathbf{A}\mathbf{x} = \mathbf{b}$. However, if the rows of $\mathbf{A}$ are linearly dependent, then the corresponding system of linear equations may have an infinite number of solutions, or no solution. The elimination process will reveal which is the case.

End-of-section Exercise

Exercise 1.7 _____

In the following systems of linear equations, determine which has a single solution, which has an infinite number of solutions, and which has no solution. Where the equations have a unique solution, find it. Where the equations have an infinite number of solutions, find the general solution and a non-trivial linear combination of the rows of $\mathbf{A}|\mathbf{b}$ that gives a row of zeros.

(a)
$$\begin{cases} x_1 - 2x_2 + 5x_3 = 7 \\ x_1 + 3x_2 - 4x_3 = 20 \\ x_1 + 18x_2 - 31x_3 = 40 \end{cases}$$

(b)
$$\begin{cases} x_1 - 2x_2 + 5x_3 = 6 \\ x_1 + 3x_2 - 4x_3 = 7 \\ 2x_1 + 6x_2 - 12x_3 = 12 \end{cases}$$

(c)
$$\begin{cases} x_1 - 4x_2 + x_3 = 14 \\ 5x_1 - x_2 - x_3 = 2 \\ 6x_1 + 14x_2 - 6x_3 = -52 \end{cases}$$

2 Properties of matrices

In this section we review the algebraic properties of matrices, and show how solving the matrix equation $\mathbf{Ax} = \mathbf{b}$ can be interpreted as finding the vector $\mathbf{x}$ that is mapped to the vector $\mathbf{b}$ by the transformation defined by $\mathbf{A}$. Then we investigate a related number, called the *determinant* of the matrix, that can be used to decide whether a given system of linear equations has a unique solution. Finally, we look at some applications of determinants.

2.1 Algebra of matrices

A matrix of **order** or **size** $m \times n$ is a rectangular array of elements (usually real numbers) with m rows and n columns. If $m = n$, the matrix is a **square matrix**, an example of which is the 2×2 matrix $\begin{bmatrix} 1 & 1 \\ 1 & 2 \end{bmatrix}$. If $m = 1$, the matrix can be regarded as a **row vector**, an example of which is the 1×3 matrix $\begin{bmatrix} 2 & 3 & 4 \end{bmatrix}$. If $n = 1$, the matrix can be regarded as a **column vector**, an example of which is the 2×1 matrix $\begin{bmatrix} 5 \\ 7 \end{bmatrix}$, which we often write in text as $[5 \quad 7]^T$. The general $m \times n$ matrix $\mathbf{A}$ can be written as $[a_{ij}]$ to denote the matrix

$$\mathbf{A} = \begin{bmatrix} a_{11} & a_{12} & \cdots & a_{1n} \\ a_{21} & a_{22} & \cdots & a_{2n} \\ \vdots & \vdots & \vdots & \vdots \\ a_{m1} & a_{m2} & \cdots & a_{mn} \end{bmatrix}.$$

Matrices were first used in 1858 by the English mathematician Arthur Cayley.

You met these notations for column vectors in *Unit 4*.

The element a_{ij} is in the ith row and the jth column.

Two matrices $\mathbf{A} = [a_{ij}]$ and $\mathbf{B} = [b_{ij}]$ are **equal** if they have the same order and $a_{ij} = b_{ij}$ for all $i = 1, 2, \ldots, m$ and $j = 1, 2, \ldots, n$. If all the elements of a matrix are zero, the matrix is the **zero matrix**, denoted by $\mathbf{0}$.

Strictly speaking, we should write the $m \times n$ zero matrix as $\mathbf{0}_{mn}$, but the size of the zero matrix will always be clear from the context.

Addition and scalar multiplication of $m \times n$ matrices

If $\mathbf{A} = [a_{ij}]$ and $\mathbf{B} = [b_{ij}]$ are matrices of the same order, we can form the **sum**

$$\mathbf{A} + \mathbf{B} = [a_{ij} + b_{ij}] \quad \text{(component-wise addition)}.$$

For any matrix $\mathbf{A}$, and $\mathbf{0}$ of the same order,

$$\mathbf{A} + \mathbf{0} = \mathbf{A} \quad \text{(the components are unaltered)}.$$

The **scalar multiple** of a matrix $\mathbf{A} = [a_{ij}]$ by a number k is given by

$$k\mathbf{A} = [ka_{ij}] \quad \text{(multiply each component by k)}.$$

The **negative** of the matrix $\mathbf{A} = [a_{ij}]$ is $-\mathbf{A} = [-a_{ij}]$, so

$$\mathbf{A} + (-\mathbf{A}) = \mathbf{0}.$$

For two matrices $\mathbf{A}$ and $\mathbf{B}$ of the same order, $\mathbf{A} - \mathbf{B}$ is given by

$$\mathbf{A} + (-\mathbf{B}).$$

Matrix addition is commutative,
$\mathbf{A} + \mathbf{B} = \mathbf{B} + \mathbf{A}$,
and associative,
$(\mathbf{A} + \mathbf{B}) + \mathbf{C} = \mathbf{A} + (\mathbf{B} + \mathbf{C})$.

In this context, the number k is sometimes referred to as a *scalar* in order to distinguish it from a matrix. The same idea was used in *Unit 4* in the context of vectors.

Exercise 2.1 _____

Let $\mathbf{A} = \begin{bmatrix} 1 & 2 & 3 \\ 4 & 5 & 6 \end{bmatrix}$, $\mathbf{B} = \begin{bmatrix} 1 & 3 & 7 \\ 4 & -5 & 0 \end{bmatrix}$ and $\mathbf{C} = \begin{bmatrix} -2 & 1 & -6 \\ -5 & 3 & 3 \end{bmatrix}$.

(a) Calculate $3\mathbf{A}$ and $-\mathbf{A}$.

(b) Calculate $\mathbf{A} + \mathbf{B}$ and $\mathbf{B} + \mathbf{C}$.

(c) Use the results of part (b) to verify that $(\mathbf{A} + \mathbf{B}) + \mathbf{C} = \mathbf{A} + (\mathbf{B} + \mathbf{C})$.

Exercise 2.2 _____

Let $\mathbf{A} = \begin{bmatrix} 1 & -2 \\ 7 & -3 \end{bmatrix}$ and $\mathbf{B} = \begin{bmatrix} -3 & 0 \\ 4 & -5 \end{bmatrix}$.

(a) Calculate $\mathbf{A} - \mathbf{B}$ and $\mathbf{B} - \mathbf{A}$.

(b) Verify that $\mathbf{B} - \mathbf{A} = -(\mathbf{A} - \mathbf{B})$.

*Exercise 2.3 _____

Let $\mathbf{A} = \begin{bmatrix} 1 & 2 & 3 \\ 4 & 5 & 6 \end{bmatrix}$ and $\mathbf{B} = \begin{bmatrix} 1 & 3 & 7 \\ 4 & -5 & 0 \end{bmatrix}$.

(a) Calculate $2\mathbf{A} - 5\mathbf{B}$.

(b) Verify that $3(\mathbf{A} + \mathbf{B}) = 3\mathbf{A} + 3\mathbf{B}$.

The multiplication of matrices is more complicated. We illustrate the method by forming the product of two 2×2 matrices.

Let $\mathbf{A} = \begin{bmatrix} 1 & 2 \\ 3 & 4 \end{bmatrix}$ and $\mathbf{B} = \begin{bmatrix} 5 & 6 \\ 7 & 8 \end{bmatrix}$. To form the product $\mathbf{AB} = \mathbf{C}$, we define c_{ij} using the ith row of $\mathbf{A}$ and the jth column of $\mathbf{B}$, so that

$$c_{11} = a_{11}b_{11} + a_{12}b_{21} = (1 \times 5) + (2 \times 7) = 19,$$
$$c_{12} = a_{11}b_{12} + a_{12}b_{22} = (1 \times 6) + (2 \times 8) = 22,$$
$$c_{21} = a_{21}b_{11} + a_{22}b_{21} = (3 \times 5) + (4 \times 7) = 43,$$
$$c_{22} = a_{21}b_{12} + a_{22}b_{22} = (3 \times 6) + (4 \times 8) = 50.$$

Thus

$$\mathbf{C} = \mathbf{AB} = \begin{bmatrix} 1 & 2 \\ 3 & 4 \end{bmatrix} \begin{bmatrix} 5 & 6 \\ 7 & 8 \end{bmatrix} = \begin{bmatrix} 19 & 22 \\ 43 & 50 \end{bmatrix}.$$

Similarly, if $\mathbf{A} = \begin{bmatrix} 1 & 2 & 3 \\ 4 & 5 & 6 \end{bmatrix}$ and $\mathbf{B} = \begin{bmatrix} 2 & 4 \\ -1 & -2 \\ 5 & 3 \end{bmatrix}$, then

$$\mathbf{AB} = \begin{bmatrix} (1 \times 2) + (2 \times (-1)) + (3 \times 5) & (1 \times 4) + (2 \times (-2)) + (3 \times 3) \\ (4 \times 2) + (5 \times (-1)) + (6 \times 5) & (4 \times 4) + (5 \times (-2)) + (6 \times 3) \end{bmatrix}$$

$$= \begin{bmatrix} 15 & 9 \\ 33 & 24 \end{bmatrix}.$$

The above procedure can be carried out only when the number of columns of $\mathbf{A}$ is equal to the number of rows of $\mathbf{B}$.

Matrix multiplication

The **product** of an $m \times p$ matrix $\mathbf{A}$ and a $p \times n$ matrix $\mathbf{B}$ is the $m \times n$ matrix $\mathbf{C} = \mathbf{AB}$, where c_{ij} is formed using the ith row of $\mathbf{A}$ and the jth column of $\mathbf{B}$, so that

$$c_{ij} = a_{i1}b_{1j} + a_{i2}b_{2j} + \cdots + a_{ip}b_{pj}.$$

Exercise 2.4

Calculate the following matrix products, where they exist.

(a) $\begin{bmatrix} 1 & 2 \\ 2 & -3 \end{bmatrix} \begin{bmatrix} 1 & 3 \\ 2 & -1 \end{bmatrix}$ (b) $\begin{bmatrix} 2 & 1 \end{bmatrix} \begin{bmatrix} 1 & 6 \\ 0 & 2 \end{bmatrix}$ (c) $\begin{bmatrix} 1 \\ 2 \end{bmatrix} \begin{bmatrix} 3 & 0 & -4 \end{bmatrix}$

(d) $\begin{bmatrix} 3 & 1 & 2 \\ 0 & 5 & 1 \end{bmatrix} \begin{bmatrix} -2 & 0 & 1 \\ 1 & 3 & 0 \\ 4 & 1 & -1 \end{bmatrix}$ (e) $\begin{bmatrix} 2 \\ 4 \\ -1 \end{bmatrix} \begin{bmatrix} 3 & 2 \\ 4 & -1 \end{bmatrix}$

Exercise 2.5

Calculate $\mathbf{Ax}$ when $\mathbf{A} = \begin{bmatrix} 3 & -1 & 5 \\ 6 & 4 & 7 \\ 2 & -3 & 0 \end{bmatrix}$ and $\mathbf{x} = \begin{bmatrix} x_1 \\ x_2 \\ x_3 \end{bmatrix}$, and hence show that the equation $\mathbf{Ax} = \mathbf{b}$, where $\mathbf{b} = \begin{bmatrix} 2 & 5 & 6 \end{bmatrix}^T$, is equivalent to the system of equations

$$\begin{cases} 3x_1 - x_2 + 5x_3 = 2, \\ 6x_1 + 4x_2 + 7x_3 = 5, \\ 2x_1 - 3x_2 \quad\quad = 6. \end{cases}$$

In Section 1 we referred to $\mathbf{Ax} = \mathbf{b}$ as a convenient representation of a system of equations. This is consistent with the interpretation of $\mathbf{Ax}$ as the matrix product of $\mathbf{A}$ with $\mathbf{x}$, as we show here.

Earlier, you saw that addition of matrices is commutative and associative. We now give the rules for matrix multiplication.

Rules of matrix multiplication

For any matrices $\mathbf{A}$, $\mathbf{B}$ and $\mathbf{C}$ of appropriate sizes, matrix multiplication is **associative**, i.e.

$$(\mathbf{AB})\mathbf{C} = \mathbf{A}(\mathbf{BC}),$$

and **distributive** over matrix addition, i.e.

$$\mathbf{A}(\mathbf{B} + \mathbf{C}) = \mathbf{AB} + \mathbf{AC}.$$

The phrase 'of appropriate sizes' means that all the matrix sums and products can be formed.
In general, matrix multiplication is *not commutative*, so $\mathbf{AB}$ may not be equal to $\mathbf{BA}$. But multiplication of numbers *is* commutative, i.e. $ab = ba$, for any numbers a and b. So this is a significant difference between the algebra of matrices and the algebra of numbers.

Exercise 2.6

Let $\mathbf{A} = \begin{bmatrix} 1 & 1 \\ 3 & 2 \end{bmatrix}$, $\mathbf{B} = \begin{bmatrix} 1 & 4 \\ 2 & 1 \end{bmatrix}$ and $\mathbf{C} = \begin{bmatrix} 2 & 0 \\ 1 & 5 \end{bmatrix}$.

Verify each of the following statements.

(a) $\mathbf{AB} \neq \mathbf{BA}$ (b) $(\mathbf{AB})\mathbf{C} = \mathbf{A}(\mathbf{BC})$ (c) $\mathbf{A}(\mathbf{B} + \mathbf{C}) = \mathbf{AB} + \mathbf{AC}$

For a square matrix $\mathbf{A}$, we define **powers** of the matrix in the obvious way: $\mathbf{A}^2 = \mathbf{AA}$, $\mathbf{A}^3 = \mathbf{AAA}$, and so on.

An operation that we can apply to any matrix $\mathbf{A}$ is to form its **transpose** $\mathbf{A}^T$ by interchanging its rows and columns. Thus the rows of $\mathbf{A}^T$ are the columns of $\mathbf{A}$, and the columns of $\mathbf{A}^T$ are the rows of $\mathbf{A}$, taken in the same order. If $\mathbf{A}$ is an $m \times n$ matrix, then $\mathbf{A}^T$ is an $n \times m$ matrix. Examples of transposes are

$\mathbf{A}^T$ is read as 'A transpose'.

If we denote $\mathbf{A}$ by $[a_{ij}]$ and $\mathbf{A}^T$ by $[a_{ij}^T]$, then $a_{ij}^T = a_{ji}$.

$$\begin{bmatrix} 1 & 2 & 3 \\ 4 & 5 & 6 \\ 7 & 8 & 9 \end{bmatrix}^T = \begin{bmatrix} 1 & 4 & 7 \\ 2 & 5 & 8 \\ 3 & 6 & 9 \end{bmatrix}, \quad \begin{bmatrix} 2 & 7 \\ -6 & 1 \\ 0 & 4 \end{bmatrix}^T = \begin{bmatrix} 2 & -6 & 0 \\ 7 & 1 & 4 \end{bmatrix}.$$

Rules for transposes of matrices

For any matrix $\mathbf{A}$,
$$(\mathbf{A}^T)^T = \mathbf{A}.$$

For any matrices $\mathbf{A}$ and $\mathbf{B}$ of the same size,
$$(\mathbf{A} + \mathbf{B})^T = \mathbf{A}^T + \mathbf{B}^T.$$

If $\mathbf{A}$ is an $m \times p$ matrix and $\mathbf{B}$ is a $p \times n$ matrix, then
$$(\mathbf{AB})^T = \mathbf{B}^T \mathbf{A}^T.$$

Notice the change in order of the terms involving $\mathbf{A}$ and $\mathbf{B}$.

Notice in passing that the dot product of two vectors can be written using matrix multiplication: if $\mathbf{a} = \begin{bmatrix} a_1 & a_2 & a_3 \end{bmatrix}^T$ and $\mathbf{b} = \begin{bmatrix} b_1 & b_2 & b_3 \end{bmatrix}^T$, then

Remember that a vector is simply a matrix with one column.

$$\mathbf{a} \cdot \mathbf{b} = a_1 b_1 + a_2 b_2 + a_3 b_3 = \begin{bmatrix} a_1 & a_2 & a_3 \end{bmatrix} \begin{bmatrix} b_1 \\ b_2 \\ b_3 \end{bmatrix} = \mathbf{a}^T \mathbf{b}.$$

This fact will turn out to be extremely useful when we come to discuss vector calculus later in the course.

A square matrix $\mathbf{A}$ is **symmetric** if $\mathbf{A} = \mathbf{A}^T$. Symmetric here refers to symmetry about the leading diagonal. The matrices $\begin{bmatrix} 1 & 2 \\ 2 & 3 \end{bmatrix}$ and $\begin{bmatrix} 1 & 2 & 3 \\ 2 & 3 & 4 \\ 3 & 4 & 5 \end{bmatrix}$ are examples of symmetric matrices.

Exercise 2.7

Let $\mathbf{A} = \begin{bmatrix} 1 & 2 \\ 3 & 4 \\ 5 & 6 \end{bmatrix}$, $\mathbf{B} = \begin{bmatrix} 2 & 5 \\ -1 & -4 \\ 3 & 1 \end{bmatrix}$ and $\mathbf{C} = \begin{bmatrix} 1 & 0 \\ 2 & 3 \end{bmatrix}$.

(a) Write down $\mathbf{A}^T$, $\mathbf{B}^T$ and $\mathbf{C}^T$.

(b) Verify that $(\mathbf{A} + \mathbf{B})^T = \mathbf{A}^T + \mathbf{B}^T$.

(c) Verify that $(\mathbf{AC})^T = \mathbf{C}^T \mathbf{A}^T$.

Of particular importance in the solution of simultaneous linear equations are the triangular matrices. An **upper triangular matrix** is a square matrix in which each entry below the leading diagonal is 0. A **lower triangular matrix** is a square matrix in which each entry above the leading diagonal is 0. A **diagonal matrix** is a square matrix where all the elements off the leading diagonal are 0. A matrix that is upper triangular, lower triangular or both (i.e. diagonal) is sometimes referred to simply as a **triangular matrix**. For example, the matrix on the left below is upper triangular, the one in the middle is lower triangular, and the one on the right is diagonal:

You met examples of an upper triangular matrix $\mathbf{U}$ in Section 1.

$$\begin{bmatrix} 1 & 2 & 3 \\ 0 & 4 & 5 \\ 0 & 0 & 6 \end{bmatrix}, \quad \begin{bmatrix} 1 & 0 & 0 \\ 2 & 4 & 0 \\ 0 & 5 & 6 \end{bmatrix}, \quad \begin{bmatrix} 1 & 0 & 0 \\ 0 & 4 & 0 \\ 0 & 0 & 6 \end{bmatrix}.$$

The transpose of an upper triangular matrix is a lower triangular matrix, and vice versa.

Exercise 2.8

For each of the following matrices, state whether it is upper triangular, lower triangular, diagonal, or none of these.

(a) $\begin{bmatrix} 1 & 1 & 0 \\ 0 & 0 & 3 \\ 0 & 0 & 3 \end{bmatrix}$ (b) $\begin{bmatrix} 0 & 0 & 1 \\ 0 & 1 & 2 \\ 1 & 2 & 3 \end{bmatrix}$ (c) $\begin{bmatrix} 6 & 0 & 0 \\ 0 & 5 & 0 \\ 0 & 0 & 4 \end{bmatrix}$

Earlier, you met the $m \times n$ zero matrix $\mathbf{0}$, which has the property that $\mathbf{A} + \mathbf{0} = \mathbf{A}$ for each $m \times n$ matrix $\mathbf{A}$. The analogue for matrix multiplication is the $n \times n$ **identity matrix** $\mathbf{I}$, which is a diagonal matrix where each diagonal entry is 1. For example, the 3×3 identity matrix is

Strictly speaking, we should write the $n \times n$ identity matrix as $\mathbf{I}_n$, but the size of any identity matrix will be clear from the context.

$$\mathbf{I} = \begin{bmatrix} 1 & 0 & 0 \\ 0 & 1 & 0 \\ 0 & 0 & 1 \end{bmatrix}.$$

If $\mathbf{A}$ is an $n \times n$ matrix and $\mathbf{I}$ is the $n \times n$ identity matrix, then

$$\mathbf{IA} = \mathbf{AI} = \mathbf{A}.$$

If there exists a matrix $\mathbf{B}$ such that $\mathbf{AB} = \mathbf{BA} = \mathbf{I}$, then $\mathbf{B}$ is called the **inverse** of $\mathbf{A}$, and we write $\mathbf{B} = \mathbf{A}^{-1}$. Only square matrices can have inverses. A matrix that has an inverse is called **invertible** (and a matrix that does not have an inverse is called **non-invertible!**).

$\mathbf{A}^{-1}$ is read as 'A inverse'.

An invertible matrix is sometimes called *non-singular*, whilst a non-invertible matrix is called *singular*.

Exercise 2.9

For each of the following pairs of matrices $\mathbf{A}$ and $\mathbf{B}$, calculate $\mathbf{AB}$ and deduce that $\mathbf{B} = \mathbf{A}^{-1}$.

(a) $\mathbf{A} = \begin{bmatrix} 2 & 1 \\ 7 & 8 \end{bmatrix}$ and $\mathbf{B} = \begin{bmatrix} \frac{8}{9} & -\frac{1}{9} \\ -\frac{7}{9} & \frac{2}{9} \end{bmatrix}.$

(b) $\mathbf{A} = \begin{bmatrix} 1 & 3 & -1 \\ -2 & -5 & 1 \\ 4 & 11 & -2 \end{bmatrix}$ and $\mathbf{B} = \begin{bmatrix} -1 & -5 & -2 \\ 0 & 2 & 1 \\ -2 & 1 & 1 \end{bmatrix}.$

Finding the inverse of an invertible matrix

There is a way to compute the inverse of an invertible square matrix using row operations similar to those that you used for Gaussian elimination. An example will make the method clear.

Example 2.1

Find the inverse of the invertible matrix

$$\mathbf{A} = \begin{bmatrix} 2 & 2 & -1 \\ 3 & 5 & 1 \\ 1 & 2 & 1 \end{bmatrix}.$$

Solution

Form the augmented 6×3 matrix

$$\begin{bmatrix} 2 & 2 & -1 & | & 1 & 0 & 0 \\ 3 & 5 & 1 & | & 0 & 1 & 0 \\ 1 & 2 & 1 & | & 0 & 0 & 1 \end{bmatrix} \begin{matrix} \mathbf{R}_1 \\ \mathbf{R}_2 \\ \mathbf{R}_3 \end{matrix}$$

consisting of $\mathbf{A}$ together with the identity matrix. Then perform row operations in order to reduce the left-hand matrix to the identity, as follows.

Stage 1(a)   We reduce the elements below the leading diagonal in column 1 to zero.

$$\begin{matrix} \\ \mathbf{R}_2 - \frac{3}{2}\mathbf{R}_1 \\ \mathbf{R}_3 - \frac{1}{2}\mathbf{R}_1 \end{matrix} \begin{bmatrix} 2 & 2 & -1 & | & 1 & 0 & 0 \\ 0 & 2 & \frac{5}{2} & | & -\frac{3}{2} & 1 & 0 \\ 0 & 1 & \frac{3}{2} & | & -\frac{1}{2} & 0 & 1 \end{bmatrix} \begin{matrix} \mathbf{R}_1 \\ \mathbf{R}_{2a} \\ \mathbf{R}_{3a} \end{matrix}$$

Stage 1(b)   We reduce the element below the leading diagonal in column 2 to zero.

$$\begin{matrix} \\ \\ \mathbf{R}_{3a} - \frac{1}{2}\mathbf{R}_{2a} \end{matrix} \begin{bmatrix} 2 & 2 & -1 & | & 1 & 0 & 0 \\ 0 & 2 & \frac{5}{2} & | & -\frac{3}{2} & 1 & 0 \\ 0 & 0 & \frac{1}{4} & | & \frac{1}{4} & -\frac{1}{2} & 1 \end{bmatrix} \begin{matrix} \mathbf{R}_1 \\ \mathbf{R}_{2a} \\ \mathbf{R}_{3b} \end{matrix}$$

Note that the left-hand matrix is now in upper triangular form.

Stage 2(a)   We adjust the element at the bottom of column 3 to one.

$$\begin{matrix} \\ \\ 4\mathbf{R}_{3b} \end{matrix} \begin{bmatrix} 2 & 2 & -1 & | & 1 & 0 & 0 \\ 0 & 2 & \frac{5}{2} & | & -\frac{3}{2} & 1 & 0 \\ 0 & 0 & 1 & | & 1 & -2 & 4 \end{bmatrix} \begin{matrix} \mathbf{R}_1 \\ \mathbf{R}_{2a} \\ \mathbf{R}_{3c} \end{matrix}$$

Stage 2(b)   We reduce the elements above the leading diagonal in column 3 to zero.

$$\begin{matrix} \mathbf{R}_1 + \mathbf{R}_{3c} \\ \mathbf{R}_{2a} - \frac{5}{2}\mathbf{R}_{3c} \\ \\ \end{matrix} \begin{bmatrix} 2 & 2 & 0 & | & 2 & -2 & 4 \\ 0 & 2 & 0 & | & -4 & 6 & -10 \\ 0 & 0 & 1 & | & 1 & -2 & 4 \end{bmatrix} \begin{matrix} \mathbf{R}_{1a} \\ \mathbf{R}_{2b} \\ \mathbf{R}_{3c} \end{matrix}$$

Stage 2(c)   We adjust the element on the leading diagonal in column 2 to one.

$$\begin{matrix} \\ \frac{1}{2}\mathbf{R}_{2b} \\ \\ \end{matrix} \begin{bmatrix} 2 & 2 & 0 & | & 2 & -2 & 4 \\ 0 & 1 & 0 & | & -2 & 3 & -5 \\ 0 & 0 & 1 & | & 1 & -2 & 4 \end{bmatrix} \begin{matrix} \mathbf{R}_{1a} \\ \mathbf{R}_{2c} \\ \mathbf{R}_{3c} \end{matrix}$$

Stage 2(d)   We reduce the element at the top of column 2 to zero.

$$\begin{matrix} \mathbf{R}_{1a} - 2\mathbf{R}_{2c} \\ \\ \\ \end{matrix} \begin{bmatrix} 2 & 0 & 0 & | & 6 & -8 & 14 \\ 0 & 1 & 0 & | & -2 & 3 & -5 \\ 0 & 0 & 1 & | & 1 & -2 & 4 \end{bmatrix} \begin{matrix} \mathbf{R}_{1b} \\ \mathbf{R}_{2c} \\ \mathbf{R}_{3c} \end{matrix}$$

Stage 2(e)   We adjust the element at the top of column 1 to one.

$$\begin{matrix} \frac{1}{2}\mathbf{R}_{1b} \\ \\ \\ \end{matrix} \begin{bmatrix} 1 & 0 & 0 & | & 3 & -4 & 7 \\ 0 & 1 & 0 & | & -2 & 3 & -5 \\ 0 & 0 & 1 & | & 1 & -2 & 4 \end{bmatrix} \begin{matrix} \mathbf{R}_{1c} \\ \mathbf{R}_{2c} \\ \mathbf{R}_{3c} \end{matrix}$$

The resulting matrix on the right-hand side is the required inverse,

$$\mathbf{A}^{-1} = \begin{bmatrix} 3 & -4 & 7 \\ -2 & 3 & -5 \\ 1 & -2 & 4 \end{bmatrix},$$

as you can readily check. ■

This technique extends to larger square matrices, but because it is rather inefficient, it is not widely used.

Procedure 2.1   Finding the inverse of an invertible square matrix

To find the inverse of an invertible square matrix $\mathbf{A}$, carry out the following steps.

(a) Form the augmented matrix $\mathbf{A}|\mathbf{I}$, where $\mathbf{I}$ is the identity matrix of the same size as $\mathbf{A}$.

(b) Use row operations to reduce the left-hand side to the identity matrix $\mathbf{I}$.

(c) The matrix on the right-hand side is the inverse of $\mathbf{A}$.

Row interchanges will be necessary if one or more of the pivots is zero.

Exercise 2.10

Use Procedure 2.1 to find the inverse of a general 2×2 matrix

$$\mathbf{A} = \begin{bmatrix} a & b \\ c & d \end{bmatrix} \quad (ad - bc \neq 0).$$

Note that you will have to treat $a = 0$ as a special case.

The existence (or otherwise) of the inverse of a given square matrix $\mathbf{A}$ depends solely on the value of a single number called the *determinant* of $\mathbf{A}$, written $\det \mathbf{A}$. For a 2×2 matrix, Exercise 2.10 yields the following result (which saves working through Procedure 2.1).

It is sometimes convenient to write $\det(\mathbf{A})$ rather than $\det \mathbf{A}$. We study determinants in Subsection 2.3.

Inverse of an invertible 2×2 matrix

If $\mathbf{A} = \begin{bmatrix} a & b \\ c & d \end{bmatrix}$, then the **determinant** of $\mathbf{A}$ is $\det \mathbf{A} = ad - bc$.

If $\det \mathbf{A} \neq 0$, then $\mathbf{A}$ is invertible and $\mathbf{A}^{-1} = \dfrac{1}{ad - bc} \begin{bmatrix} d & -b \\ -c & a \end{bmatrix}$.

So to find the inverse of a 2×2 matrix, interchange the diagonal entries, take the negatives of the other two entries, and divide each resulting entry by the determinant. You may like to check that $\mathbf{A}\mathbf{A}^{-1} = \mathbf{I}$.

We shall see shortly that it is possible to define $\det \mathbf{A}$ for all square matrices, and the following result holds (although we shall not prove it).

Condition for invertibility of a matrix A

A matrix $\mathbf{A}$ is invertible if and only if $\det \mathbf{A} \neq 0$.

This is equivalent to saying that a matrix $\mathbf{A}$ is non-invertible if and only if $\det \mathbf{A} = 0$.

Exercise 2.11

For each of the following 2×2 matrices $\mathbf{A}$, calculate $\det \mathbf{A}$ and determine $\mathbf{A}^{-1}$, if it exists.

(a) $\mathbf{A} = \begin{bmatrix} 7 & 4 \\ 5 & 3 \end{bmatrix}$ (b) $\mathbf{A} = \begin{bmatrix} 6 & 2 \\ 9 & 3 \end{bmatrix}$ (c) $\mathbf{A} = \begin{bmatrix} 4 & 2 \\ 5 & 3 \end{bmatrix}$

Properties of invertible matrices

The inverse of an invertible matrix $\mathbf{A}$ is unique (i.e. if $\mathbf{AB} = \mathbf{I}$ and $\mathbf{AC} = \mathbf{I}$, then $\mathbf{B} = \mathbf{C} = \mathbf{A}^{-1}$).

If $\mathbf{AB} = \mathbf{I}$, then $\mathbf{BA} = \mathbf{I}$, so $\mathbf{AA}^{-1} = \mathbf{A}^{-1}\mathbf{A} = \mathbf{I}$, and hence the inverse of $\mathbf{A}^{-1}$ is $\mathbf{A}$.

The rows of a square matrix are linearly independent if and only if the matrix is invertible.

If $\mathbf{A}$ and $\mathbf{B}$ are invertible matrices of the same size, then $\mathbf{AB}$ is invertible and $(\mathbf{AB})^{-1} = \mathbf{B}^{-1}\mathbf{A}^{-1}$.

We do not prove these properties here.

Notice the change in order of the terms involving $\mathbf{A}$ and $\mathbf{B}$.

Exercise 2.12 _____

(a) Show that if $\mathbf{A}$ and $\mathbf{B}$ are any two square matrices of the same size, then $(\mathbf{AB})^{-1} = \mathbf{B}^{-1}\mathbf{A}^{-1}$.

Let $\mathbf{A} = \begin{bmatrix} 2 & 2 \\ 4 & 5 \end{bmatrix}$ and $\mathbf{B} = \begin{bmatrix} 3 & 4 \\ -1 & -2 \end{bmatrix}$.

(b) Find $\mathbf{A}^{-1}$ and $\mathbf{B}^{-1}$.

(c) Verify that $(\mathbf{A} + \mathbf{B})^{-1} \neq \mathbf{A}^{-1} + \mathbf{B}^{-1}$.

(d) Verify that $(\mathbf{AB})^{-1} = \mathbf{B}^{-1}\mathbf{A}^{-1}$.

2.2   *Linear transformations of the (x, y)-plane*

Linear transformations of the (x, y)-plane provide examples of a use of matrices.

You will see further examples in Unit 10.

Definition

A **linear transformation** of the plane is a function that maps a two-dimensional vector $[x \quad y]^T$ to the image vector $[ax + by \quad cx + dy]^T$, where a, b, c and d are real numbers.

The transformation is called linear because straight lines are mapped to straight lines.

We can represent any such linear transformation by the matrix $\mathbf{A} = \begin{bmatrix} a & b \\ c & d \end{bmatrix}$, since $\mathbf{A}\begin{bmatrix} x \\ y \end{bmatrix} = \begin{bmatrix} a & b \\ c & d \end{bmatrix}\begin{bmatrix} x \\ y \end{bmatrix} = \begin{bmatrix} ax + by \\ cx + dy \end{bmatrix}$. The image of any given vector can then be calculated. For example, the matrix $\mathbf{A} = \begin{bmatrix} 3 & 2 \\ 1 & 4 \end{bmatrix}$ maps $\begin{bmatrix} 2 \\ 1 \end{bmatrix}$ to

$$\mathbf{A}\begin{bmatrix} 2 \\ 1 \end{bmatrix} = \begin{bmatrix} 3 & 2 \\ 1 & 4 \end{bmatrix}\begin{bmatrix} 2 \\ 1 \end{bmatrix} = \begin{bmatrix} 8 \\ 6 \end{bmatrix}.$$

Exercise 2.13 _____

Consider the linear transformation that maps a vector $[x \quad y]^T$ to the image vector $[x + 2y \quad 3x + 4y]^T$.

(a) Write down the matrix $\mathbf{A}$ for this linear transformation.

(b) Use the matrix $\mathbf{A}$ to find the image of each of the following vectors.

(i) $\begin{bmatrix} 3 \\ 1 \end{bmatrix}$ (ii) $\begin{bmatrix} -1 \\ 1 \end{bmatrix}$ (iii) $\begin{bmatrix} 0 \\ 0 \end{bmatrix}$

For any linear transformation with matrix $\mathbf{A}$, the images of the Cartesian unit vectors $\mathbf{i} = [1 \ \ 0]^T$ and $\mathbf{j} = [0 \ \ 1]^T$ are the columns of $\mathbf{A}$. To see this, consider the general linear transformation that maps each vector $[x \ \ y]^T$ to the image vector $[a_{11}x + a_{12}y \ \ a_{21}x + a_{22}y]^T$. Then

$$\text{the image of } \begin{bmatrix} 1 \\ 0 \end{bmatrix} \text{ is } \begin{bmatrix} a_{11} \times 1 + a_{12} \times 0 \\ a_{21} \times 1 + a_{22} \times 0 \end{bmatrix} = \begin{bmatrix} a_{11} \\ a_{21} \end{bmatrix},$$

and

$$\text{the image of } \begin{bmatrix} 0 \\ 1 \end{bmatrix} \text{ is } \begin{bmatrix} a_{11} \times 0 + a_{12} \times 1 \\ a_{21} \times 0 + a_{22} \times 1 \end{bmatrix} = \begin{bmatrix} a_{12} \\ a_{22} \end{bmatrix}.$$

These images are the columns of the matrix $\mathbf{A} = \begin{bmatrix} a_{11} & a_{12} \\ a_{21} & a_{22} \end{bmatrix}$.

An interesting offshoot of these ideas concerns the *determinant* of the matrix of a linear transformation.

Consider the general linear transformation with matrix $\mathbf{A} = \begin{bmatrix} a & b \\ c & d \end{bmatrix}$. The image of $[1 \ \ 0]^T$ is $[a \ \ c]^T$, and the image of $[0 \ \ 1]^T$ is $[b \ \ d]^T$. It can be shown that the unit square (with vertices at the points $(0,0)$, $(1,0)$, $(1,1)$ and $(0,1)$) is mapped to the parallelogram defined by these image vectors, as shown in Figure 2.1. From *Unit 4*, we know that the area of this parallelogram is the magnitude of the cross product of the two position vectors $[a \ \ c]^T$ and $[b \ \ d]^T$, which is $|(a\mathbf{i} + c\mathbf{j}) \times (b\mathbf{i} + d\mathbf{j})| = |ad - bc|$. The determinant $\det \mathbf{A}$ of the 2×2 matrix $\mathbf{A} = \begin{bmatrix} a & b \\ c & d \end{bmatrix}$ is $ad - bc$. So the area of the parallelogram is the magnitude of $\det \mathbf{A}$. But the parallelogram is the image of the unit square defined by the two vectors $[1 \ \ 0]^T$ and $[0 \ \ 1]^T$, so $|\det \mathbf{A}|$ is the area of the image of the unit square. Accordingly, the larger $|\det \mathbf{A}|$, the larger the images of shapes under the transformation.

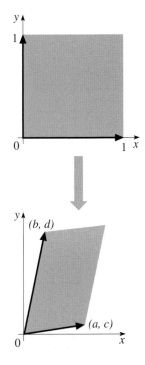

Figure 2.1

Exercise 2.14

For each of the following matrices, calculate $\det \mathbf{A}$ and compare your answer with the area of the parallelogram defined by the images of the Cartesian unit vectors $\mathbf{i}$ and $\mathbf{j}$.

(a) $\mathbf{A} = \begin{bmatrix} 1 & 1 \\ -1 & 1 \end{bmatrix}$ (b) $\mathbf{A} = \begin{bmatrix} 3 & 2 \\ 1 & -6 \end{bmatrix}$ (c) $\mathbf{A} = \begin{bmatrix} 4 & 6 \\ 2 & 3 \end{bmatrix}$

We can also link these ideas with systems of linear equations. For example, the system of linear equations

$$\begin{cases} x_1 + \ \ x_2 = 0, \\ x_1 + 2x_2 = 1, \end{cases} \tag{2.1}$$

can be written in matrix form as $\mathbf{Ax} = \mathbf{b}$, given by

$$\begin{bmatrix} 1 & 1 \\ 1 & 2 \end{bmatrix} \begin{bmatrix} x_1 \\ x_2 \end{bmatrix} = \begin{bmatrix} 0 \\ 1 \end{bmatrix}. \tag{2.2}$$

Solving Equations (2.1) is equivalent to finding the vector $\mathbf{x}$ that is mapped to the vector $\mathbf{b}$ by the linear transformation with matrix $\mathbf{A}$ as shown in Equation (2.2). This is the 'inverse process' of our earlier work (for example in Exercise 2.13), where we were given $\mathbf{x}$ and asked to find the image vector $\mathbf{b} = \mathbf{Ax}$. This suggests that we might consider using the inverse matrix as a way of solving such systems of linear equations.

For the matrix $\mathbf{A}$ in Equation (2.2),

$$\mathbf{A}^{-1} = \begin{bmatrix} 1 & 1 \\ 1 & 2 \end{bmatrix}^{-1} = \begin{bmatrix} 2 & -1 \\ -1 & 1 \end{bmatrix}.$$

Here $\det \mathbf{A} = 1$.

We wish to multiply the equation $\mathbf{Ax} = \mathbf{b}$ by $\mathbf{A}^{-1}$, but we must be careful with the order of the multiplication. Multiplying both sides of the equation *on the left* by $\mathbf{A}^{-1}$, we obtain

$$\mathbf{A}^{-1}\mathbf{Ax} = \mathbf{A}^{-1}\mathbf{b}.$$

Since $\mathbf{A}^{-1}\mathbf{A} = \mathbf{I}$, we have

$$\mathbf{x} = \mathbf{A}^{-1}\mathbf{b},$$

Here we use the associative law: $\mathbf{A}^{-1}(\mathbf{Ax}) = (\mathbf{A}^{-1}\mathbf{A})\mathbf{x}$.

so $\mathbf{x}$ is the image of $\mathbf{b}$ under transformation by the inverse matrix $\mathbf{A}^{-1}$. Therefore

$$\begin{bmatrix} x_1 \\ x_2 \end{bmatrix} = \begin{bmatrix} 2 & -1 \\ -1 & 1 \end{bmatrix} \begin{bmatrix} 0 \\ 1 \end{bmatrix} = \begin{bmatrix} -1 \\ 1 \end{bmatrix}.$$

Thus $x_1 = -1$, $x_2 = 1$ is the solution of this system of linear equations.

This matrix approach to solving a system of linear equations can be used whenever the matrix $\mathbf{A}^{-1}$ exists, i.e. whenever $\mathbf{A}$ is invertible. However, except for 2×2 matrices, the inverse matrix is usually tedious to calculate, and it is more efficient to use the Gaussian elimination method to solve the system of equations.

We come now to a result that is important with respect to the material in the next unit. Suppose that $\mathbf{b} = \mathbf{0}$, so that we are looking for a solution to $\mathbf{Ax} = \mathbf{0}$. What can we say about $\mathbf{x}$? If $\mathbf{A}$ has an inverse, then multiplying both sides of $\mathbf{Ax} = \mathbf{0}$ on the left by $\mathbf{A}^{-1}$ gives $\mathbf{A}^{-1}\mathbf{Ax} = \mathbf{A}^{-1}\mathbf{0}$, so $\mathbf{x} = \mathbf{0}$. Therefore, if $\mathbf{Ax} = \mathbf{0}$ is to have a non-zero solution $\mathbf{x}$, then $\mathbf{A}$ cannot have an inverse, i.e. it must be non-invertible. So we have the following result.

Non-invertible square matrix

If $\mathbf{A}$ is a square matrix and $\mathbf{Ax} = \mathbf{0}$ with $\mathbf{x} \neq \mathbf{0}$, then $\mathbf{A}$ is non-invertible.

So $\det \mathbf{A} = 0$.

2.3 Determinants

In this subsection we summarize the main properties of determinants of 2×2 matrices and extend the ideas to $n \times n$ matrices.

Properties of 2×2 determinants

Recall that if $\mathbf{A} = \begin{bmatrix} a & b \\ c & d \end{bmatrix}$, then $\det \mathbf{A} = ad - bc$.

We frequently use the 'vertical line' notation for determinants:

$$\det \mathbf{A} = \begin{vmatrix} a & b \\ c & d \end{vmatrix} = ad - bc.$$

Earlier in this section you saw that if $\det \mathbf{A} \neq 0$, then $\mathbf{A}$ is invertible. In the following exercise we investigate some further properties of 2×2 determinants.

Exercise 2.15

Calculate the following determinants.

(a) $\begin{vmatrix} a & 0 \\ c & d \end{vmatrix}$, $\begin{vmatrix} a & b \\ 0 & d \end{vmatrix}$ and $\begin{vmatrix} a & 0 \\ 0 & d \end{vmatrix}$ (b) $\begin{vmatrix} c & d \\ a & b \end{vmatrix}$ and $\begin{vmatrix} b & a \\ d & c \end{vmatrix}$

(c) $\begin{vmatrix} a & c \\ b & d \end{vmatrix}$ (d) $\begin{vmatrix} a & b \\ a & b \end{vmatrix}$ and $\begin{vmatrix} a & a \\ c & c \end{vmatrix}$ (e) $\begin{vmatrix} ka & kb \\ c & d \end{vmatrix}$ and $\begin{vmatrix} ka & b \\ kc & d \end{vmatrix}$

(f) $\begin{vmatrix} ka & kb \\ kc & kd \end{vmatrix}$ (g) $\begin{vmatrix} a & b \\ c-ma & d-mb \end{vmatrix}$ and $\begin{vmatrix} a-mc & b-md \\ c & d \end{vmatrix}$

(h) $\begin{vmatrix} \dfrac{d}{ad-bc} & -\dfrac{b}{ad-bc} \\[2ex] -\dfrac{c}{ad-bc} & \dfrac{a}{ad-bc} \end{vmatrix}$

In parts (b), (c), (e), (f), (g) and (h), compare your answer with $\det \mathbf{A}$, where $\mathbf{A} = \begin{bmatrix} a & b \\ c & d \end{bmatrix}$.

In Exercise 2.15 we have (with respect to the matrix $\mathbf{A}$, where appropriate) illustrations of:
(a) lower and upper triangular matrices, and a diagonal matrix;
(b) interchanges of rows and columns;
(c) a transpose;
(d) linearly dependent rows and columns;
(e) multiplying rows and columns by a scalar;
(f) multiplying each element by a scalar;
(g) subtracting a multiple of one row from another;
(h) an inverse matrix.

We shall refer back to the results in Exercise 2.15 later.

Introducing 3×3 *and* $n \times n$ *determinants*

Just as the magnitude of the 2×2 determinant

$$\begin{vmatrix} a_1 & a_2 \\ b_1 & b_2 \end{vmatrix}$$

represents the area of the parallelogram defined by the vectors $[a_1 \quad a_2]^T$ and $[b_1 \quad b_2]^T$, so we can define a 3×3 determinant

$$\begin{vmatrix} a_1 & a_2 & a_3 \\ b_1 & b_2 & b_3 \\ c_1 & c_2 & c_3 \end{vmatrix}$$

whose magnitude represents the volume of the parallelepiped defined by the vectors $\mathbf{a} = [a_1 \quad a_2 \quad a_3]^T$, $\mathbf{b} = [b_1 \quad b_2 \quad b_3]^T$ and $\mathbf{c} = [c_1 \quad c_2 \quad c_3]^T$, as shown in Figure 2.2.

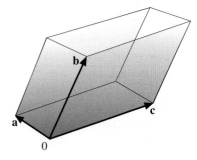

Figure 2.2

Definition

The **determinant** of the 3×3 matrix

$$\mathbf{A} = \begin{bmatrix} a_1 & a_2 & a_3 \\ b_1 & b_2 & b_3 \\ c_1 & c_2 & c_3 \end{bmatrix}$$

is given by

$$\det \mathbf{A} = a_1 \begin{vmatrix} b_2 & b_3 \\ c_2 & c_3 \end{vmatrix} - a_2 \begin{vmatrix} b_1 & b_3 \\ c_1 & c_3 \end{vmatrix} + a_3 \begin{vmatrix} b_1 & b_2 \\ c_1 & c_2 \end{vmatrix}$$

$$= a_1 b_2 c_3 - a_1 b_3 c_2 - a_2 b_1 c_3 + a_2 b_3 c_1 + a_3 b_1 c_2 - a_3 b_2 c_1. \quad (2.3)$$

This is sometimes known as 'expanding the determinant by the top row'. Notice the minus sign before the second term.

As before, we frequently use 'vertical line' notation. For example,

$$\begin{vmatrix} 1 & 2 & 4 \\ 3 & 1 & -1 \\ 2 & 5 & 6 \end{vmatrix} = 1 \begin{vmatrix} 1 & -1 \\ 5 & 6 \end{vmatrix} - 2 \begin{vmatrix} 3 & -1 \\ 2 & 6 \end{vmatrix} + 4 \begin{vmatrix} 3 & 1 \\ 2 & 5 \end{vmatrix} = 11 - 40 + 52 = 23.$$

A simple way to remember formula (2.3) is related to Sarrus's Rule (see *Unit 4*). Draw a tableau with a_1, a_2 and a_3 in the top row, then repeat a_1 and a_2. In the second row do the same with the second row of the matrix, and in the third row with the third. Then following the diagonal lines as shown, and multiplying the entries, gives the corresponding terms of the determinant det $\mathbf{A}$, which are the elements on the fourth row of the tableau.

This tableau method does not extend to $n \times n$ matrices for $n > 3$.

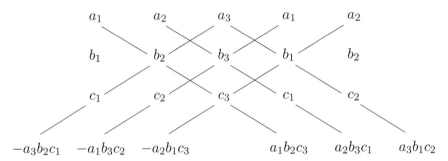

(The diagonals pointing to the right yield a positive term, those pointing left have a minus sign.)

*Exercise 2.16

Evaluate the following determinants.

(a) $\begin{vmatrix} 4 & 1 & 0 \\ 0 & 2 & -1 \\ 2 & 3 & 1 \end{vmatrix}$ (b) $\begin{vmatrix} 1 & 2 & 3 \\ 4 & 5 & 6 \\ 7 & 8 & 9 \end{vmatrix}$ (c) $\begin{vmatrix} 1 & 2 & 3 \\ 0 & 4 & 5 \\ 0 & 0 & 6 \end{vmatrix}$

The result of using the tableau shown above does not change under cyclic permutations of the rows (i.e. of the symbols a, b, c). However, as you can check, it changes sign if two adjacent rows are interchanged. This shows that the determinant can be expanded using any row of the matrix, provided that the rows are then taken in the correct order. If the order is reversed, then a minus sign is introduced. For example,

$$
\begin{aligned}
\det \mathbf{A} &= a_1 \begin{vmatrix} b_2 & b_3 \\ c_2 & c_3 \end{vmatrix} - a_2 \begin{vmatrix} b_1 & b_3 \\ c_1 & c_3 \end{vmatrix} + a_3 \begin{vmatrix} b_1 & b_2 \\ c_1 & c_2 \end{vmatrix} \\
&= -a_1 \begin{vmatrix} c_2 & c_3 \\ b_2 & b_3 \end{vmatrix} + a_2 \begin{vmatrix} c_1 & c_3 \\ b_1 & b_3 \end{vmatrix} - a_3 \begin{vmatrix} c_1 & c_2 \\ b_1 & b_2 \end{vmatrix} \\
&= -b_1 \begin{vmatrix} a_2 & a_3 \\ c_2 & c_3 \end{vmatrix} + b_2 \begin{vmatrix} a_1 & a_3 \\ c_1 & c_3 \end{vmatrix} - b_3 \begin{vmatrix} a_1 & a_2 \\ c_1 & c_2 \end{vmatrix} \\
&= c_1 \begin{vmatrix} a_2 & a_3 \\ b_2 & b_3 \end{vmatrix} - c_2 \begin{vmatrix} a_1 & a_3 \\ b_1 & b_3 \end{vmatrix} + c_3 \begin{vmatrix} a_1 & a_2 \\ b_1 & b_2 \end{vmatrix}.
\end{aligned}
$$

Another interesting thing occurs if we use the tableau method to evaluate det $\mathbf{A}^T$ (the determinant of the transpose of $\mathbf{A}$).

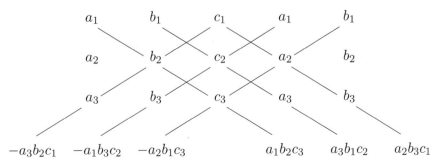

As you can see,

$$\det(\mathbf{A}^T) = \det \mathbf{A},$$

a result that extends to $n \times n$ matrices (though we shall not prove this). This means that to evaluate $\det \mathbf{A}$ we can expand using columns in place of rows, as shown in Example 2.2 below.

In fact, these observations make it easy to evaluate any 3×3 determinant in which one row or column is particularly simple.

Example 2.2

Evaluate the determinant of each of the following.

(a) $\mathbf{A} = \begin{bmatrix} 8 & 9 & -6 \\ 1 & 0 & 0 \\ 32 & -7 & 14 \end{bmatrix}$ (b) $\mathbf{B} = \begin{bmatrix} 8 & 9 & 0 \\ 13 & -4 & 2 \\ -6 & 2 & 0 \end{bmatrix}$

Solution

(a) We can expand $\det \mathbf{A}$ by the second row:

$$\begin{vmatrix} 8 & 9 & -6 \\ 1 & 0 & 0 \\ 32 & -7 & 14 \end{vmatrix} = -1 \begin{vmatrix} 9 & -6 \\ -7 & 14 \end{vmatrix} + 0 \begin{vmatrix} 8 & -6 \\ 32 & 14 \end{vmatrix} - 0 \begin{vmatrix} 8 & 9 \\ 32 & -7 \end{vmatrix}$$
$$= -1(126 - 42)$$
$$= -84.$$

(b) We can expand $\det \mathbf{B}$ by the third column:

$$\begin{vmatrix} 8 & 9 & 0 \\ 13 & -4 & 2 \\ -6 & 2 & 0 \end{vmatrix} = 0 \begin{vmatrix} 13 & -4 \\ -6 & 2 \end{vmatrix} - 2 \begin{vmatrix} 8 & 9 \\ -6 & 2 \end{vmatrix} + 0 \begin{vmatrix} 8 & 9 \\ 13 & -4 \end{vmatrix}$$
$$= -2(16 + 54)$$
$$= -140. \quad \blacksquare$$

The armoury of techniques for evaluating determinants can be expanded by noting some general rules.

Rules for $n \times n$ determinants

(a) If $\mathbf{A}$ is a diagonal, upper triangular or lower triangular matrix, then $\det \mathbf{A}$ is the product of the diagonal entries.

(b) Interchanging any two rows or any two columns of $\mathbf{A}$ changes the sign of $\det \mathbf{A}$.

(c) $\det(\mathbf{A}^T) = \det \mathbf{A}$.

(d) If the rows or columns of $\mathbf{A}$ are linearly dependent, then $\det \mathbf{A} = 0$; otherwise $\det \mathbf{A} \neq 0$.

(e) Multiplying any row or any column of $\mathbf{A}$ by a scalar k multiplies $\det \mathbf{A}$ by k.

(f) For any number k, $\det(k\mathbf{A}) = k^n \det \mathbf{A}$.

(g) Adding a multiple of one row of $\mathbf{A}$ to another row does not change $\det \mathbf{A}$.

(h) The matrix $\mathbf{A}$ is non-invertible if and only if $\det \mathbf{A} = 0$. If $\det \mathbf{A} \neq 0$, then $\det(\mathbf{A}^{-1}) = 1/\det \mathbf{A}$.

(i) For any two $n \times n$ matrices $\mathbf{A}$ and $\mathbf{B}$ we have
$$\det(\mathbf{AB}) = \det \mathbf{A} \det \mathbf{B}.$$

The general $n \times n$ determinant is defined below. You may find it helpful to compare these general rules with the results we obtained for a 2×2 matrix in Exercise 2.15. The letters (a) to (h) here relate to the relevant parts of that exercise.

The multiple can be negative or positive, so (g) covers subtracting a multiple of one row from another row.

Rule (d) tells us that $\det \mathbf{A} = 0$ if and only if the rows of $\mathbf{A}$ are linearly dependent. Hence any system of linear equations with coefficient matrix $\mathbf{A}$ has a *unique* solution if and only if $\det \mathbf{A} \neq 0$. If $\det \mathbf{A} = 0$, then the system has an infinite number of solutions or no solution.

Note that since $\det(\mathbf{A}^T) = \det \mathbf{A}$, we can also deduce that $\det \mathbf{A} = 0$ if and only if the *columns* of $\mathbf{A}$ are linearly dependent.

Exercise 2.17 _____

(a) Calculate $\begin{vmatrix} 2 & 1 & 3 \\ 0 & 2 & 1 \\ 3 & 1 & 6 \end{vmatrix}$.

(b) Use the result of part (a) and the above rules to *write down* the values of the following determinants.

(i) $\begin{vmatrix} 2 & 1 & 3 \\ 3 & 1 & 6 \\ 0 & 2 & 1 \end{vmatrix}$ (ii) $\begin{vmatrix} 2 & 0 & 3 \\ 1 & 2 & 1 \\ 3 & 1 & 6 \end{vmatrix}$ (iii) $\begin{vmatrix} 2 & 3 & 3 \\ 3 & 3 & 6 \\ 0 & 6 & 1 \end{vmatrix}$

(c) Let $\mathbf{A} = \begin{bmatrix} 1 & 3 & 2 \\ 0 & 1 & -1 \\ 0 & 2 & 3 \end{bmatrix}$. Calculate $\det \mathbf{A}$. Subtract twice the second row of $\mathbf{A}$ from the third row to obtain an upper triangular matrix $\mathbf{U}$. Calculate $\det \mathbf{U}$ using the definition of a 3×3 determinant, and compare this with the product of the diagonal elements of $\mathbf{U}$.

It is also possible to define larger determinants. To do this, we proceed one step at a time, defining an $n \times n$ determinant in terms of $(n-1) \times (n-1)$ determinants. For example, to define a 4×4 determinant, we write

$$\begin{vmatrix} a_1 & a_2 & a_3 & a_4 \\ b_1 & b_2 & b_3 & b_4 \\ c_1 & c_2 & c_3 & c_4 \\ d_1 & d_2 & d_3 & d_4 \end{vmatrix} = a_1 \begin{vmatrix} b_2 & b_3 & b_4 \\ c_2 & c_3 & c_4 \\ d_2 & d_3 & d_4 \end{vmatrix} - a_2 \begin{vmatrix} b_1 & b_3 & b_4 \\ c_1 & c_3 & c_4 \\ d_1 & d_3 & d_4 \end{vmatrix}$$

Note that alternate terms in the expansion have a minus sign.

$$+ a_3 \begin{vmatrix} b_1 & b_2 & b_4 \\ c_1 & c_2 & c_4 \\ d_1 & d_2 & d_4 \end{vmatrix} - a_4 \begin{vmatrix} b_1 & b_2 & b_3 \\ c_1 & c_2 & c_3 \\ d_1 & d_2 & d_3 \end{vmatrix}.$$

Except in special cases, the calculation of large determinants like this can be very tedious. However, rule (g) for determinants provides the clue to a simpler method. Procedure 1.1 (Gaussian elimination) applied to the matrix $\mathbf{A}$ consists of a sequence of row operations where a multiple of one row is added to another. Each such operation does not change the value of the determinant. Thus we can deduce that $\det \mathbf{A} = \det \mathbf{U}$, where $\mathbf{U}$ is the upper triangular matrix obtained at the end of the elimination stage. Since the determinant of an upper triangular matrix is the product of the diagonal elements, Procedure 1.1 also provides an efficient way of calculating determinants of any size.

If we need to make essential row interchanges to avoid a zero pivot, we note that each row interchange will change the sign of the determinant (see rule (b)).

Exercise 2.18 _____

In Example 1.3 we applied the Gaussian elimination method to the matrix

$$\mathbf{A} = \begin{bmatrix} 1 & -4 & 2 \\ 3 & -2 & 3 \\ 8 & -2 & 9 \end{bmatrix} \text{ to obtain } \mathbf{U} = \begin{bmatrix} 1 & -4 & 2 \\ 0 & 10 & -3 \\ 0 & 0 & 2 \end{bmatrix}.$$

Calculate $\det \mathbf{A}$ and $\det \mathbf{U}$, and hence show that $\det \mathbf{A} = \det \mathbf{U}$.

2.4 Some applications

We conclude this section by illustrating how 3×3 determinants can be used to represent areas and volumes, and products of vectors. We start by revisiting the scalar triple product.

Scalar triple products and the other topics in this subsection were mentioned in Unit 4.

Scalar triple product

Let $\mathbf{a} = a_1\mathbf{i} + a_2\mathbf{j} + a_3\mathbf{k}$, $\mathbf{b} = b_1\mathbf{i} + b_2\mathbf{j} + b_3\mathbf{k}$ and $\mathbf{c} = c_1\mathbf{i} + c_2\mathbf{j} + c_3\mathbf{k}$. The volume of the parallelepiped with sides defined by the vectors $\mathbf{a}$, $\mathbf{b}$ and $\mathbf{c}$ is given by the magnitude of the scalar triple product $(\mathbf{b} \times \mathbf{c}) \cdot \mathbf{a}$, which you will recall from *Unit 4* can also be written as $\mathbf{a} \cdot (\mathbf{b} \times \mathbf{c})$. The cross product of vectors $\mathbf{b}$ and $\mathbf{c}$ is

$$\mathbf{b} \times \mathbf{c} = (b_2c_3 - b_3c_2)\mathbf{i} + (b_3c_1 - b_1c_3)\mathbf{j} + (b_1c_2 - b_2c_1)\mathbf{k}$$

$$= \begin{vmatrix} b_2 & b_3 \\ c_2 & c_3 \end{vmatrix} \mathbf{i} - \begin{vmatrix} b_1 & b_3 \\ c_1 & c_3 \end{vmatrix} \mathbf{j} + \begin{vmatrix} b_1 & b_2 \\ c_1 & c_2 \end{vmatrix} \mathbf{k},$$

hence

$$\mathbf{a} \cdot (\mathbf{b} \times \mathbf{c}) = a_1 \begin{vmatrix} b_2 & b_3 \\ c_2 & c_3 \end{vmatrix} - a_2 \begin{vmatrix} b_1 & b_3 \\ c_1 & c_3 \end{vmatrix} + a_3 \begin{vmatrix} b_1 & b_2 \\ c_1 & c_2 \end{vmatrix}$$

$$= \begin{vmatrix} a_1 & a_2 & a_3 \\ b_1 & b_2 & b_3 \\ c_1 & c_2 & c_3 \end{vmatrix}. \tag{2.4}$$

*Exercise 2.19

Use the result of Exercise 2.17(a) to find the scalar triple product $\mathbf{a} \cdot (\mathbf{b} \times \mathbf{c})$ when $\mathbf{a} = 2\mathbf{i} + \mathbf{j} + 3\mathbf{k}$, $\mathbf{b} = 2\mathbf{j} + \mathbf{k}$ and $\mathbf{c} = 3\mathbf{i} + \mathbf{j} + 6\mathbf{k}$.

Exercise 2.20

Use Equation (2.4) to find the volume of the parallelepiped defined by the vectors $\mathbf{a} = \mathbf{i} + \mathbf{k}$, $\mathbf{b} = \mathbf{i} + 2\mathbf{j}$ and $\mathbf{c} = \mathbf{j} + 3\mathbf{k}$.

Cross product

The similarity between the formula for a 3×3 determinant and Sarrus's Rule (in *Unit 4*) for evaluating the cross product of two vectors gives another way of remembering the formula for the cross product. We have seen above that if $\mathbf{b} = [b_1 \quad b_2 \quad b_3]^T$ and $\mathbf{c} = [c_1 \quad c_2 \quad c_3]^T$, then

$$\mathbf{b} \times \mathbf{c} = \begin{vmatrix} b_2 & b_3 \\ c_2 & c_3 \end{vmatrix} \mathbf{i} - \begin{vmatrix} b_1 & b_3 \\ c_1 & c_3 \end{vmatrix} \mathbf{j} + \begin{vmatrix} b_1 & b_2 \\ c_1 & c_2 \end{vmatrix} \mathbf{k}.$$

This expression can be remembered more easily if we write it as a 3×3 determinant:

$$\mathbf{b} \times \mathbf{c} = \begin{vmatrix} \mathbf{i} & \mathbf{j} & \mathbf{k} \\ b_1 & b_2 & b_3 \\ c_1 & c_2 & c_3 \end{vmatrix}.$$

Exercise 2.21

Express $\mathbf{b} \times \mathbf{c}$ as a determinant, and calculate its value, when:

(a) $\mathbf{b} = 3\mathbf{i} + 2\mathbf{j} - 4\mathbf{k}$ and $\mathbf{c} = \mathbf{i} - \mathbf{j} + 3\mathbf{k}$;

(b) $\mathbf{b} = [1 \quad 2 \quad 3]^T$ and $\mathbf{c} = [6 \quad 5 \quad 4]^T$.

Area of a triangle in the (x, y)-plane

Consider the triangle defined by the origin and the points with position vectors $\mathbf{a} = [a_1 \quad a_2 \quad 0]^T$ and $\mathbf{b} = [b_1 \quad b_2 \quad 0]^T$, as shown in Figure 2.3. Its area A is given by

$$A = \tfrac{1}{2} |\mathbf{a} \times \mathbf{b}|$$

$$= \tfrac{1}{2} \left| \det \begin{bmatrix} \mathbf{i} & \mathbf{j} & \mathbf{k} \\ a_1 & a_2 & 0 \\ b_1 & b_2 & 0 \end{bmatrix} \right|$$

$$= \tfrac{1}{2} |(a_1 b_2 - a_2 b_1)\mathbf{k}|$$

$$= \tfrac{1}{2} |a_1 b_2 - a_2 b_1|$$

$$= \tfrac{1}{2} \left| \det \begin{bmatrix} a_1 & a_2 \\ b_1 & b_2 \end{bmatrix} \right|. \tag{2.5}$$

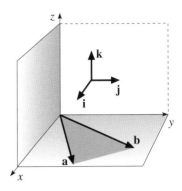

Figure 2.3

We use det for determinant here, rather than | |, to avoid confusion with the modulus function, which is also present.

The formula (2.5) agrees with our earlier interpretation of the magnitude of the determinant as the area of the parallelogram defined by $\mathbf{a}$ and $\mathbf{b}$.

We can extend this result to give a formula containing determinants for the area of a triangle whose vertices have position vectors $\mathbf{a} = [a_1 \quad a_2 \quad 0]^T$, $\mathbf{b} = [b_1 \quad b_2 \quad 0]^T$ and $\mathbf{c} = [c_1 \quad c_2 \quad 0]^T$. Two sides of the triangle are given by the vectors $\mathbf{a} - \mathbf{c}$ and $\mathbf{b} - \mathbf{c}$, so we can find the area as follows:

Remember that $\mathbf{c} \times \mathbf{c} = \mathbf{0}$ and that $-\mathbf{c} \times \mathbf{b} = \mathbf{b} \times \mathbf{c}$ (from *Unit 4*).

$$A = \tfrac{1}{2} |(\mathbf{a} - \mathbf{c}) \times (\mathbf{b} - \mathbf{c})|$$

$$= \tfrac{1}{2} |(\mathbf{a} \times \mathbf{b}) - (\mathbf{a} \times \mathbf{c}) + (\mathbf{b} \times \mathbf{c})|$$

$$= \tfrac{1}{2} \left| \det \begin{bmatrix} \mathbf{i} & \mathbf{j} & \mathbf{k} \\ a_1 & a_2 & 0 \\ b_1 & b_2 & 0 \end{bmatrix} - \det \begin{bmatrix} \mathbf{i} & \mathbf{j} & \mathbf{k} \\ a_1 & a_2 & 0 \\ c_1 & c_2 & 0 \end{bmatrix} + \det \begin{bmatrix} \mathbf{i} & \mathbf{j} & \mathbf{k} \\ b_1 & b_2 & 0 \\ c_1 & c_2 & 0 \end{bmatrix} \right|$$

$$= \tfrac{1}{2} |(a_1 b_2 - a_2 b_1)\mathbf{k} - (a_1 c_2 - a_2 c_1)\mathbf{k} + (b_1 c_2 - b_2 c_1)\mathbf{k}|$$

$$= \tfrac{1}{2} |(a_1 b_2 - a_2 b_1) - (a_1 c_2 - a_2 c_1) + (b_1 c_2 - b_2 c_1)|$$

$$= \tfrac{1}{2} \left| \det \begin{bmatrix} 1 & 1 & 1 \\ a_1 & b_1 & c_1 \\ a_2 & b_2 & c_2 \end{bmatrix} \right|. \tag{2.6}$$

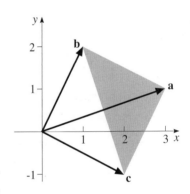

Figure 2.4

Exercise 2.22

Use Equation (2.6) to find the area of the triangle whose vertices are $\mathbf{a} = 3\mathbf{i} + \mathbf{j}$, $\mathbf{b} = \mathbf{i} + 2\mathbf{j}$ and $\mathbf{c} = 2\mathbf{i} - \mathbf{j}$ (see Figure 2.4).

End-of-section Exercises

Exercise 2.23

Given the symmetric matrices $\mathbf{A} = \begin{bmatrix} 1 & 2 & 1 \\ 2 & 3 & -1 \\ 1 & -1 & 0 \end{bmatrix}$ and $\mathbf{B} = \begin{bmatrix} 1 & 1 & 0 \\ 1 & 0 & 1 \\ 0 & 1 & 1 \end{bmatrix}$,

show that $\mathbf{AB}$ is not symmetric. Verify that $(\mathbf{AB})^T = \mathbf{B}^T \mathbf{A}^T$.

Exercise 2.24

Given $\mathbf{A} = \begin{bmatrix} 1 & 2 \\ -1 & 1 \end{bmatrix}$, calculate $\det \mathbf{A}$ and $\mathbf{A}^{-1}$. Hence write down the solution of the system of equations

$$\begin{cases} x + 2y = 1, \\ -x + y = -1. \end{cases}$$

3 Matrices in action

In Section 1 we used matrix notation to describe the solution of systems of linear equations by the Gaussian elimination method. The ubiquitous nature of matrices is partially explained by the fact that such systems of equations arise in many areas of applied mathematics, numerical analysis and statistics. In this section we look at two applications that involve solving systems of linear equations: *polynomial interpolation* and *least squares approximations*. In each application, we are given a set of $n+1$ data points (x_i, y_i), $i = 0, 1, \ldots, n$, where $x_0 < x_1 < \cdots < x_n$, as shown in Figure 3.1.

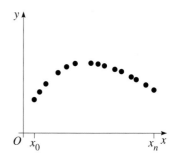

In the first application, we determine the polynomial $y(x) = a_0 + a_1 x + \cdots + a_n x^n$ such that $y(x_i) = y_i$, $i = 0, 1, \ldots, n$. This polynomial, defined on the interval $x_0 \le x \le x_n$, is called the **interpolating polynomial**. The graph of such a function passes through each data point.

Figure 3.1

The second application arises, for example, when we conduct an experiment and, for each x_i, the corresponding measurement of y_i contains an experimental error. In such situations it may be preferable to construct a polynomial of lower degree that 'best approximates' the data, rather than a polynomial that passes through every point.

3.1 Polynomial interpolation

We are often given a table of values showing the variation of one variable with another. For example, in Example 2.1 of *Unit 2* we met the initial-value problem

$$\frac{dy}{dx} = x + y, \quad y(0) = 1. \tag{3.1}$$

Using Euler's method with step size $h = 0.2$, we obtained a table of approximate values for the solution (see Table 3.1).

Table 3.1

i	x_i	Y_i
0	0	1
1	0.2	1.2
2	0.4	1.48
3	0.6	1.856
4	0.8	2.3472
5	1.0	2.97664

Suppose that we wish to approximate the solution at $x = 0.47$. One way of doing this is to construct a polynomial through some or all of the data values and then use this interpolating polynomial to approximate the solution at $x = 0.47$. There are many ways of constructing interpolating polynomials, but we shall present just one method here. We start with a straight line approximation through the two points closest to $x = 0.47$.

Example 3.1

Find the equation of the straight line through $(0.4, 1.48)$ and $(0.6, 1.856)$, and use it to approximate the solution of system (3.1) at $x = 0.47$.

Solution

Suppose that the line is $y = a_0 + a_1 x$. Since, from Table 3.1, $y = 1.48$ when $x = 0.4$, and $y = 1.856$ when $x = 0.6$, we obtain the system of equations

$$\begin{cases} a_0 + 0.4 a_1 = 1.48, \\ a_0 + 0.6 a_1 = 1.856. \end{cases}$$

The solution of these equations is $a_0 = 0.728$, $a_1 = 1.88$. Hence the equation of the straight line is

$$y = 0.728 + 1.88x.$$

When $x = 0.47$, we have $y = 0.728 + 1.88 \times 0.47 = 1.6116.$ ∎

In general, if we require the line through (x_0, y_0) and (x_1, y_1), we have (as in Example 3.1)

$$\begin{cases} a_0 + a_1 x_0 = y_0, \\ a_0 + a_1 x_1 = y_1, \end{cases}$$

which can be written in matrix form as

$$\begin{bmatrix} 1 & x_0 \\ 1 & x_1 \end{bmatrix} \begin{bmatrix} a_0 \\ a_1 \end{bmatrix} = \begin{bmatrix} y_0 \\ y_1 \end{bmatrix};$$

that is,

$$\mathbf{X}\mathbf{a} = \mathbf{y}, \qquad\qquad (3.2)$$

where the matrix $\mathbf{X}$ contains the given values x_i, and the vector $\mathbf{y}$ contains the given values y_i $(i = 1, 2)$. We wish to determine the vector $\mathbf{a}$, and this could be done, for example, by using Gaussian elimination.

Exercise 3.1 ⎯⎯⎯⎯⎯⎯⎯⎯⎯⎯⎯⎯⎯⎯⎯⎯⎯⎯⎯⎯⎯

Consider the data in Table 3.1. Find the straight line through the points $(0.6, 1.856)$ and $(0.8, 2.3472)$, and use it to find an approximation to the value of y at $x = 0.65$ and at $x = 0.47$.

⎯⎯⎯⎯⎯⎯⎯⎯⎯⎯⎯⎯⎯⎯⎯⎯⎯⎯⎯⎯⎯⎯⎯⎯⎯⎯⎯⎯

We now have two approximations for $y(0.47)$, which do not agree, even to one decimal place. However, in Example 3.1 the value of $x = 0.47$ lies within the domain $0.4 \leq x \leq 0.6$ of the interpolating polynomial, and we have *interpolated* a straight line to obtain the approximation. In Exercise 3.1 the value of $x = 0.47$ lies outside the domain $0.6 \leq x \leq 0.8$ of the interpolating polynomial, and we have *extrapolated* a straight line to obtain the approximation. **Extrapolation** is, in general, less accurate than interpolation, and we should use the result for the approximate value of $y(0.47)$ from Example 3.1 rather than that from Exercise 3.1.

In general, given $n + 1$ data points, we can determine the interpolating polynomial of degree n of the form

$$y = a_0 + a_1 x + a_2 x^2 + \cdots + a_n x^n \qquad\qquad (3.3)$$

in a similar way, so we can fit a straight line through two points, a quadratic through three points, a cubic through four points, and so on.

Example 3.2

Find the interpolating quadratic polynomial for the three data points $(0.4, 1.48)$, $(0.6, 1.856)$ and $(0.8, 2.3472)$, and use it to find an approximation to the value of y at $x = 0.47$.

Solution

The three data points give rise to the system of linear equations

$$\begin{cases} a_0 + 0.4a_1 + (0.4)^2 a_2 = 1.48, \\ a_0 + 0.6a_1 + (0.6)^2 a_2 = 1.856, \\ a_0 + 0.8a_1 + (0.8)^2 a_2 = 2.3472, \end{cases}$$

that is,

$$\underbrace{\begin{bmatrix} 1 & 0.4 & 0.16 \\ 1 & 0.6 & 0.36 \\ 1 & 0.8 & 0.64 \end{bmatrix}}_{\mathbf{X}} \underbrace{\begin{bmatrix} a_0 \\ a_1 \\ a_2 \end{bmatrix}}_{\mathbf{a}} = \underbrace{\begin{bmatrix} 1.48 \\ 1.856 \\ 2.3472 \end{bmatrix}}_{\mathbf{y}}.$$

Using the Gaussian elimination method to solve these equations, we find $a_0 = 1.0736$, $a_1 = 0.44$, $a_2 = 1.44$. Hence the interpolating quadratic polynomial is

$$y = 1.0736 + 0.44x + 1.44x^2.$$

So $y(0.47) = 1.598\,496.$ ■

This value for $y(0.47)$ is fairly close to the solution found in Example 3.1.

Procedure 3.1   *Polynomial interpolation*

To determine the interpolating polynomial of degree n

$$y = a_0 + a_1 x + a_2 x^2 + \cdots + a_n x^n,$$

through $n+1$ data points (x_i, y_i), $i = 0, 1, \ldots, n$, proceed as follows.

Solve, for the coefficients $a_0, a_1, \ldots, a_n$, the system of equations $\mathbf{Xa} = \mathbf{y}$ given by

$$\begin{bmatrix} 1 & x_0 & x_0^2 & \cdots & x_0^n \\ 1 & x_1 & x_1^2 & \cdots & x_1^n \\ \vdots & \vdots & \vdots & \vdots & \vdots \\ 1 & x_n & x_n^2 & \cdots & x_n^n \end{bmatrix} \begin{bmatrix} a_0 \\ a_1 \\ \vdots \\ a_n \end{bmatrix} = \begin{bmatrix} y_0 \\ y_1 \\ \vdots \\ y_n \end{bmatrix}.$$

There are a number of questions that should be asked at this stage.

(a) *Will we always obtain a unique polynomial?*
The answer is yes, provided that all the x_i values are different.

(b) *How accurate is any estimate obtained from an interpolating polynomial?*
This depends on the accuracy of the data. For accurate data, it is often sufficient to obtain interpolating polynomials of increasing degree and then to look for consistency in the estimates. Estimates for values of x close to the data points are likely to be more accurate than those that are further away from the data points. Interpolation is, in general, more accurate than extrapolation.

Table 3.1 provides only an approximate solution to the differential equation at the specified values of x_i, and this illustrates a case where the initial data do not represent values of the 'true' function. The accuracy of the interpolated values is then limited by the accuracy of the values of y_i.

(c) *What degree polynomial should we use?*
This again depends on the accuracy of the data. In theory, if the data are very accurate, then we can use polynomials of high degree. In practice, as you will see in the computing activities, high-degree interpolating polynomials often oscillate rapidly, which may cause difficulties. A sensible strategy is to start with a low-degree polynomial and increase the degree while looking for an appropriate level of consistency in the estimates.

(d) *Which points should we use?*
The best strategy, when using an interpolating polynomial of degree n, is to select the $n+1$ points which are closest to the value of x for which you want to estimate the value of the underlying function. Unfortunately, if you need estimates at several different points, this might involve calculating several different interpolating polynomials of degree n, each based on a different subset of $n+1$ points selected from the data points. A sensible compromise might be to use a different interpolating polynomial of degree n for each subinterval $x_i \le x \le x_{i+1}$, based on the $n+1$ data points closest to this subinterval.

Exercise 3.2

Determine the quadratic polynomial that passes through the data points $(0.2, 1.2)$, $(0.4, 1.48)$ and $(0.6, 1.856)$ from Table 3.1. Use it to estimate the solution of the initial-value problem $dy/dx = x + y$, $y(0) = 1$ at $x = 0.47$. Is this estimate likely to be more accurate than that found in Example 3.2?

3.2 Least squares approximations

In the previous subsection we described a method of finding the interpolating polynomial of degree n that passes through $n + 1$ data points. However, in many practical problems, where the data are subject to random errors, it is often preferable to approximate a set of data points using a polynomial of low degree that passes close to, rather than through, the data points. We may, for example, attempt to find the 'best' straight line corresponding to a set of data points.

In statistics, this is called *linear regression*.

Such problems can arise in modelling, where we may have obtained a relationship between two variables and wish to test this relationship by comparing it with experimental results. For example, suppose that a set of measurements has produced the values shown in Table 3.2. Looking at a plot of these values (see Figure 3.2), it is clear that, within the range of possible experimental error, a linear relationship exists between y and x. The question arises as to which line gives the best fit.

Table 3.2

x	1	2	3	4
y	0.9	2.1	2.9	4.1

We are looking for a relationship of the form $y = a_0 + a_1 x$. Suppose that we write the equations as

$$\begin{cases} a_0 + a_1 = 0.9, \\ a_0 + 2a_1 = 2.1, \\ a_0 + 3a_1 = 2.9, \\ a_0 + 4a_1 = 4.1. \end{cases}$$

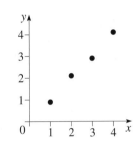

Figure 3.2

There are four equations and only two unknowns: this is an example of an **overdetermined system of equations**, i.e. a system where the number of equations is greater than the number of unknowns. We would be extremely lucky if there were values of a_0 and a_1 such that all the equations were satisfied exactly. It is more usual to find that the system has no solution, i.e. we have an inconsistent system of equations. Since the data we are considering here are subject to experimental error, we cannot expect to find values of a_0 and a_1 that will satisfy exactly all the equations.

Suppose that we measure the deviation d_i as the vertical (y) distance of each data point from the straight line $y = a_0 + a_1 x$, whose equation we wish to find, so that

$$d_i = (a_0 + a_1 x_i) - y_i \quad (i = 1, 2, 3, 4). \tag{3.4}$$

We wish to find the line that is 'closest', in some sense, to our set of data points, and we choose the sum of the squares of the deviations as our measure of 'closeness'. (The sum of the deviations would not do, because negative deviations would cancel out positive deviations.)

For the *least squares method* we seek the straight line that minimizes the sum of the squares of these deviations. Thus, for our experimental data, we wish to minimize $d_1^2 + d_2^2 + d_3^2 + d_4^2$, and this involves solving a system of linear equations.

In other words, we seek the values of a_0 and a_1 that minimize this sum of squares.

We can write Equations (3.4) in vector form as $\mathbf{d} = \mathbf{Xa} - \mathbf{y}$, where

$$\mathbf{d} = [d_1 \quad d_2 \quad d_3 \quad d_4]^T, \quad \mathbf{X} = \begin{bmatrix} 1 & 1 & 1 & 1 \\ 1 & 2 & 3 & 4 \end{bmatrix}^T,$$

$$\mathbf{a} = [a_0 \quad a_1]^T \quad \text{and} \quad \mathbf{y} = [0.9 \quad 2.1 \quad 2.9 \quad 4.1]^T.$$

From the definition of the transpose, we know that

$$\mathbf{d}^T\mathbf{d} = d_1^2 + d_2^2 + d_3^2 + d_4^2,$$

and this is the sum that we are trying to minimize with respect to a_0 and a_1. Writing

$$\mathbf{d}^T = (\mathbf{Xa} - \mathbf{y})^T = (\mathbf{Xa})^T - \mathbf{y}^T = \mathbf{a}^T\mathbf{X}^T - \mathbf{y}^T,$$

we have

$$\begin{aligned} \mathbf{d}^T\mathbf{d} &= (\mathbf{a}^T\mathbf{X}^T - \mathbf{y}^T)(\mathbf{Xa} - \mathbf{y}) \\ &= \mathbf{a}^T\mathbf{X}^T\mathbf{Xa} - \mathbf{a}^T\mathbf{X}^T\mathbf{y} - \mathbf{y}^T\mathbf{Xa} + \mathbf{y}^T\mathbf{y} \\ &= \mathbf{a}^T\mathbf{X}^T\mathbf{Xa} - 2\mathbf{a}^T\mathbf{X}^T\mathbf{y} + \mathbf{y}^T\mathbf{y}. \end{aligned}$$

For our particular example, this equation is given by

$$\mathbf{d}^T\mathbf{d} = [a_0 \quad a_1]\begin{bmatrix} 4 & 10 \\ 10 & 30 \end{bmatrix}\begin{bmatrix} a_0 \\ a_1 \end{bmatrix} - 2[a_0 \quad a_1]\begin{bmatrix} 10 \\ 30.2 \end{bmatrix} + 30.44.$$

This is a function of the two variables a_0 and a_1, and we want to minimize this function with respect to a_0 and a_1. We do not yet have the mathematics to explain how to minimize a function of two variables; we postpone that explanation until *Unit 12*. However, it transpires that the vector $\mathbf{a}$ that minimizes the expression $\mathbf{a}^T\mathbf{X}^T\mathbf{Xa} - 2\mathbf{a}^T\mathbf{X}^T\mathbf{y} + \mathbf{y}^T\mathbf{y}$ satisfies

$$(\mathbf{X}^T\mathbf{X})\mathbf{a} = \mathbf{X}^T\mathbf{y}.$$

Thus we want to solve

$$\begin{bmatrix} 4 & 10 \\ 10 & 30 \end{bmatrix}\begin{bmatrix} a_0 \\ a_1 \end{bmatrix} = \begin{bmatrix} 10 \\ 30.2 \end{bmatrix},$$

and this has solution $a_0 = -0.1$, $a_1 = 1.04$. So the least squares straight line is $y = -0.1 + 1.04x$.

Strictly, $\mathbf{d}^T\mathbf{d}$ is a matrix of order 1×1, but it is common practice to treat such matrices as numbers.

Since $\mathbf{y}^T\mathbf{Xa}$ is a 1×1 matrix, we have
$\mathbf{y}^T\mathbf{Xa} = (\mathbf{y}^T\mathbf{Xa})^T = \mathbf{a}^T\mathbf{X}^T\mathbf{y}.$

Procedure 3.2   Least squares straight line

To determine the least squares straight line approximation of the form $y = a_0 + a_1x$, given $n + 1$ data points (x_0, y_0), (x_1, y_1), ..., (x_n, y_n), where $n > 1$, proceed as follows.

(a) Write down the matrix $\mathbf{X}$ and the vectors $\mathbf{a}$ and $\mathbf{y}$ given by

$$\mathbf{X} = \begin{bmatrix} 1 & x_0 \\ 1 & x_1 \\ \vdots & \vdots \\ 1 & x_n \end{bmatrix}, \quad \mathbf{a} = \begin{bmatrix} a_0 \\ a_1 \end{bmatrix}, \quad \mathbf{y} = \begin{bmatrix} y_0 \\ y_1 \\ \vdots \\ y_n \end{bmatrix}.$$

(b) Solve the pair of linear equations represented by $(\mathbf{X}^T\mathbf{X})\mathbf{a} = \mathbf{X}^T\mathbf{y}$ to determine the vector $\mathbf{a}$, whose elements are the coefficients of the straight line approximation.

A useful check on the calculations is that the matrix $\mathbf{X}^T\mathbf{X}$ is symmetric, since $(\mathbf{X}^T\mathbf{X})^T = \mathbf{X}^T(\mathbf{X}^T)^T = \mathbf{X}^T\mathbf{X}.$

Exercise 3.3

Find the least squares straight line for the points $(1, 2)$, $(2, 2)$, $(2, 2)$ and $(3, 4)$. Sketch the graph of your solution.

Exercise 3.4 ————————————————————————

Find the least squares straight line for the points $(-1,-1)$, $(0,0)$ and $(1,1)$, and comment on the accuracy of your solution.

Exercise 3.5 ————————————————————————

Find the least squares straight line for the points $(1,1)$, $(2,4)$, $(3,9)$ and $(4,16)$, and comment on the accuracy of your solution.

End-of-section Exercise

Exercise 3.6 ————————————————————————

You are given the data points $(-1,0)$, $(0,-1)$, $(1,0)$ and $(2,1)$.

(a) Find the least squares straight line approximation, and evaluate the least squares deviation $\mathbf{d}^T\mathbf{d}$.

(b) Find the interpolating cubic polynomial.

4   Ill-conditioning

In this section we examine briefly a difficulty that may occur when we attempt to find the numerical solution to a given problem. This arises because some problems are inherently unstable in the sense that very small changes to the input data (due perhaps to experimental errors or rounding errors) may dramatically alter the output numerical values. Such problems are said to be **ill-conditioned**.

Such changes 'perturb' the data.

Problems that are not ill-conditioned are said to be **well-conditioned**.

4.1   Ill-conditioning in practice

In this subsection we use examples to help us define what we mean by ill-conditioning for a system of linear equations $\mathbf{Ax} = \mathbf{b}$. A proper analysis of ill-conditioning for such a system would include a discussion of the effect of small changes to the coefficient matrix $\mathbf{A}$, but, to simplify the theory, we discuss only the effect of small changes to the right-hand-side vector $\mathbf{b}$, and we assume that $\mathbf{A}$ is exact.

In earlier courses, we introduced the idea of absolute error: for real numbers, the error in an estimate $\bar{x}$ of the exact value x is $\bar{x} - x$, and the absolute error is $|\bar{x} - x|$. We need to extend this idea to vectors. There are a number of ways of doing this; we shall do it by defining the **norm of a vector** $\mathbf{x} = [x_1 \quad x_2 \quad \cdots \quad x_n]^T$ as the magnitude of the element of largest magnitude in $\mathbf{x}$. Thus the norm of $\mathbf{x}$, using the notation $\|\mathbf{x}\|$, is

See Subsection 4.2 of the Handbook.

$$\|\mathbf{x}\| = \max_{i=1,\ldots,n} |x_i|.$$

For example, if $\mathbf{x} = [2 \quad -3 \quad 1]^T$, then $\|\mathbf{x}\| = \max\{2,3,1\} = 3$.

Suppose that we have two vectors, $\mathbf{x}$ and $\bar{\mathbf{x}}$, where $\bar{\mathbf{x}}$ is an estimate of the exact vector $\mathbf{x}$. The **change** in $\mathbf{x}$ is $\delta\mathbf{x} = \bar{\mathbf{x}} - \mathbf{x}$, and the **absolute change** is $\|\delta\mathbf{x}\| = \|\bar{\mathbf{x}} - \mathbf{x}\|$.

We prefer to discuss changes here rather than errors, since we are making small changes to the data to see the effect on the solution.

Example 4.1

Suppose that $\mathbf{x} = [2 \quad -3 \quad 1]^T$, and that $\overline{\mathbf{x}} = [2.02 \quad -3.11 \quad 1.03]^T$ is an approximation to $\mathbf{x}$. Compute the change and the absolute change in $\mathbf{x}$.

Solution

The change is $\delta\mathbf{x} = \overline{\mathbf{x}} - \mathbf{x} = [0.02 \quad -0.11 \quad 0.03]^T$. The absolute change is $\|\delta\mathbf{x}\| = \max\{0.02, 0.11, 0.03\} = 0.11$. ∎

Exercise 4.1

Determine the absolute change in the approximation $\overline{\mathbf{x}} = [3.04 \quad 2.03 \quad 0.95]^T$ to the exact vector $\mathbf{x} = [3 \quad 2 \quad 1]^T$.

In discussing ill-conditioning, we are interested in the solution $\mathbf{x}$ of the equation

$$\mathbf{A}\mathbf{x} = \mathbf{b},$$

and, in particular, in how small changes in $\mathbf{b}$ give rise to changes in $\mathbf{x}$. The solution may be written as $\mathbf{x} = \mathbf{A}^{-1}\mathbf{b}$, which we can regard as a linear transformation of $\mathbf{b}$ to $\mathbf{x}$. If we allow each element of $\mathbf{b}$ to change by the small amount $\pm\varepsilon$, forming the vector $\overline{\mathbf{b}} = \mathbf{b} + \delta\mathbf{b}$, then the solution we obtain will be $\overline{\mathbf{x}} = \mathbf{A}^{-1}(\mathbf{b} + \delta\mathbf{b})$, where the change is

We assume that $\mathbf{A}$ is invertible.

$$\delta\mathbf{x} = \overline{\mathbf{x}} - \mathbf{x} = \mathbf{A}^{-1}(\mathbf{b} + \delta\mathbf{b}) - \mathbf{A}^{-1}\mathbf{b} = \mathbf{A}^{-1}\delta\mathbf{b}. \tag{4.1}$$

If $\|\delta\mathbf{x}\|$ is large compared to $\|\delta\mathbf{b}\|$, then we know that the system of equations is ill-conditioned.

Example 4.2

Consider the equation

$$\begin{bmatrix} 1 & -2 \\ 1 & -1.9 \end{bmatrix} \mathbf{x} = \begin{bmatrix} -1 \\ -0.8 \end{bmatrix}. \tag{4.2}$$

If the values on the right-hand side are changed by ± 0.1, how big a change in the solution might arise?

Solution

We have

$$\mathbf{A} = \begin{bmatrix} 1 & -2 \\ 1 & -1.9 \end{bmatrix}, \quad \mathbf{b} = \begin{bmatrix} -1 \\ -0.8 \end{bmatrix}, \quad \text{so} \quad \mathbf{A}^{-1} = \begin{bmatrix} -19 & 20 \\ -10 & 10 \end{bmatrix}.$$

Thus the solution of Equation (4.2) is

$$\mathbf{x} = \begin{bmatrix} -19 & 20 \\ -10 & 10 \end{bmatrix} \begin{bmatrix} -1 \\ -0.8 \end{bmatrix} = \begin{bmatrix} 3 \\ 2 \end{bmatrix}.$$

Now taking $\varepsilon = 0.1$, the possible values for $\overline{\mathbf{b}}$ are

$$\begin{bmatrix} -1.1 \\ -0.9 \end{bmatrix}, \quad \begin{bmatrix} -1.1 \\ -0.7 \end{bmatrix}, \quad \begin{bmatrix} -0.9 \\ -0.9 \end{bmatrix}, \quad \begin{bmatrix} -0.9 \\ -0.7 \end{bmatrix},$$

with corresponding values for $\delta\mathbf{b}$

$$\begin{bmatrix} -0.1 \\ -0.1 \end{bmatrix}, \quad \begin{bmatrix} -0.1 \\ 0.1 \end{bmatrix}, \quad \begin{bmatrix} 0.1 \\ -0.1 \end{bmatrix}, \quad \begin{bmatrix} 0.1 \\ 0.1 \end{bmatrix}.$$

Note that $\|\delta\mathbf{b}\| = 0.1$ for each of these vectors.

Applying $\mathbf{A}^{-1}$ to each $\delta\mathbf{b}$ above yields, respectively, the following values of $\delta\mathbf{x}$:

$$\begin{bmatrix} -0.1 \\ 0 \end{bmatrix}, \quad \begin{bmatrix} 3.9 \\ 2 \end{bmatrix}, \quad \begin{bmatrix} -3.9 \\ -2 \end{bmatrix}, \quad \begin{bmatrix} 0.1 \\ 0 \end{bmatrix}.$$

Looking at the norm of $\delta \mathbf{x}$ in each case, we see that the middle two vectors have

$$\|\delta \mathbf{x}\| = 3.9,$$

which is 39 times bigger than the norm of $\delta \mathbf{b}$. Thus a change of magnitude 0.1 in the entries of $\mathbf{b}$ may cause a change of magnitude 3.9 in the entries of the solution. ∎

A geometric interpretation will help to make this clearer. If, in Example 4.2, we change the elements of $\mathbf{b}$ by ± 0.1, then the changed vector $\overline{\mathbf{b}}$ lies at a corner of the square with centre $\mathbf{b} = [-1 \quad -0.8]^T$ shown in Figure 4.1 (which is not drawn to scale).

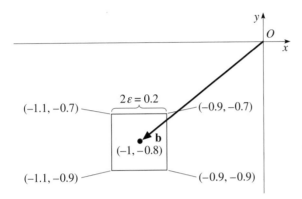

Figure 4.1

Such a point $\overline{\mathbf{b}}$ is mapped to a point $\overline{\mathbf{x}}$ under the linear transformation represented by $\mathbf{A}^{-1}$, i.e. $\overline{\mathbf{x}} = \mathbf{A}^{-1}\overline{\mathbf{b}}$, so the point $\overline{\mathbf{x}}$ must lie at a corner of the parallelogram shown in Figure 4.2. (You saw in Subsection 2.2 how linear transformations map squares to parallelograms.)

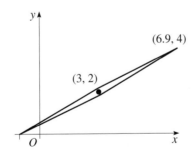

Figure 4.2

The greatest change in $\mathbf{x}$ occurs when $\overline{\mathbf{x}}$ is at a vertex furthest from (the exact solution) $\mathbf{x} = [3 \quad 2]^T$ in Figure 4.2, in other words either at $\overline{\mathbf{x}} = [6.9 \quad 4]^T$, or at $\overline{\mathbf{x}} = [-0.9 \quad 0]^T$.

The vertex $\overline{\mathbf{x}} = [6.9 \quad 4]^T$ arises from choosing $\overline{\mathbf{b}} = [-1.1 \quad -0.7]^T$, and $\overline{\mathbf{x}} = [-0.9 \quad 0]^T$ arises from choosing $\overline{\mathbf{b}} = [-0.9 \quad -0.9]^T$.

In either case, $\|\delta \mathbf{x}\| = \|\overline{\mathbf{x}} - \mathbf{x}\| = 3.9$, as we have seen. So here we have a situation in which a numerical change of 0.1 in the elements of $\mathbf{b}$ has caused a change of 3.9 in an element of the solution. We would certainly regard such a system of equations as ill-conditioned. It is the ratio of $\|\delta \mathbf{x}\|$ to $\|\delta \mathbf{b}\|$ that is relevant here. In this instance, we have found a point $\overline{\mathbf{b}}$ and its image $\overline{\mathbf{x}}$ for which this ratio is $3.9/0.1 = 39$ (a rather large number). Once we have found one instance of $\overline{\mathbf{b}}$ for which the ratio is large, we say that the system of equations is ill-conditioned.

We define the **absolute condition number** k_a for the problem of solving $\mathbf{Ax} = \mathbf{b}$, when $\mathbf{b}$ is subject to small changes of up to ε in magnitude, to be the largest possible value of the ratio of $\|\delta\mathbf{x}\|$ to $\|\delta\mathbf{b}\|$, i.e.

$$k_a = \max_{\|\delta\mathbf{b}\|\le\varepsilon} \frac{\|\delta\mathbf{x}\|}{\|\delta\mathbf{b}\|}.$$

Because $\mathbf{A}^{-1}$ represents a linear transformation, this largest value occurs when the perturbed vector $\overline{\mathbf{b}}$ lies at a corner of the square of side 2ε centred on $\mathbf{b}$. In the example above, we have shown that $k_a = 39$, which tells us that the system of equations is *absolutely ill-conditioned*.

We do not prove this here.

The cause of the ill-conditioning can be deduced by a re-examination of Equation (4.2). Solving this equation corresponds to finding the point of intersection of the two lines $x - 2y = -1$ and $x - 1.9y = -0.8$. These lines are almost parallel, so a small change in $\mathbf{b}$ can give rise to a large change in the solution.

We shall discuss methods of determining k_a and specific criteria for absolute ill-conditioning shortly.

These ideas can be applied to many problems other than those involving systems of linear equations.

Criteria for absolute ill-conditioning

Suppose that small changes are made in the data for a problem. The problem is **absolutely ill-conditioned** if it is possible for the absolute change in the solution to be significantly larger than the absolute change in the data.

Alternatively, we can think of small errors or uncertainties in the data giving rise to significantly larger errors or uncertainties in the solution.

Normally, the interpretation of *significantly larger* is dependent on the context. However, for the sake of clarity and certainty, we shall adopt the following course convention. A problem is judged to be:

- absolutely well-conditioned if the absolute condition number k_a for the problem is less than 5;

- neither absolutely well-conditioned nor absolutely ill-conditioned if k_a is greater than 5, but less than 10;

- absolutely ill-conditioned if k_a is greater than 10.

Different numbers might be more appropriate for large systems of equations, but 5 and 10 are suitable choices for systems of two or three linear equations.

For very large systems of equations, we may try to detect ill-conditioning by making small changes in the data. If, for the changes we try, the changes in the solution remain small, then we can say only that we have found *no evidence of ill-conditioning* and that the problem *may* be well-conditioned. For small systems of equations, however, where it is feasible to compute the inverse matrix $\mathbf{A}^{-1}$, we can give a much better way of detecting ill-conditioning or well-conditioning.

Changes that we have not tried might cause significantly larger changes in the solution.

From Equation (4.1) we have

$$\delta\mathbf{x} = \mathbf{A}^{-1}\delta\mathbf{b}.$$

Hence any change in the right-hand-side vector $\mathbf{b}$ will be multiplied by $\mathbf{A}^{-1}$ to give the change in the solution.

To see how this works, we return to the linear problem in Example 4.2:

$$\begin{bmatrix} 1 & -2 \\ 1 & -1.9 \end{bmatrix} \mathbf{x} = \begin{bmatrix} -1 \\ -0.8 \end{bmatrix},$$

where

$$\mathbf{A}^{-1} = \begin{bmatrix} -19 & 20 \\ -10 & 10 \end{bmatrix}.$$

The argument will be clearer if we let $\delta \mathbf{b} = [\varepsilon_1 \quad \varepsilon_2]^T$, where $\varepsilon_1 = \pm\varepsilon$ and $\varepsilon_2 = \pm\varepsilon$. Then we have

$$\delta \mathbf{x} = \mathbf{A}^{-1}\delta \mathbf{b} = \begin{bmatrix} -19 & 20 \\ -10 & 10 \end{bmatrix} \begin{bmatrix} \varepsilon_1 \\ \varepsilon_2 \end{bmatrix}$$

$$= \begin{bmatrix} -19\varepsilon_1 + 20\varepsilon_2 \\ -10\varepsilon_1 + 10\varepsilon_2 \end{bmatrix}.$$

We can see that the largest element of $\delta \mathbf{x}$ occurs when $\varepsilon_1 = -\varepsilon$ and $\varepsilon_2 = \varepsilon$, giving $\delta \mathbf{x} = [39\varepsilon \quad 20\varepsilon]^T$ and $\|\delta \mathbf{x}\| = 39\varepsilon$.

Notice that the sign of ε_i is chosen to give the largest possible result for $\|\delta \mathbf{x}\|$.

Now $\|\delta \mathbf{b}\| = \varepsilon$, therefore $k_a = 39$, as we observed above. It is no coincidence that this is also the maximum row sum of the magnitudes of the elements of $\mathbf{A}^{-1}$.

This example illustrates the following result (which we do not prove here).

Absolute condition number of an invertible $n \times n$ matrix

The absolute condition number for small changes to the right-hand-side vector $\mathbf{b}$ in the solution of $\mathbf{A}\mathbf{x} = \mathbf{b}$ is given by the maximum row sum of the magnitudes of the elements of $\mathbf{A}^{-1}$, i.e.

$$k_a = \max_i \left\{ |c_{i1}| + |c_{i2}| + \cdots + |c_{in}| \right\},$$

where the c_{ij} are the elements of the matrix $\mathbf{C} = \mathbf{A}^{-1}$.

Exercise 4.2

Determine the absolute condition number for small changes to the right-hand-side vector $\mathbf{b}$ in the solution of $\mathbf{A}\mathbf{x} = \mathbf{b}$ when $\mathbf{A}$ and its inverse are given by

$$\mathbf{A} = \begin{bmatrix} 6 & 4 & 3 \\ 7.5 & 6 & 5 \\ 10 & 7.5 & 6 \end{bmatrix}, \quad \mathbf{A}^{-1} = \begin{bmatrix} 6 & 6 & -8 \\ -20 & -24 & 30 \\ 15 & 20 & -24 \end{bmatrix}.$$

In order to determine the conditioning of a problem, we have had to do what we had hoped to avoid: calculate the inverse of the matrix $\mathbf{A}$. However, this may be the price we have to pay if we are worried that our problem may be sensitive to small changes in the data.

The cure for ill-conditioning is fairly drastic. We can abandon the current equations and try to find some more data — or even abandon the model.

Remember also that we have not discussed the effect of changes to the entries in $\mathbf{A}$.

Exercise 4.3

For each of the following examples, determine the absolute condition number and comment on the conditioning of the problem.

These examples are also considered in Activity 5.2(a).

(a) $\mathbf{A} = \begin{bmatrix} 1 & 1 \\ 1 & -2 \end{bmatrix}$, $\mathbf{b} = \begin{bmatrix} 5 \\ -1 \end{bmatrix}$.

(b) $\mathbf{A} = \begin{bmatrix} 1.4 & 1 \\ 2 & 1.4 \end{bmatrix}$, $\mathbf{b} = \begin{bmatrix} 3.7 \\ 5.2 \end{bmatrix}$.

5 Computing activities

In this section there are two computing activities involving the computer algebra package for the course. The first activity is designed to help you consolidate the material in the first three sections of the unit, while the second deals with ill-conditioning.

Use your computer to carry out the following activities.

PC

*Activity 5.1

Use the Gaussian elimination method with essential row interchanges to solve $\mathbf{Ax} = \mathbf{b}$ to determine $\mathbf{x}$ for each of the following examples. Compare this solution with the solution obtained using the computer algebra package's linear equation solver. Compare $\det \mathbf{A}$ and $\det \mathbf{U}$, and comment on your findings.

(a) $\mathbf{A} = \begin{bmatrix} 1 & -4 & 2 \\ 3 & -2 & 3 \\ 8 & -2 & 9 \end{bmatrix}$, $\mathbf{b} = \begin{bmatrix} -9 \\ 7 \\ 34 \end{bmatrix}$.

(b) $\mathbf{A} = \begin{bmatrix} 0 & 10 & -3 \\ 1 & -4 & 2 \\ 0 & 0 & 2 \end{bmatrix}$, $\mathbf{b} = \begin{bmatrix} 34 \\ -9 \\ 4 \end{bmatrix}$.

(c) $\mathbf{A} = \begin{bmatrix} 1 & 4 & -3 \\ 1 & 2 & 2 \\ 2 & 2 & 9 \end{bmatrix}$, $\mathbf{b} = \begin{bmatrix} 2 \\ 5 \\ 7 \end{bmatrix}$.

(d) $\mathbf{A} = \begin{bmatrix} 1 & 4 & -3 \\ 1 & 2 & 2 \\ 2 & 2 & 9 \end{bmatrix}$, $\mathbf{b} = \begin{bmatrix} 2 \\ 5 \\ 13 \end{bmatrix}$.

*Activity 5.2

(a) This part of the activity allows you to explore *absolute ill-conditioning* graphically for systems of two equations in two unknowns.

For each of the following systems, investigate whether perturbations (small changes) of $\pm\varepsilon$ to each of the elements of $\mathbf{b}$ cause significantly larger changes in the solution. Hence determine whether or not the problem is absolutely ill-conditioned.

(i) $\mathbf{A} = \begin{bmatrix} 1 & 1 \\ 1 & -2 \end{bmatrix}$, $\mathbf{b} = \begin{bmatrix} 5 \\ -1 \end{bmatrix}$, $\varepsilon = 0.2$.

(ii) $\mathbf{A} = \begin{bmatrix} 1 & -2 \\ 1 & -1.9 \end{bmatrix}$, $\mathbf{b} = \begin{bmatrix} -1 \\ -0.8 \end{bmatrix}$, $\varepsilon = 0.1$.

(iii) $\mathbf{A} = \begin{bmatrix} 1.4 & 1 \\ 2 & 1.4 \end{bmatrix}$, $\mathbf{b} = \begin{bmatrix} 3.7 \\ 5.2 \end{bmatrix}$, $\varepsilon = 0.1$.

(b) Consider the problem in Example 1.2, where the coefficient matrix $\mathbf{A}$ and the right-hand-side vector $\mathbf{b}$ are

$$\mathbf{A} = \begin{bmatrix} 1 & -4 & 2 \\ 3 & -2 & 3 \\ 8 & -2 & 9 \end{bmatrix}, \quad \mathbf{b} = \begin{bmatrix} -9 \\ 7 \\ 34 \end{bmatrix}.$$

Investigate whether this problem suffers from ill-conditioning. You may like to try $\varepsilon = 0.1$ for all the elements of $\mathbf{b}$ and then a different ε for each element of $\mathbf{b}$.

Outcomes

After studying this unit you should be able to:

- understand how a system of linear equations can be represented using matrices;
- solve 2×2 and 3×3 systems of linear equations by the Gaussian elimination method, using essential row interchanges where necessary;
- add, subtract and multiply matrices of suitable sizes, and multiply a matrix by a scalar;
- understand the terms transpose of a matrix, symmetric matrix, diagonal matrix, upper triangular matrix, lower triangular matrix, zero matrix, identity matrix, inverse matrix, invertible matrix and non-invertible matrix;
- understand that a matrix can be used to represent a linear transformation, and know what this means geometrically for a 2×2 matrix;
- find the inverse of a 2×2 matrix;
- evaluate the determinant of an $n \times n$ matrix, by hand when $n = 2$ or 3, and using the Gaussian elimination method for $n > 3$;
- use the determinant of a matrix to evaluate cross products, areas and volumes;
- find the interpolating polynomial of degree n passing through $n + 1$ data points, by hand for $n \le 3$;
- determine the least squares straight line approximating a set of data points;
- understand what is meant by absolute ill-conditioning for a system of linear equations, and know how to determine whether a particular problem is absolutely ill-conditioned;
- use the computer algebra package for the course to solve many of the problems posed in this unit.

Solutions to the exercises

Section 1

1.1 *Stage 1(a)* We eliminate x_1 using $E_2 - 5E_1$, which gives

$$-3x_2 + 7x_3 = 10, \qquad\qquad E_{2a}$$

followed by $E_3 - 4E_1$, which gives

$$-6x_2 + x_3 = 7. \qquad\qquad E_{3a}$$

Stage 1(b) We eliminate x_2 using $E_{3a} - 2E_{2a}$, which gives

$$-13x_3 = -13. \qquad\qquad E_{3b}$$

Stage 2 The solution is obtained by back substitution. From E_{3b}, we find $x_3 = 1$. Substituting this into E_{2a} gives $-3x_2 + 7 = 10$, hence $x_2 = -1$. From E_1, $x_1 - 1 - 1 = 2$, hence $x_1 = 4$. So the solution is

$$x_1 = 4, \quad x_2 = -1, \quad x_3 = 1.$$

1.2 (a) $\mathbf{A}|\mathbf{b} = \begin{bmatrix} 3 & -5 & 8 \\ 4 & 7 & 11 \end{bmatrix}$

(b) $\mathbf{A}|\mathbf{b} = \begin{bmatrix} 1 & 2 & 0 & 3 \\ 2 & -1 & 1 & 1 \\ 0 & 1 & -1 & -1 \end{bmatrix}$

1.3 The augmented matrix representing these equations is as follows.

$$\begin{bmatrix} 1 & 2 & 4 \\ 3 & -1 & 5 \end{bmatrix} \begin{matrix} \mathbf{R}_1 \\ \mathbf{R}_2 \end{matrix}$$

Stage 1 We reduce to zero the element below the leading diagonal.

$$\begin{matrix} \\ \mathbf{R}_2 - 3\mathbf{R}_1 \end{matrix} \begin{bmatrix} 1 & 2 & 4 \\ 0 & -7 & -7 \end{bmatrix} \begin{matrix} \mathbf{R}_1 \\ \mathbf{R}_{2a} \end{matrix}$$

Stage 2 The equations represented by the new matrix are

$$\begin{cases} x_1 + 2x_2 = 4, & E_1 \\ \quad -7x_2 = -7. & E_{2a} \end{cases}$$

From E_{2a}, we find $x_2 = 1$. Substituting this into E_1, we obtain $x_1 + 2 = 4$. Hence $x_1 = 2$, giving the solution

$$x_1 = 2, \quad x_2 = 1.$$

1.4 The augmented matrix representing these equations is as follows.

$$\begin{bmatrix} 1 & 1 & -1 & 2 \\ 5 & 2 & 2 & 20 \\ 4 & -2 & -3 & 15 \end{bmatrix} \begin{matrix} \mathbf{R}_1 \\ \mathbf{R}_2 \\ \mathbf{R}_3 \end{matrix}$$

Stage 1(a) We reduce the elements below the leading diagonal in column 1 to zero.

$$\begin{matrix} \\ \mathbf{R}_2 - 5\mathbf{R}_1 \\ \mathbf{R}_3 - 4\mathbf{R}_1 \end{matrix} \begin{bmatrix} 1 & 1 & -1 & 2 \\ 0 & -3 & 7 & 10 \\ 0 & -6 & 1 & 7 \end{bmatrix} \begin{matrix} \mathbf{R}_1 \\ \mathbf{R}_{2a} \\ \mathbf{R}_{3a} \end{matrix}$$

Stage 1(b) We reduce the element below the leading diagonal in column 2 to zero.

$$\begin{matrix} \\ \\ \mathbf{R}_{3a} - 2\mathbf{R}_{2a} \end{matrix} \begin{bmatrix} 1 & 1 & -1 & 2 \\ 0 & -3 & 7 & 10 \\ 0 & 0 & -13 & -13 \end{bmatrix} \begin{matrix} \mathbf{R}_1 \\ \mathbf{R}_{2a} \\ \mathbf{R}_{3b} \end{matrix}$$

Stage 2 The equations represented by the new matrix are

$$\begin{cases} x_1 + x_2 - x_3 = 2, & E_1 \\ \quad -3x_2 + 7x_3 = 10, & E_{2a} \\ \quad\quad -13x_3 = -13. & E_{3b} \end{cases}$$

From E_{3b}, we have $x_3 = 1$.
From E_{2a}, we have $-3x_2 + 7 = 10$, so $x_2 = -1$.
From E_1, we have $x_1 - 1 - 1 = 2$, so $x_1 = 4$.
Hence the solution is

$$x_1 = 4, \quad x_2 = -1, \quad x_3 = 1,$$

as we saw in Solution 1.1.

1.5 The graphs of the four pairs of equations are sketched below.

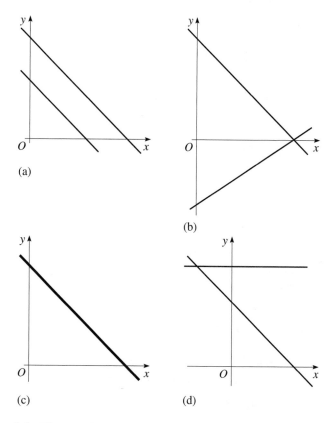

(a)

(b)

(c)

(d)

(a) The two lines are parallel, so there is no solution.

(b) There is one solution, at the intersection of the two lines.

(c) The two lines coincide, so there is an infinite number of solutions, consisting of all the points that lie on the line.

(d) There is one solution, at the intersection of the two lines.

1.6 For the two lines to be parallel they must have the same slope. Assuming that $b \neq 0$ (which then requires $d \neq 0$), the first line has slope $-a/b$, while the second line has slope $-c/d$. Hence the two lines are parallel if

$$\text{either} \quad b = d = 0 \quad \text{or} \quad \frac{a}{b} = \frac{c}{d}.$$

1.7 (a) Write down the augmented matrix.

$$\mathbf{A}|\mathbf{b} = \begin{bmatrix} 1 & -2 & 5 & 7 \\ 1 & 3 & -4 & 20 \\ 1 & 18 & -31 & 40 \end{bmatrix} \begin{matrix} \mathbf{R}_1 \\ \mathbf{R}_2 \\ \mathbf{R}_3 \end{matrix}$$

Stage 1(a) Reduce to zero in column 1.

$$\begin{matrix} \\ \mathbf{R}_2 - \mathbf{R}_1 \\ \mathbf{R}_3 - \mathbf{R}_1 \end{matrix} \begin{bmatrix} 1 & -2 & 5 & 7 \\ 0 & 5 & -9 & 13 \\ 0 & 20 & -36 & 33 \end{bmatrix} \begin{matrix} \mathbf{R}_1 \\ \mathbf{R}_{2a} \\ \mathbf{R}_{3a} \end{matrix}$$

Stage 1(b) Reduce to zero in column 2.

$$\begin{matrix} \\ \\ \mathbf{R}_{3a} - 4\mathbf{R}_{2a} \end{matrix} \begin{bmatrix} 1 & -2 & 5 & 7 \\ 0 & 5 & -9 & 13 \\ 0 & 0 & 0 & -19 \end{bmatrix} \begin{matrix} \mathbf{R}_1 \\ \mathbf{R}_{2a} \\ \mathbf{R}_{3b} \end{matrix}$$

Stage 2 Try to solve the equations represented by the rows of the above matrix.

Since the rows of $\mathbf{A}$ are linearly dependent, but the rows of $\mathbf{A}|\mathbf{b}$ are not, there is no solution.

(b) Write down the augmented matrix.

$$\mathbf{A}|\mathbf{b} = \begin{bmatrix} 1 & -2 & 5 & 6 \\ 1 & 3 & -4 & 7 \\ 2 & 6 & -12 & 12 \end{bmatrix} \begin{matrix} \mathbf{R}_1 \\ \mathbf{R}_2 \\ \mathbf{R}_3 \end{matrix}$$

Stage 1(a) Reduce to zero in column 1.

$$\begin{matrix} \\ \mathbf{R}_2 - \mathbf{R}_1 \\ \mathbf{R}_3 - 2\mathbf{R}_1 \end{matrix} \begin{bmatrix} 1 & -2 & 5 & 6 \\ 0 & 5 & -9 & 1 \\ 0 & 10 & -22 & 0 \end{bmatrix} \begin{matrix} \mathbf{R}_1 \\ \mathbf{R}_{2a} \\ \mathbf{R}_{3a} \end{matrix}$$

Stage 1(b) Reduce to zero in column 2.

$$\begin{matrix} \\ \\ \mathbf{R}_{3a} - 2\mathbf{R}_{2a} \end{matrix} \begin{bmatrix} 1 & -2 & 5 & 6 \\ 0 & 5 & -9 & 1 \\ 0 & 0 & -4 & -2 \end{bmatrix} \begin{matrix} \mathbf{R}_1 \\ \mathbf{R}_{2a} \\ \mathbf{R}_{3b} \end{matrix}$$

Stage 2 Solve the equations by back substitution.

Since the rows of $\mathbf{A}$ are linearly independent, there is a unique solution. Back substitution gives

$$x_1 = 5.7, \quad x_2 = 1.1, \quad x_3 = 0.5.$$

(c) Write down the augmented matrix.

$$\mathbf{A}|\mathbf{b} = \begin{bmatrix} 1 & -4 & 1 & 14 \\ 5 & -1 & -1 & 2 \\ 6 & 14 & -6 & -52 \end{bmatrix} \begin{matrix} \mathbf{R}_1 \\ \mathbf{R}_2 \\ \mathbf{R}_3 \end{matrix}$$

Stage 1(a) Reduce to zero in column 1.

$$\begin{matrix} \\ \mathbf{R}_2 - 5\mathbf{R}_1 \\ \mathbf{R}_3 - 6\mathbf{R}_1 \end{matrix} \begin{bmatrix} 1 & -4 & 1 & 14 \\ 0 & 19 & -6 & -68 \\ 0 & 38 & -12 & -136 \end{bmatrix} \begin{matrix} \mathbf{R}_1 \\ \mathbf{R}_{2a} \\ \mathbf{R}_{3a} \end{matrix}$$

Stage 1(b) Reduce to zero in column 2.

$$\begin{matrix} \\ \\ \mathbf{R}_{3a} - 2\mathbf{R}_{2a} \end{matrix} \begin{bmatrix} 1 & -4 & 1 & 14 \\ 0 & 19 & -6 & -68 \\ 0 & 0 & 0 & 0 \end{bmatrix} \begin{matrix} \mathbf{R}_1 \\ \mathbf{R}_{2a} \\ \mathbf{R}_{3b} \end{matrix}$$

Stage 2 Solve the equations by back substitution.

Since the rows of $\mathbf{A}|\mathbf{b}$ are linearly dependent, there is an infinite number of solutions. Putting $x_3 = k$, back substitution gives the set of solutions

$$x_1 = (5k - 6)/19, \quad x_2 = (6k - 68)/19, \quad x_3 = k.$$

Here

$$\begin{aligned} \mathbf{R}_{3b} &= \mathbf{R}_{3a} - 2\mathbf{R}_{2a} \\ &= (\mathbf{R}_3 - 6\mathbf{R}_1) - 2(\mathbf{R}_2 - 5\mathbf{R}_1) \\ &= \mathbf{R}_3 - 2\mathbf{R}_2 + 4\mathbf{R}_1 = \mathbf{0}, \end{aligned}$$

which is the required non-trivial linear combination of the rows of $\mathbf{A}|\mathbf{b}$ that gives a row of zeros.

Section 2

2.1 (a) $3\mathbf{A} = \begin{bmatrix} 3 & 6 & 9 \\ 12 & 15 & 18 \end{bmatrix}$,

$$-\mathbf{A} = \begin{bmatrix} -1 & -2 & -3 \\ -4 & -5 & -6 \end{bmatrix}.$$

(b) $\mathbf{A} + \mathbf{B} = \begin{bmatrix} 1+1 & 2+3 & 3+7 \\ 4+4 & 5+(-5) & 6+0 \end{bmatrix}$

$$= \begin{bmatrix} 2 & 5 & 10 \\ 8 & 0 & 6 \end{bmatrix},$$

$$\mathbf{B} + \mathbf{C} = \begin{bmatrix} 1+(-2) & 3+1 & 7+(-6) \\ 4+(-5) & (-5)+3 & 0+3 \end{bmatrix}$$

$$= \begin{bmatrix} -1 & 4 & 1 \\ -1 & -2 & 3 \end{bmatrix}.$$

(c) $(\mathbf{A} + \mathbf{B}) + \mathbf{C} = \begin{bmatrix} 2 & 5 & 10 \\ 8 & 0 & 6 \end{bmatrix} + \begin{bmatrix} -2 & 1 & -6 \\ -5 & 3 & 3 \end{bmatrix}$

$$= \begin{bmatrix} 0 & 6 & 4 \\ 3 & 3 & 9 \end{bmatrix},$$

$$\mathbf{A} + (\mathbf{B} + \mathbf{C}) = \begin{bmatrix} 1 & 2 & 3 \\ 4 & 5 & 6 \end{bmatrix} + \begin{bmatrix} -1 & 4 & 1 \\ -1 & -2 & 3 \end{bmatrix}$$

$$= \begin{bmatrix} 0 & 6 & 4 \\ 3 & 3 & 9 \end{bmatrix}.$$

Thus $(\mathbf{A} + \mathbf{B}) + \mathbf{C} = \mathbf{A} + (\mathbf{B} + \mathbf{C})$.

2.2 (a) $\mathbf{A} - \mathbf{B} = \begin{bmatrix} 1 & -2 \\ 7 & -3 \end{bmatrix} - \begin{bmatrix} -3 & 0 \\ 4 & -5 \end{bmatrix}$

$$= \begin{bmatrix} 1-(-3) & -2-0 \\ 7-4 & -3-(-5) \end{bmatrix}$$

$$= \begin{bmatrix} 4 & -2 \\ 3 & 2 \end{bmatrix},$$

$$\mathbf{B} - \mathbf{A} = \begin{bmatrix} -3 & 0 \\ 4 & -5 \end{bmatrix} - \begin{bmatrix} 1 & -2 \\ 7 & -3 \end{bmatrix}$$

$$= \begin{bmatrix} -3-1 & 0-(-2) \\ 4-7 & -5-(-3) \end{bmatrix} = \begin{bmatrix} -4 & 2 \\ -3 & -2 \end{bmatrix}.$$

(b) From part (a) we have $\mathbf{B} - \mathbf{A} = -(\mathbf{A} - \mathbf{B})$.

2.3 (a) $2\mathbf{A} - 5\mathbf{B} = \begin{bmatrix} 2 & 4 & 6 \\ 8 & 10 & 12 \end{bmatrix} - \begin{bmatrix} 5 & 15 & 35 \\ 20 & -25 & 0 \end{bmatrix}$

$\qquad\qquad\quad = \begin{bmatrix} -3 & -11 & -29 \\ -12 & 35 & 12 \end{bmatrix}.$

(b) $3(\mathbf{A} + \mathbf{B}) = 3\begin{bmatrix} 2 & 5 & 10 \\ 8 & 0 & 6 \end{bmatrix} = \begin{bmatrix} 6 & 15 & 30 \\ 24 & 0 & 18 \end{bmatrix},$

$3\mathbf{A} + 3\mathbf{B} = \begin{bmatrix} 3 & 6 & 9 \\ 12 & 15 & 18 \end{bmatrix} + \begin{bmatrix} 3 & 9 & 21 \\ 12 & -15 & 0 \end{bmatrix}$

$\qquad\qquad\quad = \begin{bmatrix} 6 & 15 & 30 \\ 24 & 0 & 18 \end{bmatrix}.$

Thus $3(\mathbf{A} + \mathbf{B}) = 3\mathbf{A} + 3\mathbf{B}$.

2.4 (a) $\begin{bmatrix} 1 & 2 \\ 2 & -3 \end{bmatrix}\begin{bmatrix} 1 & 3 \\ 2 & -1 \end{bmatrix} = \begin{bmatrix} 5 & 1 \\ -4 & 9 \end{bmatrix}$

(b) $\begin{bmatrix} 2 & 1 \end{bmatrix}\begin{bmatrix} 1 & 6 \\ 0 & 2 \end{bmatrix} = \begin{bmatrix} 2 & 14 \end{bmatrix}$

(c) $\begin{bmatrix} 1 \\ 2 \end{bmatrix}\begin{bmatrix} 3 & 0 & -4 \end{bmatrix} = \begin{bmatrix} 3 & 0 & -4 \\ 6 & 0 & -8 \end{bmatrix}$

(d) $\begin{bmatrix} 3 & 1 & 2 \\ 0 & 5 & 1 \end{bmatrix}\begin{bmatrix} -2 & 0 & 1 \\ 1 & 3 & 0 \\ 4 & 1 & -1 \end{bmatrix} = \begin{bmatrix} 3 & 5 & 1 \\ 9 & 16 & -1 \end{bmatrix}$

(e) The product does not exist, because the left-hand matrix has only 1 column, whereas the right-hand matrix has 2 rows.

2.5 $\mathbf{Ax} = \begin{bmatrix} 3 & -1 & 5 \\ 6 & 4 & 7 \\ 2 & -3 & 0 \end{bmatrix}\begin{bmatrix} x_1 \\ x_2 \\ x_3 \end{bmatrix}$

$\qquad = \begin{bmatrix} 3x_1 - x_2 + 5x_3 \\ 6x_1 + 4x_2 + 7x_3 \\ 2x_1 - 3x_2 \end{bmatrix}.$

The two matrices $\mathbf{Ax}$ and $\mathbf{b}$ are equal only if

$\begin{cases} 3x_1 - x_2 + 5x_3 = 2, \\ 6x_1 + 4x_2 + 7x_3 = 5, \\ 2x_1 - 3x_2 \quad\ = 6. \end{cases}$

Hence the equation $\mathbf{Ax} = \mathbf{b}$ is equivalent to the system of linear equations.

2.6 (a) $\mathbf{AB} = \begin{bmatrix} 1 & 1 \\ 3 & 2 \end{bmatrix}\begin{bmatrix} 1 & 4 \\ 2 & 1 \end{bmatrix} = \begin{bmatrix} 3 & 5 \\ 7 & 14 \end{bmatrix},$

$\mathbf{BA} = \begin{bmatrix} 1 & 4 \\ 2 & 1 \end{bmatrix}\begin{bmatrix} 1 & 1 \\ 3 & 2 \end{bmatrix} = \begin{bmatrix} 13 & 9 \\ 5 & 4 \end{bmatrix}.$

Thus $\mathbf{AB} \neq \mathbf{BA}$.

(b) $(\mathbf{AB})\mathbf{C} = \begin{bmatrix} 3 & 5 \\ 7 & 14 \end{bmatrix}\begin{bmatrix} 2 & 0 \\ 1 & 5 \end{bmatrix} = \begin{bmatrix} 11 & 25 \\ 28 & 70 \end{bmatrix},$

$\mathbf{A}(\mathbf{BC}) = \begin{bmatrix} 1 & 1 \\ 3 & 2 \end{bmatrix}\left(\begin{bmatrix} 1 & 4 \\ 2 & 1 \end{bmatrix}\begin{bmatrix} 2 & 0 \\ 1 & 5 \end{bmatrix}\right)$

$\qquad = \begin{bmatrix} 1 & 1 \\ 3 & 2 \end{bmatrix}\begin{bmatrix} 6 & 20 \\ 5 & 5 \end{bmatrix}$

$\qquad = \begin{bmatrix} 11 & 25 \\ 28 & 70 \end{bmatrix}.$

Thus $(\mathbf{AB})\mathbf{C} = \mathbf{A}(\mathbf{BC})$.

(c) $\mathbf{A}(\mathbf{B} + \mathbf{C}) = \begin{bmatrix} 1 & 1 \\ 3 & 2 \end{bmatrix}\left(\begin{bmatrix} 1 & 4 \\ 2 & 1 \end{bmatrix} + \begin{bmatrix} 2 & 0 \\ 1 & 5 \end{bmatrix}\right)$

$\qquad = \begin{bmatrix} 1 & 1 \\ 3 & 2 \end{bmatrix}\begin{bmatrix} 3 & 4 \\ 3 & 6 \end{bmatrix} = \begin{bmatrix} 6 & 10 \\ 15 & 24 \end{bmatrix},$

$\mathbf{AB} + \mathbf{AC} = \begin{bmatrix} 1 & 1 \\ 3 & 2 \end{bmatrix}\begin{bmatrix} 1 & 4 \\ 2 & 1 \end{bmatrix} + \begin{bmatrix} 1 & 1 \\ 3 & 2 \end{bmatrix}\begin{bmatrix} 2 & 0 \\ 1 & 5 \end{bmatrix}$

$\qquad = \begin{bmatrix} 3 & 5 \\ 7 & 14 \end{bmatrix} + \begin{bmatrix} 3 & 5 \\ 8 & 10 \end{bmatrix} = \begin{bmatrix} 6 & 10 \\ 15 & 24 \end{bmatrix}.$

Thus $\mathbf{A}(\mathbf{B} + \mathbf{C}) = \mathbf{AB} + \mathbf{AC}$.

2.7 (a) $\mathbf{A}^T = \begin{bmatrix} 1 & 3 & 5 \\ 2 & 4 & 6 \end{bmatrix},\quad \mathbf{B}^T = \begin{bmatrix} 2 & -1 & 3 \\ 5 & -4 & 1 \end{bmatrix},$

$\mathbf{C}^T = \begin{bmatrix} 1 & 2 \\ 0 & 3 \end{bmatrix}.$

(b) $(\mathbf{A} + \mathbf{B})^T = \left(\begin{bmatrix} 1 & 2 \\ 3 & 4 \\ 5 & 6 \end{bmatrix} + \begin{bmatrix} 2 & 5 \\ -1 & -4 \\ 3 & 1 \end{bmatrix}\right)^T$

$\qquad = \begin{bmatrix} 3 & 7 \\ 2 & 0 \\ 8 & 7 \end{bmatrix}^T = \begin{bmatrix} 3 & 2 & 8 \\ 7 & 0 & 7 \end{bmatrix},$

$\mathbf{A}^T + \mathbf{B}^T = \begin{bmatrix} 1 & 3 & 5 \\ 2 & 4 & 6 \end{bmatrix} + \begin{bmatrix} 2 & -1 & 3 \\ 5 & -4 & 1 \end{bmatrix}$

$\qquad = \begin{bmatrix} 3 & 2 & 8 \\ 7 & 0 & 7 \end{bmatrix}.$

Thus $(\mathbf{A} + \mathbf{B})^T = \mathbf{A}^T + \mathbf{B}^T$.

(c) $(\mathbf{AC})^T = \left(\begin{bmatrix} 1 & 2 \\ 3 & 4 \\ 5 & 6 \end{bmatrix}\begin{bmatrix} 1 & 0 \\ 2 & 3 \end{bmatrix}\right)^T$

$\qquad = \begin{bmatrix} 5 & 6 \\ 11 & 12 \\ 17 & 18 \end{bmatrix}^T = \begin{bmatrix} 5 & 11 & 17 \\ 6 & 12 & 18 \end{bmatrix},$

$\mathbf{C}^T\mathbf{A}^T = \begin{bmatrix} 1 & 2 \\ 0 & 3 \end{bmatrix}\begin{bmatrix} 1 & 3 & 5 \\ 2 & 4 & 6 \end{bmatrix} = \begin{bmatrix} 5 & 11 & 17 \\ 6 & 12 & 18 \end{bmatrix}.$

Thus $(\mathbf{AC})^T = \mathbf{C}^T\mathbf{A}^T$.

2.8 (a) The matrix is upper triangular.

(b) The matrix is neither upper triangular nor lower triangular and so cannot be diagonal.

(c) The matrix is upper triangular and lower triangular and hence diagonal.

2.9 (a) $\mathbf{AB} = \begin{bmatrix} 2 & 1 \\ 7 & 8 \end{bmatrix}\begin{bmatrix} \frac{8}{9} & -\frac{1}{9} \\ -\frac{7}{9} & \frac{2}{9} \end{bmatrix} = \begin{bmatrix} 1 & 0 \\ 0 & 1 \end{bmatrix} = \mathbf{I}.$

Since $\mathbf{AB} = \mathbf{I}$, it follows that $\mathbf{B} = \mathbf{A}^{-1}$.

(b) $\mathbf{AB} = \begin{bmatrix} 1 & 3 & -1 \\ -2 & -5 & 1 \\ 4 & 11 & -2 \end{bmatrix}\begin{bmatrix} -1 & -5 & -2 \\ 0 & 2 & 1 \\ -2 & 1 & 1 \end{bmatrix}$

$\qquad = \begin{bmatrix} 1 & 0 & 0 \\ 0 & 1 & 0 \\ 0 & 0 & 1 \end{bmatrix} = \mathbf{I}.$

Since $\mathbf{AB} = \mathbf{I}$, it follows that $\mathbf{B} = \mathbf{A}^{-1}$.

2.10 We form the 4×2 augmented matrix.

$$\begin{bmatrix} a & b & | & 1 & 0 \\ c & d & | & 0 & 1 \end{bmatrix} \begin{matrix} \mathbf{R}_1 \\ \mathbf{R}_2 \end{matrix}$$

Going through the stages of Procedure 2.1 in turn we obtain, for $a \neq 0$, the following.

$$\mathbf{R}_2 - \frac{c}{a}\mathbf{R}_1 \begin{bmatrix} a & b & | & 1 & 0 \\ 0 & d - \frac{c}{a}b & | & -\frac{c}{a} & 1 \end{bmatrix} \begin{matrix} \mathbf{R}_1 \\ \mathbf{R}_{2a} \end{matrix}$$

$$\frac{a}{ad-bc}\mathbf{R}_{2a} \begin{bmatrix} a & b & | & 1 & 0 \\ 0 & 1 & | & -\frac{c}{ad-bc} & \frac{a}{ad-bc} \end{bmatrix} \begin{matrix} \mathbf{R}_1 \\ \mathbf{R}_{2b} \end{matrix}$$

$$\mathbf{R}_1 - b\mathbf{R}_{2b} \begin{bmatrix} a & 0 & | & \frac{ad}{ad-bc} & -\frac{ab}{ad-bc} \\ 0 & 1 & | & -\frac{c}{ad-bc} & \frac{a}{ad-bc} \end{bmatrix} \begin{matrix} \mathbf{R}_{1a} \\ \mathbf{R}_{2b} \end{matrix}$$

$$\frac{1}{a}\mathbf{R}_{1a} \begin{bmatrix} 1 & 0 & | & \frac{d}{ad-bc} & -\frac{b}{ad-bc} \\ 0 & 1 & | & -\frac{c}{ad-bc} & \frac{a}{ad-bc} \end{bmatrix} \begin{matrix} \mathbf{R}_{1b} \\ \mathbf{R}_{2b} \end{matrix}$$

Hence

$$\mathbf{A}^{-1} = \frac{1}{ad-bc} \begin{bmatrix} d & -b \\ -c & a \end{bmatrix}.$$

If $a = 0$, we must start by interchanging $\mathbf{R}_1$ and $\mathbf{R}_2$.

$$\mathbf{R}_1 \leftrightarrow \mathbf{R}_2 \begin{bmatrix} c & d & | & 0 & 1 \\ 0 & b & | & 1 & 0 \end{bmatrix} \begin{matrix} \mathbf{R}_{1a} \\ \mathbf{R}_{2a} \end{matrix}$$

Again, going through the stages of Procedure 2.1 in turn, noting that $bc \neq 0$ since $ad - bc \neq 0$, we obtain the following.

$$\frac{1}{b}\mathbf{R}_{2a} \begin{bmatrix} c & d & | & 0 & 1 \\ 0 & 1 & | & \frac{1}{b} & 0 \end{bmatrix} \begin{matrix} \mathbf{R}_{1a} \\ \mathbf{R}_{2b} \end{matrix}$$

$$\mathbf{R}_{1a} - d\mathbf{R}_{2b} \begin{bmatrix} c & 0 & | & -\frac{d}{b} & 1 \\ 0 & 1 & | & \frac{1}{b} & 0 \end{bmatrix} \begin{matrix} \mathbf{R}_{1b} \\ \mathbf{R}_{2b} \end{matrix}$$

$$\frac{1}{c}\mathbf{R}_{1b} \begin{bmatrix} 1 & 0 & | & -\frac{d}{bc} & \frac{1}{c} \\ 0 & 1 & | & \frac{1}{b} & 0 \end{bmatrix} \begin{matrix} \mathbf{R}_{1c} \\ \mathbf{R}_{2b} \end{matrix}$$

This gives the same inverse matrix as substituting $a = 0$ into the inverse matrix found earlier.

2.11 (a) Since $\det \mathbf{A} = (7 \times 3) - (4 \times 5) = 1$,

$$\mathbf{A}^{-1} = \begin{bmatrix} 3 & -4 \\ -5 & 7 \end{bmatrix}.$$

(b) Since $\det \mathbf{A} = (6 \times 3) - (2 \times 9) = 0$, $\mathbf{A}^{-1}$ does not exist.

(c) Since $\det \mathbf{A} = (4 \times 3) - (2 \times 5) = 2$,

$$\mathbf{A}^{-1} = \frac{1}{2} \begin{bmatrix} 3 & -2 \\ -5 & 4 \end{bmatrix} = \begin{bmatrix} \frac{3}{2} & -1 \\ -\frac{5}{2} & 2 \end{bmatrix}.$$

2.12 (a) We have

$$\begin{aligned} (\mathbf{B}^{-1}\mathbf{A}^{-1})(\mathbf{A}\mathbf{B}) &= \mathbf{B}^{-1}(\mathbf{A}^{-1}\mathbf{A})\mathbf{B} \\ &= \mathbf{B}^{-1}\mathbf{I}\mathbf{B} \\ &= \mathbf{B}^{-1}\mathbf{B} = \mathbf{I} \end{aligned}$$

and

$$(\mathbf{A}\mathbf{B})(\mathbf{B}^{-1}\mathbf{A}^{-1}) = \mathbf{A}(\mathbf{B}\mathbf{B}^{-1})\mathbf{A}^{-1} = \mathbf{A}\mathbf{A}^{-1} = \mathbf{I},$$

hence $(\mathbf{A}\mathbf{B})^{-1} = \mathbf{B}^{-1}\mathbf{A}^{-1}$.

(b) Since $\det \mathbf{A} = 2$, we have

$$\mathbf{A}^{-1} = \frac{1}{2} \begin{bmatrix} 5 & -2 \\ -4 & 2 \end{bmatrix} = \begin{bmatrix} \frac{5}{2} & -1 \\ -2 & 1 \end{bmatrix}.$$

Since $\det \mathbf{B} = -2$, we have

$$\mathbf{B}^{-1} = \frac{1}{-2} \begin{bmatrix} -2 & -4 \\ 1 & 3 \end{bmatrix} = \begin{bmatrix} 1 & 2 \\ -\frac{1}{2} & -\frac{3}{2} \end{bmatrix}.$$

(c) $(\mathbf{A} + \mathbf{B})^{-1} = \begin{bmatrix} 5 & 6 \\ 3 & 3 \end{bmatrix}^{-1}$

$$= \frac{1}{-3} \begin{bmatrix} 3 & -6 \\ -3 & 5 \end{bmatrix}$$

$$= \begin{bmatrix} -1 & 2 \\ 1 & -\frac{5}{3} \end{bmatrix},$$

$$\mathbf{A}^{-1} + \mathbf{B}^{-1} = \begin{bmatrix} \frac{5}{2} & -1 \\ -2 & 1 \end{bmatrix} + \begin{bmatrix} 1 & 2 \\ -\frac{1}{2} & -\frac{3}{2} \end{bmatrix}$$

$$= \begin{bmatrix} \frac{7}{2} & 1 \\ -\frac{5}{2} & -\frac{1}{2} \end{bmatrix}.$$

Thus $(\mathbf{A} + \mathbf{B})^{-1} \neq \mathbf{A}^{-1} + \mathbf{B}^{-1}$.

(d) $(\mathbf{A}\mathbf{B})^{-1} = \left(\begin{bmatrix} 2 & 2 \\ 4 & 5 \end{bmatrix} \begin{bmatrix} 3 & 4 \\ -1 & -2 \end{bmatrix} \right)^{-1}$

$$= \begin{bmatrix} 4 & 4 \\ 7 & 6 \end{bmatrix}^{-1}$$

$$= -\frac{1}{4} \begin{bmatrix} 6 & -4 \\ -7 & 4 \end{bmatrix}$$

$$= \begin{bmatrix} -\frac{3}{2} & 1 \\ \frac{7}{4} & -1 \end{bmatrix},$$

$$\mathbf{B}^{-1}\mathbf{A}^{-1} = \begin{bmatrix} 1 & 2 \\ -\frac{1}{2} & -\frac{3}{2} \end{bmatrix} \begin{bmatrix} \frac{5}{2} & -1 \\ -2 & 1 \end{bmatrix}$$

$$= \begin{bmatrix} -\frac{3}{2} & 1 \\ \frac{7}{4} & -1 \end{bmatrix}.$$

Thus $(\mathbf{A}\mathbf{B})^{-1} = \mathbf{B}^{-1}\mathbf{A}^{-1}$.

2.13 (a) $\mathbf{A} = \begin{bmatrix} 1 & 2 \\ 3 & 4 \end{bmatrix}$

(b) (i) $\mathbf{A} \begin{bmatrix} 3 \\ 1 \end{bmatrix} = \begin{bmatrix} 1 & 2 \\ 3 & 4 \end{bmatrix} \begin{bmatrix} 3 \\ 1 \end{bmatrix} = \begin{bmatrix} 5 \\ 13 \end{bmatrix}$

(ii) $\mathbf{A} \begin{bmatrix} -1 \\ 1 \end{bmatrix} = \begin{bmatrix} 1 & 2 \\ 3 & 4 \end{bmatrix} \begin{bmatrix} -1 \\ 1 \end{bmatrix} = \begin{bmatrix} 1 \\ 1 \end{bmatrix}$

(iii) $\mathbf{A} \begin{bmatrix} 0 \\ 0 \end{bmatrix} = \begin{bmatrix} 1 & 2 \\ 3 & 4 \end{bmatrix} \begin{bmatrix} 0 \\ 0 \end{bmatrix} = \begin{bmatrix} 0 \\ 0 \end{bmatrix}$

2.14 In each case, the area of the parallelogram is the magnitude of det $\mathbf{A}$. (Note that in each case the parallelogram is a rectangle!)

(a) We have det $\mathbf{A} = 2$, so the area of the parallelogram is 2.

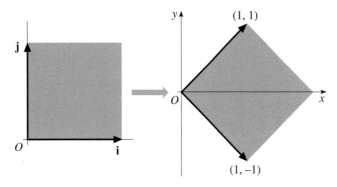

(b) We have det $\mathbf{A} = -20$, so the area of the parallelogram is 20.

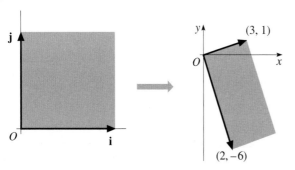

(c) We have det $\mathbf{A} = 0$, so the area of the parallelogram is 0.

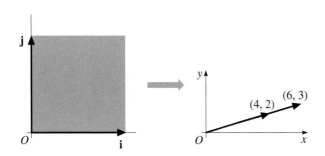

2.15 (a) $\begin{vmatrix} a & 0 \\ c & d \end{vmatrix} = \begin{vmatrix} a & b \\ 0 & d \end{vmatrix} = \begin{vmatrix} a & 0 \\ 0 & d \end{vmatrix} = ad$

(b) $\begin{vmatrix} c & d \\ a & b \end{vmatrix} = \begin{vmatrix} b & a \\ d & c \end{vmatrix}$

$= bc - ad = -(ad - bc) = -\det \mathbf{A}$

(c) $\begin{vmatrix} a & c \\ b & d \end{vmatrix} = ad - bc = \det \mathbf{A}$

(d) $\begin{vmatrix} a & b \\ a & b \end{vmatrix} = \begin{vmatrix} a & a \\ c & c \end{vmatrix} = 0$

(e) $\begin{vmatrix} ka & kb \\ c & d \end{vmatrix} = \begin{vmatrix} ka & b \\ kc & d \end{vmatrix} = k(ad - bc) = k \det \mathbf{A}$

(f) $\begin{vmatrix} ka & kb \\ kc & kd \end{vmatrix} = k^2(ad - bc) = k^2 \det \mathbf{A}$

(g) $\begin{vmatrix} a & b \\ c - ma & d - mb \end{vmatrix} = ad - amb - bc + bma$

$= ad - bc = \det \mathbf{A},$

$\begin{vmatrix} a - mc & b - md \\ c & d \end{vmatrix} = ad - mcd - bc + mdc$

$= ad - bc = \det \mathbf{A}.$

(h) From part (f), with $k = (ad - bc)^{-1}$, we have

$\begin{vmatrix} \dfrac{d}{ad - bc} & -\dfrac{b}{ad - bc} \\ -\dfrac{c}{ad - bc} & \dfrac{a}{ad - bc} \end{vmatrix} = \dfrac{1}{(ad - bc)^2} \begin{vmatrix} d & -b \\ -c & a \end{vmatrix}$

$= \dfrac{1}{ad - bc} = \dfrac{1}{\det \mathbf{A}}.$

2.16

(a) $\begin{vmatrix} 4 & 1 & 0 \\ 0 & 2 & -1 \\ 2 & 3 & 1 \end{vmatrix} = 4\begin{vmatrix} 2 & -1 \\ 3 & 1 \end{vmatrix} - 1\begin{vmatrix} 0 & -1 \\ 2 & 1 \end{vmatrix} + 0\begin{vmatrix} 0 & 2 \\ 2 & 3 \end{vmatrix}$

$= (4 \times 5) - (1 \times 2) + 0 = 18$

(b) $\begin{vmatrix} 1 & 2 & 3 \\ 4 & 5 & 6 \\ 7 & 8 & 9 \end{vmatrix} = 1\begin{vmatrix} 5 & 6 \\ 8 & 9 \end{vmatrix} - 2\begin{vmatrix} 4 & 6 \\ 7 & 9 \end{vmatrix} + 3\begin{vmatrix} 4 & 5 \\ 7 & 8 \end{vmatrix}$

$= (1 \times (-3)) - (2 \times (-6)) + (3 \times (-3))$

$= -3 + 12 - 9 = 0$

(c) $\begin{vmatrix} 1 & 2 & 3 \\ 0 & 4 & 5 \\ 0 & 0 & 6 \end{vmatrix} = 1\begin{vmatrix} 4 & 5 \\ 0 & 6 \end{vmatrix} - 2\begin{vmatrix} 0 & 5 \\ 0 & 6 \end{vmatrix} + 3\begin{vmatrix} 0 & 4 \\ 0 & 0 \end{vmatrix}$

$= (1 \times 24) - (2 \times 0) + (3 \times 0) = 24$

2.17 (a) We have

$\begin{vmatrix} 2 & 1 & 3 \\ 0 & 2 & 1 \\ 3 & 1 & 6 \end{vmatrix} = 2\begin{vmatrix} 2 & 1 \\ 1 & 6 \end{vmatrix} - 1\begin{vmatrix} 0 & 1 \\ 3 & 6 \end{vmatrix} + 3\begin{vmatrix} 0 & 2 \\ 3 & 1 \end{vmatrix}$

$= (2 \times 11) - (1 \times (-3)) + (3 \times (-6))$

$= 22 + 3 - 18 = 7.$

(b) (i) We obtain -7 (interchanging two rows).

(ii) We obtain 7 (taking the transpose).

(iii) We obtain -21 (interchanging two rows, as in (i), then multiplying column 2 by 3).

(c) Expanding by the first column, we have

$\det \mathbf{A} = 1\begin{vmatrix} 1 & -1 \\ 2 & 3 \end{vmatrix} - 0\begin{vmatrix} 3 & 2 \\ 2 & 3 \end{vmatrix} + 0\begin{vmatrix} 3 & 2 \\ 1 & -1 \end{vmatrix} = 5.$

We obtain

$$\mathbf{U} = \begin{bmatrix} 1 & 3 & 2 \\ 0 & 1 & -1 \\ 0 & 0 & 5 \end{bmatrix},$$

then

$\det \mathbf{U} = 1\begin{vmatrix} 1 & -1 \\ 0 & 5 \end{vmatrix} - 3\begin{vmatrix} 0 & -1 \\ 0 & 5 \end{vmatrix} + 2\begin{vmatrix} 0 & 1 \\ 0 & 0 \end{vmatrix} = 5.$

The product of the diagonal elements of $\mathbf{U}$ is also $1 \times 1 \times 5 = 5$.

2.18 We have
$$\begin{vmatrix} 1 & -4 & 2 \\ 3 & -2 & 3 \\ 8 & -2 & 9 \end{vmatrix} = 1\begin{vmatrix} -2 & 3 \\ -2 & 9 \end{vmatrix} - (-4)\begin{vmatrix} 3 & 3 \\ 8 & 9 \end{vmatrix} + 2\begin{vmatrix} 3 & -2 \\ 8 & -2 \end{vmatrix}$$
$$= -12 + 12 + 20 = 20.$$

Also, $\det \mathbf{U} = \begin{vmatrix} 1 & -4 & 2 \\ 0 & 10 & -3 \\ 0 & 0 & 2 \end{vmatrix} = 20 = \det \mathbf{A}.$

2.19 By Exercise 2.17(a),
$$\mathbf{a} \cdot (\mathbf{b} \times \mathbf{c}) = \begin{vmatrix} 2 & 1 & 3 \\ 0 & 2 & 1 \\ 3 & 1 & 6 \end{vmatrix} = 7.$$

2.20 The volume is $\left| \det \begin{bmatrix} 1 & 0 & 1 \\ 1 & 2 & 0 \\ 0 & 1 & 3 \end{bmatrix} \right|$

$$= \left| 1 \times \det \begin{bmatrix} 2 & 0 \\ 1 & 3 \end{bmatrix} - 0 \times \det \begin{bmatrix} 1 & 0 \\ 0 & 3 \end{bmatrix} + 1 \times \det \begin{bmatrix} 1 & 2 \\ 0 & 1 \end{bmatrix} \right|$$
$$= |(1 \times 6) - 0 + (1 \times 1)| = 7.$$

2.21

(a) $\mathbf{b} \times \mathbf{c} = \begin{vmatrix} \mathbf{i} & \mathbf{j} & \mathbf{k} \\ 3 & 2 & -4 \\ 1 & -1 & 3 \end{vmatrix}$

$$= \begin{vmatrix} 2 & -4 \\ -1 & 3 \end{vmatrix}\mathbf{i} - \begin{vmatrix} 3 & -4 \\ 1 & 3 \end{vmatrix}\mathbf{j} + \begin{vmatrix} 3 & 2 \\ 1 & -1 \end{vmatrix}\mathbf{k}$$
$$= 2\mathbf{i} - 13\mathbf{j} - 5\mathbf{k}$$

(b) $\mathbf{b} \times \mathbf{c} = \begin{vmatrix} \mathbf{i} & \mathbf{j} & \mathbf{k} \\ 1 & 2 & 3 \\ 6 & 5 & 4 \end{vmatrix}$

$$= \begin{vmatrix} 2 & 3 \\ 5 & 4 \end{vmatrix}\mathbf{i} - \begin{vmatrix} 1 & 3 \\ 6 & 4 \end{vmatrix}\mathbf{j} + \begin{vmatrix} 1 & 2 \\ 6 & 5 \end{vmatrix}\mathbf{k}$$
$$= -7\mathbf{i} + 14\mathbf{j} - 7\mathbf{k}$$

2.22 The area is $\frac{1}{2}\left| \det \begin{bmatrix} 1 & 1 & 1 \\ 3 & 1 & 2 \\ 1 & 2 & -1 \end{bmatrix} \right|$

$$= \frac{1}{2}\left| 1 \times \det \begin{bmatrix} 1 & 2 \\ 2 & -1 \end{bmatrix} - 1 \times \det \begin{bmatrix} 3 & 2 \\ 1 & -1 \end{bmatrix} \right.$$
$$\left. + 1 \times \det \begin{bmatrix} 3 & 1 \\ 1 & 2 \end{bmatrix} \right|$$
$$= \frac{1}{2}|-5 + 5 + 5| = 2.5.$$

2.23 $\mathbf{AB} = \begin{bmatrix} 1 & 2 & 1 \\ 2 & 3 & -1 \\ 1 & -1 & 0 \end{bmatrix}\begin{bmatrix} 1 & 1 & 0 \\ 1 & 0 & 1 \\ 0 & 1 & 1 \end{bmatrix}$

$$= \begin{bmatrix} 3 & 2 & 3 \\ 5 & 1 & 2 \\ 0 & 1 & -1 \end{bmatrix},$$

so we see that $\mathbf{AB}$ is not symmetric.

$$(\mathbf{AB})^T = \begin{bmatrix} 3 & 5 & 0 \\ 2 & 1 & 1 \\ 3 & 2 & -1 \end{bmatrix},$$

$$\mathbf{B}^T\mathbf{A}^T = \mathbf{BA} = \begin{bmatrix} 1 & 1 & 0 \\ 1 & 0 & 1 \\ 0 & 1 & 1 \end{bmatrix}\begin{bmatrix} 1 & 2 & 1 \\ 2 & 3 & -1 \\ 1 & -1 & 0 \end{bmatrix}$$
$$= \begin{bmatrix} 3 & 5 & 0 \\ 2 & 1 & 1 \\ 3 & 2 & -1 \end{bmatrix},$$

so $(\mathbf{AB})^T = \mathbf{B}^T\mathbf{A}^T$.

2.24 $\det \mathbf{A} = 1 - (-2) = 3$ and $\mathbf{A}^{-1} = \frac{1}{3}\begin{bmatrix} 1 & -2 \\ 1 & 1 \end{bmatrix}$.
Putting $\mathbf{x} = [x \ \ y]^T$ and $\mathbf{b} = [1 \ \ -1]^T$, we need to solve $\mathbf{Ax} = \mathbf{b}$. Multiplying both sides on the left by $\mathbf{A}^{-1}$, we obtain $\mathbf{A}^{-1}\mathbf{Ax} = \mathbf{A}^{-1}\mathbf{b}$. This simplifies to
$$\mathbf{x} = \mathbf{A}^{-1}\mathbf{b} = \frac{1}{3}\begin{bmatrix} 1 & -2 \\ 1 & 1 \end{bmatrix}\begin{bmatrix} 1 \\ -1 \end{bmatrix} = \begin{bmatrix} 1 \\ 0 \end{bmatrix},$$
so $x = 1$ and $y = 0$.

Section 3

3.1 Suppose that the line is $y = a_0 + a_1x$, so the interpolation equations are
$$\begin{cases} a_0 + 0.6a_1 = 1.856, \\ a_0 + 0.8a_1 = 2.3472. \end{cases}$$
The solution of this pair of equations is $a_0 = 0.3824$ and $a_1 = 2.456$, so the equation of the interpolating straight line is
$$y = 0.3824 + 2.456x.$$
Thus $y(0.65) = 1.9788$ and $y(0.47) = 1.53672$.

3.2 Suppose that the quadratic is $y = a_0 + a_1x + a_2x^2$, so the interpolation equations are
$$\begin{cases} a_0 + 0.2a_1 + (0.2)^2a_2 = 1.2, \\ a_0 + 0.4a_1 + (0.4)^2a_2 = 1.48, \\ a_0 + 0.6a_1 + (0.6)^2a_2 = 1.856. \end{cases}$$
The augmented matrix form of these equations is
$$\mathbf{X}|\mathbf{y} = \begin{bmatrix} 1 & 0.2 & 0.04 & | & 1.2 \\ 1 & 0.4 & 0.16 & | & 1.48 \\ 1 & 0.6 & 0.36 & | & 1.856 \end{bmatrix}.$$
After Stage 1 of the Gaussian elimination method, we have
$$\mathbf{U}|\mathbf{c} = \begin{bmatrix} 1 & 0.2 & 0.04 & | & 1.2 \\ 0 & 0.2 & 0.12 & | & 0.28 \\ 0 & 0 & 0.08 & | & 0.096 \end{bmatrix}.$$
Back substitution gives $\mathbf{a} = [1.016 \ \ 0.68 \ \ 1.2]^T$, so the equation of the interpolating quadratic is
$$y = 1.016 + 0.68x + 1.2x^2.$$
This gives $y(0.47) = 1.60068$. This estimate is very close to the value 1.598496 obtained in Example 3.2. However, since the three points closest to $x = 0.47$ are 0.2, 0.4 and 0.6, the value 1.60068 would be regarded as the most reliable of the four estimates that we have so far computed, in Examples 3.1 and 3.2, and Exercises 3.1 and 3.2.

3.3 The required matrices are
$$\mathbf{X} = \begin{bmatrix} 1 & 1 \\ 1 & 2 \\ 1 & 2 \\ 1 & 3 \end{bmatrix}, \quad \mathbf{a} = \begin{bmatrix} a_0 \\ a_1 \end{bmatrix}, \quad \mathbf{y} = \begin{bmatrix} 2 \\ 2 \\ 2 \\ 4 \end{bmatrix}.$$

We compute
$$\mathbf{X}^T\mathbf{X} = \begin{bmatrix} 1 & 1 & 1 & 1 \\ 1 & 2 & 2 & 3 \end{bmatrix} \begin{bmatrix} 1 & 1 \\ 1 & 2 \\ 1 & 2 \\ 1 & 3 \end{bmatrix} = \begin{bmatrix} 4 & 8 \\ 8 & 18 \end{bmatrix},$$

$$\mathbf{X}^T\mathbf{y} = \begin{bmatrix} 1 & 1 & 1 & 1 \\ 1 & 2 & 2 & 3 \end{bmatrix} \begin{bmatrix} 2 \\ 2 \\ 2 \\ 4 \end{bmatrix} = \begin{bmatrix} 10 \\ 22 \end{bmatrix}.$$

The solution of the system of linear equations $(\mathbf{X}^T\mathbf{X})\mathbf{a} = \mathbf{X}^T\mathbf{y}$ is $\mathbf{a} = [0.5 \ \ 1]^T$, so the least squares straight line for the given data points is
$$y = 0.5 + x.$$

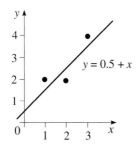

3.4 The required matrices are
$$\mathbf{X} = \begin{bmatrix} 1 & -1 \\ 1 & 0 \\ 1 & 1 \end{bmatrix}, \quad \mathbf{a} = \begin{bmatrix} a_0 \\ a_1 \end{bmatrix}, \quad \mathbf{y} = \begin{bmatrix} -1 \\ 0 \\ 1 \end{bmatrix}.$$

We compute
$$\mathbf{X}^T\mathbf{X} = \begin{bmatrix} 1 & 1 & 1 \\ -1 & 0 & 1 \end{bmatrix} \begin{bmatrix} 1 & -1 \\ 1 & 0 \\ 1 & 1 \end{bmatrix} = \begin{bmatrix} 3 & 0 \\ 0 & 2 \end{bmatrix},$$

$$\mathbf{X}^T\mathbf{y} = \begin{bmatrix} 1 & 1 & 1 \\ -1 & 0 & 1 \end{bmatrix} \begin{bmatrix} -1 \\ 0 \\ 1 \end{bmatrix} = \begin{bmatrix} 0 \\ 2 \end{bmatrix}.$$

The solution of the system of linear equations $(\mathbf{X}^T\mathbf{X})\mathbf{a} = \mathbf{X}^T\mathbf{y}$ is $\mathbf{a} = [0 \ \ 1]^T$, so the least squares straight line for the given data points is
$$y = x.$$

This result might have been expected, since all the data points lie on the line $y = x$.

3.5 The required matrices are
$$\mathbf{X} = \begin{bmatrix} 1 & 1 \\ 1 & 2 \\ 1 & 3 \\ 1 & 4 \end{bmatrix}, \quad \mathbf{a} = \begin{bmatrix} a_0 \\ a_1 \end{bmatrix}, \quad \mathbf{y} = \begin{bmatrix} 1 \\ 4 \\ 9 \\ 16 \end{bmatrix}.$$

We compute
$$\mathbf{X}^T\mathbf{X} = \begin{bmatrix} 1 & 1 & 1 & 1 \\ 1 & 2 & 3 & 4 \end{bmatrix} \begin{bmatrix} 1 & 1 \\ 1 & 2 \\ 1 & 3 \\ 1 & 4 \end{bmatrix} = \begin{bmatrix} 4 & 10 \\ 10 & 30 \end{bmatrix},$$

$$\mathbf{X}^T\mathbf{y} = \begin{bmatrix} 1 & 1 & 1 & 1 \\ 1 & 2 & 3 & 4 \end{bmatrix} \begin{bmatrix} 1 \\ 4 \\ 9 \\ 16 \end{bmatrix} = \begin{bmatrix} 30 \\ 100 \end{bmatrix}.$$

The solution of the system of linear equations $(\mathbf{X}^T\mathbf{X})\mathbf{a} = \mathbf{X}^T\mathbf{y}$ is $\mathbf{a} = [-5 \ \ 5]^T$, so the least squares straight line for the given data points is
$$y = -5 + 5x.$$

This solution is not particularly good, since the values it gives at the data points are 0, 5, 10 and 15, rather than 1, 4, 9 and 16, respectively. However, a straight line is not really appropriate for these data, which lie on the quadratic $y = x^2$; see the figure below.

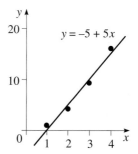

3.6 (a) For the least squares straight line, we have
$$\mathbf{X} = \begin{bmatrix} 1 & -1 \\ 1 & 0 \\ 1 & 1 \\ 1 & 2 \end{bmatrix}, \quad \mathbf{y} = \begin{bmatrix} 0 \\ -1 \\ 0 \\ 1 \end{bmatrix}, \quad \mathbf{a} = \begin{bmatrix} a_0 \\ a_1 \end{bmatrix}.$$

We compute
$$\mathbf{X}^T\mathbf{X} = \begin{bmatrix} 4 & 2 \\ 2 & 6 \end{bmatrix}, \quad \mathbf{X}^T\mathbf{y} = \begin{bmatrix} 0 \\ 2 \end{bmatrix}.$$

The solution of the system of linear equations $(\mathbf{X}^T\mathbf{X})\mathbf{a} = \mathbf{X}^T\mathbf{y}$ is $\mathbf{a} = [-0.2 \ \ 0.4]^T$, so the least squares straight line is
$$y = -0.2 + 0.4x.$$

The deviation vector $\mathbf{d}$ is given by
$$\mathbf{d} = \mathbf{X}\mathbf{a} - \mathbf{y} = \begin{bmatrix} 1 & -1 \\ 1 & 0 \\ 1 & 1 \\ 1 & 2 \end{bmatrix} \begin{bmatrix} -0.2 \\ 0.4 \end{bmatrix} - \begin{bmatrix} 0 \\ -1 \\ 0 \\ 1 \end{bmatrix}$$
$$= \begin{bmatrix} -0.6 \\ 0.8 \\ 0.2 \\ -0.4 \end{bmatrix},$$

so the least squares deviation is $\mathbf{d}^T\mathbf{d} = 1.2$.

(b) For the interpolating cubic polynomial, the required matrices are

$$\mathbf{X} = \begin{bmatrix} 1 & -1 & 1 & -1 \\ 1 & 0 & 0 & 0 \\ 1 & 1 & 1 & 1 \\ 1 & 2 & 4 & 8 \end{bmatrix}, \quad \mathbf{y} = \begin{bmatrix} 0 \\ -1 \\ 0 \\ 1 \end{bmatrix}, \quad \mathbf{a} = \begin{bmatrix} a_0 \\ a_1 \\ a_2 \\ a_3 \end{bmatrix}.$$

The solution to $\mathbf{Xa} = \mathbf{y}$ is $\mathbf{a} = [-1 \quad \frac{1}{3} \quad 1 \quad -\frac{1}{3}]^T$, so the interpolating cubic polynomial is

$$y = -1 + \tfrac{1}{3}x + x^2 - \tfrac{1}{3}x^3.$$

Section 4

4.1 The change in $\mathbf{x}$ is

$$\delta\mathbf{x} = \overline{\mathbf{x}} - \mathbf{x} = [0.04 \quad 0.03 \quad -0.05]^T,$$

so the absolute change is

$$\|\delta\mathbf{x}\| = 0.05.$$

4.2 The row sums of the magnitudes of the elements of $\mathbf{A}^{-1}$ are 20, 74 and 59. Hence the absolute condition number is $k_a = 74$.

4.3 (a) The inverse matrix is

$$\mathbf{A}^{-1} = \begin{bmatrix} \frac{2}{3} & \frac{1}{3} \\ \frac{1}{3} & -\frac{1}{3} \end{bmatrix}.$$

The problem is absolutely well-conditioned, since $k_a = 1$. (The solution is

$$\mathbf{x} = \mathbf{A}^{-1} \begin{bmatrix} 5 \\ -1 \end{bmatrix} = \begin{bmatrix} 3 \\ 2 \end{bmatrix},$$

though this was not asked for.)

(b) The inverse matrix is

$$\mathbf{A}^{-1} = \begin{bmatrix} -35 & 25 \\ 50 & -35 \end{bmatrix}.$$

The problem is absolutely ill-conditioned, since $k_a = 85$. (The solution is

$$\mathbf{x} = \mathbf{A}^{-1} \begin{bmatrix} 3.7 \\ 5.2 \end{bmatrix} = \begin{bmatrix} 0.5 \\ 3 \end{bmatrix},$$

though this was not asked for.)

UNIT 10   Eigenvalues and eigenvectors

Study guide for Unit 10

This unit continues the study of linear algebra begun in *Unit 9*. It assumes knowledge of:

- matrices to represent linear transformations of points in the plane;
- the solution of systems of linear equations in two and three variables;
- the expansion of 2×2 and 3×3 determinants.

From the point of view of later studies, Sections 2 and 3 contain the most important material.

Section 1 sets the scene and provides examples for later sections. In Subsection 1.2 you will see examples that give some indication of the importance of matrices, particularly eigenvalues, in applied mathematics.

Sections 2 and 3 contain the basic algebraic techniques that you need to understand before proceeding to *Unit 11*.

In Section 3 we shall need to expand 3×3 determinants and solve cubic equations. For all the cubic equations that we ask you to solve by hand, one root will be easy to find, so you have to solve only a quadratic equation. For more general problems, use the computer algebra package for the course.

Section 4 is devoted to numerical methods for finding eigenvalues and eigenvectors, often used in real applications. These are important ideas, but we do not extend them further in this course.

The material in Sections 1–3 will be needed later in the course, particularly in *Unit 11*. The eigenvalues and eigenvectors that you calculate in Sections 2 and 3 will be used throughout *Unit 11*.

Introduction

Consider the following simplified migration problem.

The towns Exton and Wyeville have a regular interchange of population: each year, one-tenth of Exton's population migrates to Wyeville, while one-fifth of Wyeville's population migrates to Exton (see Figure 0.1). Other changes in population, such as births, deaths and other migrations, cancel each other and so can be ignored. If x_n and y_n denote, respectively, the populations of Exton and Wyeville at the beginning of year n, then the corresponding populations at the beginning of year $n + 1$ are given by

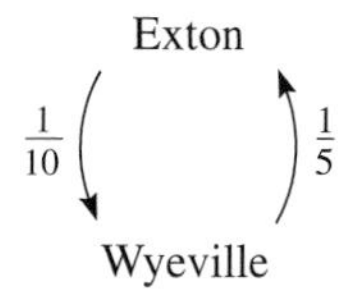

$$\begin{cases} x_{n+1} = 0.9x_n + 0.2y_n, \\ y_{n+1} = 0.1x_n + 0.8y_n, \end{cases}$$

or, in matrix form,

$$\begin{bmatrix} x_{n+1} \\ y_{n+1} \end{bmatrix} = \begin{bmatrix} 0.9 & 0.2 \\ 0.1 & 0.8 \end{bmatrix} \begin{bmatrix} x_n \\ y_n \end{bmatrix}.$$

Exton

$$\frac{1}{10} \Big(\quad \Big) \frac{1}{5}$$

Wyeville

Figure 0.1

This is an example of an *iterative process*, in which the values associated with the $(n + 1)$th iterate can be determined from the values associated with the nth iterate.

A matrix such as $\begin{bmatrix} 0.9 & 0.2 \\ 0.1 & 0.8 \end{bmatrix}$ is called a *transition matrix*. The entries in such a matrix are all non-negative, and the entries in each column sum to 1.

Suppose that initially the population of Exton is 10 000 and that of Wyeville is 8000, i.e. $x_0 = 10\,000$ and $y_0 = 8000$. Then after one year the populations are given by

$$\begin{bmatrix} x_1 \\ y_1 \end{bmatrix} = \begin{bmatrix} 0.9 & 0.2 \\ 0.1 & 0.8 \end{bmatrix} \begin{bmatrix} 10\,000 \\ 8\,000 \end{bmatrix} = \begin{bmatrix} 10\,600 \\ 7\,400 \end{bmatrix},$$

$x_1 = 10\,600,$
$y_1 = 7400.$

and after two years they are given by

$$\begin{bmatrix} x_2 \\ y_2 \end{bmatrix} = \begin{bmatrix} 0.9 & 0.2 \\ 0.1 & 0.8 \end{bmatrix} \begin{bmatrix} 10\,600 \\ 7\,400 \end{bmatrix} = \begin{bmatrix} 11\,020 \\ 6\,980 \end{bmatrix};$$

$x_2 = 11\,020,$
$y_2 = 6980.$

we can continue this process as far as we wish.

What happens in the long term? Do the populations eventually stabilize? Using the computer algebra package for the course, we can verify that the populations after 30 years are $x_{30} = 12\,000$ and $y_{30} = 6000$. It follows that after 31 years the populations are given by

$x_{30} = 12\,000,$
$y_{30} = 6000.$

$$\begin{bmatrix} x_{31} \\ y_{31} \end{bmatrix} = \begin{bmatrix} 0.9 & 0.2 \\ 0.1 & 0.8 \end{bmatrix} \begin{bmatrix} 12\,000 \\ 6\,000 \end{bmatrix}$$

$$= \begin{bmatrix} 0.9 \times 12\,000 + 0.2 \times 6000 \\ 0.1 \times 12\,000 + 0.8 \times 6000 \end{bmatrix} = \begin{bmatrix} 12\,000 \\ 6\,000 \end{bmatrix}.$$

$x_{31} = 12\,000,$
$y_{31} = 6000.$

So, if $x_{30} = 12\,000$ and $y_{30} = 6000$, then $x_{31} = x_{30}$ and $y_{31} = y_{30}$ and the sizes of the populations of the two towns do not change. Moreover, the sizes of the populations will not change in any subsequent year.

There are situations, such as the above migration problem, where a particular non-zero vector does not change under a linear transformation. However, this is more the exception than the rule. It is more useful to investigate vectors that are transformed to *scalar multiples* of themselves — geometrically this means that each such vector is transformed into another vector in the same or the opposite direction. Such vectors are called *eigenvectors*, and the corresponding scalar multipliers are called *eigenvalues*.

Section 1 considers the eigenvectors and eigenvalues associated with various linear transformations of the plane. We also outline situations where eigenvectors and eigenvalues are useful.

In many problems, such as in the above migration problem, the appropriate linear transformation is given in matrix form. In Sections 2 and 3 we investigate the various types of eigenvalue that can arise for 2×2 and 3×3 matrices.

In the migration problem, we iterated to obtain the 'steady-state' population. Section 4 follows a similar method in order to calculate the eigenvalues and eigenvectors of a matrix. Although our discussion is mainly about 2×2 and 3×3 matrices, many of the ideas can be extended to the much larger matrices that often arise from practical applications.

Here 'steady-state' refers to the fact that the populations no longer change.

1 Introducing eigenvectors

We first investigate the eigenvectors and eigenvalues that arise from various linear transformations of the plane — in particular, scaling, reflection and rotation. Do not worry about how we construct the transformation matrices — that is not important. It is the geometric properties of these matrices, and the relevance of these properties to eigenvectors and eigenvalues, that are important here. Later in this section we outline another use of eigenvectors and eigenvalues.

1.1 Eigenvectors in the plane

Consider the linear transformation of the plane specified by the matrix

$$\mathbf{A} = \begin{bmatrix} 3 & 2 \\ 1 & 4 \end{bmatrix}.$$

Using matrix multiplication, we can find the image under this linear transformation of any given vector in the plane. For example, to find the image of the vector $\mathbf{v} = \begin{bmatrix} 2 & 1 \end{bmatrix}^T$, we calculate $\mathbf{Av} = \begin{bmatrix} 3 & 2 \\ 1 & 4 \end{bmatrix} \begin{bmatrix} 2 \\ 1 \end{bmatrix} = \begin{bmatrix} 8 \\ 6 \end{bmatrix}$, so the required image is $\begin{bmatrix} 8 & 6 \end{bmatrix}^T$, as shown in Figure 1.1. In general, to find the image under this linear transformation of the vector $\mathbf{v} = \begin{bmatrix} x & y \end{bmatrix}^T$, we calculate

$$\mathbf{Av} = \begin{bmatrix} 3 & 2 \\ 1 & 4 \end{bmatrix} \begin{bmatrix} x \\ y \end{bmatrix} = \begin{bmatrix} 3x + 2y \\ x + 4y \end{bmatrix},$$

so the required image is $\begin{bmatrix} 3x + 2y & x + 4y \end{bmatrix}^T$.

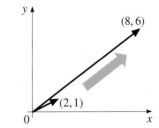

Figure 1.1

Exercise 1.1

Find the image of each of the vectors

$$\mathbf{w} = \begin{bmatrix} 3 \\ -1 \end{bmatrix}, \quad \mathbf{x} = \begin{bmatrix} 1 \\ 1 \end{bmatrix}, \quad \mathbf{y} = \begin{bmatrix} -2 \\ 1 \end{bmatrix}, \quad \mathbf{z} = \begin{bmatrix} 0 \\ 0 \end{bmatrix},$$

under the transformation matrix $\mathbf{A} = \begin{bmatrix} 3 & 2 \\ 1 & 4 \end{bmatrix}$.

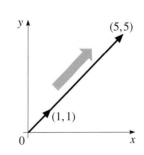

In Exercise 1.1 you saw that the image of $\mathbf{x} = \begin{bmatrix} 1 & 1 \end{bmatrix}^T$ is $\begin{bmatrix} 5 & 5 \end{bmatrix}^T$. This image is a vector in the same direction as $\mathbf{x}$, but with five times the magnitude, as shown in Figure 1.2. In symbols, we write this transformation as $\mathbf{Ax} = 5\mathbf{x}$.

Figure 1.2

In fact, as you can easily check, *any* vector in the same direction as $\mathbf{x} = \begin{bmatrix} 1 & 1 \end{bmatrix}^T$ (or in the direction opposite to $\mathbf{x}$) is transformed into another vector in the same (or opposite) direction, but with five times the magnitude, as shown in Figure 1.3. Non-zero vectors that are transformed to scalar multiples of themselves are called *eigenvectors*; the corresponding scalar multipliers are called *eigenvalues*. For the above 2×2 matrix $\mathbf{A}$, $\begin{bmatrix} 1 & 1 \end{bmatrix}^T$ is an eigenvector, with corresponding eigenvalue 5, since

$$\begin{bmatrix} 3 & 2 \\ 1 & 4 \end{bmatrix} \begin{bmatrix} 1 \\ 1 \end{bmatrix} = \begin{bmatrix} 5 \\ 5 \end{bmatrix} = 5 \begin{bmatrix} 1 \\ 1 \end{bmatrix}.$$

Similarly, since (from Exercise 1.1)

$$\begin{bmatrix} 3 & 2 \\ 1 & 4 \end{bmatrix} \begin{bmatrix} -2 \\ 1 \end{bmatrix} = \begin{bmatrix} -4 \\ 2 \end{bmatrix} = 2 \begin{bmatrix} -2 \\ 1 \end{bmatrix},$$

we can see that $\begin{bmatrix} -2 & 1 \end{bmatrix}^T$ is also an eigenvector, with corresponding eigenvalue 2.

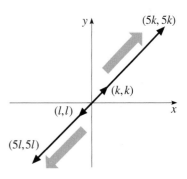

Figure 1.3

Definitions

Let $\mathbf{A}$ be any square matrix. A non-zero vector $\mathbf{v}$ is an **eigenvector** of $\mathbf{A}$ if $\mathbf{Av} = \lambda\mathbf{v}$ for some number λ. The number λ is the corresponding **eigenvalue**.

Any non-zero multiple of an eigenvector is also an eigenvector with the same eigenvalue. For example, if $\mathbf{A} = \begin{bmatrix} 3 & 2 \\ 1 & 4 \end{bmatrix}$, then for any non-zero number k, each vector $\begin{bmatrix} k & k \end{bmatrix}^T$ is an eigenvector corresponding to the eigenvalue 5, because $\begin{bmatrix} 3 & 2 \\ 1 & 4 \end{bmatrix} \begin{bmatrix} k \\ k \end{bmatrix} = 5 \begin{bmatrix} k \\ k \end{bmatrix}$; also, each vector $\begin{bmatrix} -2k & k \end{bmatrix}^T$ is an eigenvector corresponding to the eigenvalue 2, because $\begin{bmatrix} 3 & 2 \\ 1 & 4 \end{bmatrix} \begin{bmatrix} -2k \\ k \end{bmatrix} = 2 \begin{bmatrix} -2k \\ k \end{bmatrix}$.

> This is a consequence of the fact that $\mathbf{A}(k\mathbf{v}) = k(\mathbf{Av}) = k(\lambda\mathbf{v}) = \lambda(k\mathbf{v})$ for any scalar k.

We defined linear dependence for the rows of a matrix in *Unit 9*. The concept may be extended to any collection of vectors as follows.

Definitions

The vectors $\mathbf{v}_1, \mathbf{v}_2, \ldots, \mathbf{v}_n$ are **linearly dependent** if a non-zero linear combination of these vectors is equal to the zero vector, i.e.

$$q_1\mathbf{v}_1 + q_2\mathbf{v}_2 + \cdots + q_n\mathbf{v}_n = \mathbf{0}$$

where the numbers $q_1, q_2, \ldots, q_n$ are not all zero.

Vectors that are not linearly dependent are **linearly independent**.

The nature of the eigenvectors of a matrix is closely bound to the notion of linear dependence. Two (non-zero) vectors are linearly dependent if, and only if, one is a multiple of the other. Thus the eigenvectors $\begin{bmatrix} 1 & 1 \end{bmatrix}^T$ and $\begin{bmatrix} 2 & 2 \end{bmatrix}^T$ are linearly dependent, as are all the eigenvectors of the form $\begin{bmatrix} k & k \end{bmatrix}^T$ corresponding to the eigenvalue 5 of the matrix $\mathbf{A}$ above. Similarly, all the eigenvectors of the form $\begin{bmatrix} -2k & k \end{bmatrix}^T$ corresponding to the eigenvalue 2 of $\mathbf{A}$ are linearly dependent. However, the eigenvectors $\begin{bmatrix} 1 & 1 \end{bmatrix}^T$ and $\begin{bmatrix} -2 & 1 \end{bmatrix}^T$ are linearly independent.

> If
> $$q_1\mathbf{v}_1 + q_2\mathbf{v}_2 = \mathbf{0},$$
> and $q_1 \neq 0$, then
> $$\mathbf{v}_1 = -\frac{q_2}{q_1}\mathbf{v}_2.$$
> Similarly, if $q_2 \neq 0$, then
> $$\mathbf{v}_2 = -\frac{q_1}{q_2}\mathbf{v}_1.$$

The following exercise illustrates a property of linearly independent vectors that will prove useful later.

Exercise 1.2 _____

The vectors $\mathbf{v}_1 = [1 \quad 1]^T$ and $\mathbf{v}_2 = [-2 \quad 1]^T$ are linearly independent. Show that for any vector $\mathbf{v} = [x \quad y]^T$, there are numbers α and β such that $\mathbf{v} = \alpha \mathbf{v}_1 + \beta \mathbf{v}_2$. (In other words, show that any two-dimensional vector $\mathbf{v}$ can be written as a linear combination of $\mathbf{v}_1$ and $\mathbf{v}_2$.)

_____

The result in Exercise 1.2 generalizes to *any* two linearly independent vectors. That is, if $\mathbf{v}_1$ and $\mathbf{v}_2$ are any pair of linearly independent two-dimensional vectors and $\mathbf{v}$ is any two-dimensional vector, then we can find numbers α and β such that $\mathbf{v} = \alpha \mathbf{v}_1 + \beta \mathbf{v}_2$.

The result generalizes further. If $\mathbf{v}_1, \mathbf{v}_2, \ldots, \mathbf{v}_n$ are any n linearly independent n-dimensional vectors and $\mathbf{v}$ is any n-dimensional vector, then we can find numbers $\alpha_1, \alpha_2, \ldots, \alpha_n$ such that $\mathbf{v} = \alpha_1 \mathbf{v}_1 + \alpha_2 \mathbf{v}_2 + \cdots + \alpha_n \mathbf{v}_n$. We do not prove this result here.

Returning to eigenvectors, we require an eigenvector to be non-zero. This is because $\mathbf{A0} = \mathbf{0}$ for *every* square matrix $\mathbf{A}$, so $\mathbf{0}$ would otherwise be an eigenvector for *all* square matrices. Thus there is no point in including $\mathbf{0}$ as an eigenvector. However, it is possible for an eigenvalue to be 0. For example, if we choose $\mathbf{A} = \begin{bmatrix} 2 & 1 \\ 4 & 2 \end{bmatrix}$ and $\mathbf{v} = \begin{bmatrix} 1 \\ -2 \end{bmatrix}$, then $\mathbf{Av} = \begin{bmatrix} 2 & 1 \\ 4 & 2 \end{bmatrix} \begin{bmatrix} 1 \\ -2 \end{bmatrix} = \begin{bmatrix} 0 \\ 0 \end{bmatrix} = 0 \begin{bmatrix} 1 \\ -2 \end{bmatrix}$, so $[1 \quad -2]^T$ is an eigenvector of $\mathbf{A}$ with eigenvalue 0.

Exercise 1.3 _____

In each of the following cases, verify that $\mathbf{v}$ is an eigenvector of $\mathbf{A}$, and write down the corresponding eigenvalue.

(a) $\mathbf{A} = \begin{bmatrix} 2 & 3 \\ 2 & 1 \end{bmatrix}$, $\mathbf{v} = \begin{bmatrix} 3 \\ 2 \end{bmatrix}$.   (b) $\mathbf{A} = \begin{bmatrix} 2 & 3 \\ 2 & 1 \end{bmatrix}$, $\mathbf{v} = \begin{bmatrix} 1 \\ -1 \end{bmatrix}$.

(c) $\mathbf{A} = \begin{bmatrix} 2 & 0 \\ 1 & 2 \end{bmatrix}$, $\mathbf{v} = \begin{bmatrix} 0 \\ 6 \end{bmatrix}$.

Exercise 1.4 _____

Write down an eigenvector and the corresponding eigenvalue for the matrix associated with the migration problem in the Introduction, i.e. $\begin{bmatrix} 0.9 & 0.2 \\ 0.1 & 0.8 \end{bmatrix}$.

_____

Very occasionally it is possible to determine information about the eigenvectors and eigenvalues of a given matrix from its geometric properties. This is so for each of the cases in Table 1.1 below (where the image of the unit square is used in each case to indicate the behaviour of the transformation).

The unit square has vertices $(0,0)$, $(1,0)$, $(1,1)$ and $(0,1)$.

In the case of the matrix $\begin{bmatrix} 3 & 0 \\ 0 & 2 \end{bmatrix}$, it is clear from the geometric properties of the linear transformation that vectors along the coordinate axes are eigenvectors, as these are transformed to vectors in the same directions.

In the case of the matrix $\begin{bmatrix} 1 & 0 \\ 0 & -1 \end{bmatrix}$, we see that reflection in the x-axis leaves the vector $[1 \quad 0]^T$ unchanged, and reverses the direction of $[0 \quad 1]^T$, so these must be eigenvectors.

In the third case (rotation through $\frac{\pi}{4}$ anticlockwise about the origin), we do not expect to find any real eigenvectors because the direction of every vector is changed by the linear transformation. Surprisingly, even this matrix has eigenvectors of a kind, namely complex ones, but we have to adopt the algebraic approach of Section 2 in order to find them.

Table 1.1

Matrix	Comment	Transformation of the unit square	Eigenvectors	Eigenvalues
$\begin{bmatrix} 3 & 0 \\ 0 & 2 \end{bmatrix}$	A scaling by 3 in the x-direction and by 2 in the y-direction (i.e. a $(3, 2)$ scaling)		$\begin{bmatrix} 1 & 0 \end{bmatrix}^T$ $\begin{bmatrix} 0 & 1 \end{bmatrix}^T$	3 2
$\begin{bmatrix} 1 & 0 \\ 0 & -1 \end{bmatrix}$	A reflection in the x-axis		$\begin{bmatrix} 1 & 0 \end{bmatrix}^T$ $\begin{bmatrix} 0 & 1 \end{bmatrix}^T$	1 -1
$\begin{bmatrix} \frac{1}{\sqrt{2}} & -\frac{1}{\sqrt{2}} \\ \frac{1}{\sqrt{2}} & \frac{1}{\sqrt{2}} \end{bmatrix}$	A rotation through $\frac{\pi}{4}$ anticlockwise about the origin		No real eigenvectors	No real eigenvalues

Exercise 1.5

The matrix $\mathbf{A} = \begin{bmatrix} 0 & 1 \\ 1 & 0 \end{bmatrix}$ corresponds to reflection in a line through the origin at an angle $\frac{\pi}{4}$ to the x-axis. What are the eigenvectors of $\mathbf{A}$ and their corresponding eigenvalues?

(*Hint*: Find two lines through the origin that are transformed to themselves, then consider what happens to a point on each line.)

1.2 Simultaneous differential equations

We conclude this section by outlining another application of eigenvectors and eigenvalues which you will meet again in *Unit 11*.

Many mathematical models give rise to systems of simultaneous differential equations relating two or more functions and their derivatives. A simple case is shown in Example 1.1; we shall discuss the relevance of eigenvectors and eigenvalues to these equations after we have solved them.

Example 1.1

Determine the general solution of the pair of differential equations

$$\begin{cases} \dot{x} = 3x + 2y, \\ \dot{y} = \ x + 4y, \end{cases} \qquad \begin{array}{l} (1.1) \\ (1.2) \end{array} \qquad \begin{array}{l} \dot{x} \text{ is } dx/dt, \\ \dot{y} \text{ is } dy/dt. \end{array}$$

where $x(t)$ and $y(t)$ are functions of the independent variable t.

Solution

In order to solve such a system of equations, we need to find specific formulae for x and y in terms of t.

From Equation (1.2) we have

$$x = \dot{y} - 4y, \tag{1.3}$$

and differentiating this equation with respect to t gives

$$\dot{x} = \ddot{y} - 4\dot{y}. \tag{1.4}$$

Substituting for x and $\dot{x}$ in Equation (1.1) using Equations (1.3) and (1.4), we obtain $\ddot{y} - 4\dot{y} = 3(\dot{y} - 4y) + 2y$, which simplifies to

$$\ddot{y} - 7\dot{y} + 10y = 0.$$

This is a type of differential equation that you should recognize from *Unit 3*.

The general solution of this equation is obtained by solving the auxiliary equation $\lambda^2 - 7\lambda + 10 = 0$. This has solutions $\lambda = 5$ and $\lambda = 2$, so the required general solution for y is

$$y = Ae^{5t} + Be^{2t},$$

where A and B are arbitrary constants.

It follows from Equation (1.3) that

$$\begin{aligned} x &= \dot{y} - 4y \\ &= (5Ae^{5t} + 2Be^{2t}) - 4(Ae^{5t} + Be^{2t}) \\ &= Ae^{5t} - 2Be^{2t}. \end{aligned}$$

Thus the general solution of the system of equations is

$$\begin{cases} x = Ae^{5t} - 2Be^{2t}, \\ y = Ae^{5t} + Be^{2t}. \quad \blacksquare \end{cases} \tag{1.5}$$

What is the connection between eigenvalues and eigenvectors, and the equations of Example 1.1? The differential equations (1.1) and (1.2) can be written in matrix form as

$$\begin{bmatrix} \dot{x} \\ \dot{y} \end{bmatrix} = \begin{bmatrix} 3 & 2 \\ 1 & 4 \end{bmatrix} \begin{bmatrix} x \\ y \end{bmatrix}. \tag{1.6}$$

The 2×2 matrix in Equation (1.6) has eigenvectors $[1 \quad 1]^T$ and $[-2 \quad 1]^T$ with corresponding eigenvalues 5 and 2, respectively, as we saw in Subsection 1.1.

These eigenvectors and eigenvalues appear in the matrix form of the general solution given in Equations (1.5):

$$\begin{bmatrix} x \\ y \end{bmatrix} = A \begin{bmatrix} 1 \\ 1 \end{bmatrix} e^{5t} + B \begin{bmatrix} -2 \\ 1 \end{bmatrix} e^{2t}.$$

The first term on the right-hand side involves $[1 \quad 1]^T$, an eigenvector of the matrix of coefficients $\begin{bmatrix} 3 & 2 \\ 1 & 4 \end{bmatrix}$, and a term e^{5t}, where 5 is the corresponding eigenvalue. The second term on the right-hand side is of the same form, but it involves the other eigenvector and corresponding eigenvalue. That the general solution of a system of differential equations can be written explicitly in terms of eigenvectors and eigenvalues is no coincidence, as we shall explain in *Unit 11*.

End-of-section Exercises

*Exercise 1.6 _____

Show that $\begin{bmatrix} 2 \\ -3 \end{bmatrix}$ and $\begin{bmatrix} 2 \\ 3 \end{bmatrix}$ are eigenvectors of the matrix $\begin{bmatrix} 1 & 4 \\ 9 & 1 \end{bmatrix}$, and find the corresponding eigenvalues.

Exercise 1.7 _____

The matrix $\mathbf{A} = \begin{bmatrix} -1 & 0 \\ 0 & 1 \end{bmatrix}$ represents reflection in the y-axis. Write down two eigenvectors and the corresponding eigenvalues.

(*Hint*: Find two lines through the origin that are transformed to themselves, then consider what happens to a point on each line.)

Exercise 1.8 _____

Find a matrix $\mathbf{A} = \begin{bmatrix} a & b \\ c & d \end{bmatrix}$ for which $[1 \quad 2]^T$ is an eigenvector with corresponding eigenvalue 2, and $[3 \quad 1]^T$ is an eigenvector with corresponding eigenvalue 1.

2 Eigenvalues and eigenvectors of 2 × 2 matrices

In Section 1 we considered the linear transformation of the plane specified by the matrix $\mathbf{A} = \begin{bmatrix} 3 & 2 \\ 1 & 4 \end{bmatrix}$. We saw that $[1 \quad 1]^T$ and $[-2 \quad 1]^T$ are eigenvectors of $\mathbf{A}$, the corresponding eigenvalues being 5 and 2, respectively.

See page 58.

We did not show in Section 1 that these are the *only* possible eigenvalues of $\mathbf{A}$, nor did we show you how to find the eigenvectors and corresponding eigenvalues for an arbitrary matrix $\mathbf{A}$. In this section we use algebraic techniques to show you how to calculate *all* the eigenvalues and eigenvectors of any given 2 × 2 matrix $\mathbf{A}$. We also investigate the three situations that arise when the eigenvalues are:

For example:

- distinct real numbers;   5 and 2;
- one real number repeated;   2 and 2;
- complex numbers. i and $-i$, where $i^2 = -1$.

Before we begin the discussion, we need to remind you of some results from *Unit 9*.

Generally, a pair of equations with zero right-hand sides, such as

$$\begin{cases} 2x + 3y = 0, \\ x - y = 0, \end{cases} \tag{2.1}$$

has just one solution $x = 0$, $y = 0$. But this is not the case for every pair of equations of this type. For example, the equations

$$\begin{cases} x - 2y = 0, \\ -2x + 4y = 0, \end{cases} \tag{2.2}$$

have a solution $x = 2$, $y = 1$, and another solution $x = 6$, $y = 3$. In fact, $x = 2k$, $y = k$ is a solution for every value of k, i.e. there is an infinite number of solutions. This is because the equations $x - 2y = 0$ and $-2x + 4y = 0$ are essentially the same equation, since either one of the equations can be obtained from the other by multiplying by a suitable factor.

Example 2.1

Find a solution (other than $x = y = 0$) of the equations

$$\begin{cases} 3x - 5y = 0, \\ -6x + 10y = 0. \end{cases}$$

The second equation can be obtained from the first equation by multiplying it by -2.

Solution

There is an infinite number of solutions. For example, choosing $x = 5$, we find (from either equation) that $y = 3$, which gives us a solution of the pair of equations. (Any other non-zero choice of x would give another solution.) ∎

The general solution is $x = 5k$, $y = 3k$, for any constant k.

You saw in *Unit 9* that a system of linear equations $\mathbf{Ax} = \mathbf{b}$ has a unique solution if, and only if, the matrix of coefficients $\mathbf{A}$ is invertible. Thus if the system has an infinite number of solutions, then the matrix $\mathbf{A}$ must be non-invertible.

Thus the coefficient matrix $\begin{bmatrix} 1 & -2 \\ -2 & 4 \end{bmatrix}$ of Equations (2.2) must be non-invertible, as must the coefficient matrix $\begin{bmatrix} 3 & -5 \\ -6 & 10 \end{bmatrix}$ of Example 2.1, whereas the coefficient matrix $\begin{bmatrix} 2 & 3 \\ 1 & -1 \end{bmatrix}$ of Equations (2.1) must be invertible. Recall from *Unit 9* that a matrix $\mathbf{A}$ is non-invertible if and only if $\det \mathbf{A} = 0$. You may like to check that the determinants of the first two matrices are zero, but that of the last is non-zero.

2.1 Basic method

We now look at a method of finding the eigenvalues and the corresponding eigenvectors of an arbitrary 2 × 2 matrix $\mathbf{A}$. Consider the following example.

Example 2.2

Find the eigenvalues and corresponding eigenvectors of the matrix

$$\mathbf{A} = \begin{bmatrix} 3 & 2 \\ 1 & 4 \end{bmatrix}.$$

This matrix was discussed in Subsection 1.1.

Solution

We wish to find those non-zero vectors $\mathbf{v}$ that satisfy the equation

$$\mathbf{Av} = \lambda\mathbf{v}, \tag{2.3}$$

for some number λ. Writing $\mathbf{v} = [x \ \ y]^T$, we have

$$\begin{bmatrix} 3 & 2 \\ 1 & 4 \end{bmatrix}\begin{bmatrix} x \\ y \end{bmatrix} = \lambda \begin{bmatrix} x \\ y \end{bmatrix},$$

i.e. x and y must satisfy the simultaneous linear equations

$$\begin{cases} 3x + 2y = \lambda x, \\ x + 4y = \lambda y. \end{cases}$$

We are interested in only non-zero vectors $\mathbf{v}$, so x and y are not both zero. These equations will have such a solution for only certain values of λ — the eigenvalues of the matrix — and our first task is to find these values of λ. The above equations are a pair of linear equations in the unknowns x and y, where λ is a constant that has yet to be determined.

Transferring the terms λx and λy to the left-hand side, we obtain

$$\begin{cases} (3-\lambda)x + \qquad 2y = 0, \\ \qquad x + (4-\lambda)y = 0, \end{cases} \tag{2.4}$$

which can be written as

$$(\mathbf{A} - \lambda\mathbf{I})\mathbf{v} = \mathbf{0}. \tag{2.5}$$

To see this, notice that Equation (2.3) can be rewritten as $\mathbf{A}\mathbf{v} = \lambda\mathbf{I}\mathbf{v}$, where $\mathbf{I}$ is the 2×2 identity matrix, which in turn can be rewritten as $\mathbf{A}\mathbf{v} - \lambda\mathbf{I}\mathbf{v} = \mathbf{0}$ and hence as $(\mathbf{A} - \lambda\mathbf{I})\mathbf{v} = \mathbf{0}$.

It is convenient to refer to Equations (2.4) as the *eigenvector equations*.

Do not lose sight of the fact that we require $\mathbf{v} \neq \mathbf{0}$. In *Unit 9* we saw that if such a non-zero solution $\mathbf{v}$ exists, then the matrix $\mathbf{A} - \lambda\mathbf{I}$ in Equation (2.5) must be non-invertible, so $\det(\mathbf{A} - \lambda\mathbf{I}) = 0$, i.e.

$$\begin{vmatrix} 3-\lambda & 2 \\ 1 & 4-\lambda \end{vmatrix} = 0. \tag{2.6}$$

Our conclusion at this stage is that Equation (2.3) can hold for only certain values of λ, and these values must satisfy Equation (2.6). Expanding the determinant in Equation (2.6) gives

$$\begin{vmatrix} a & b \\ c & d \end{vmatrix} = ad - bc$$

$$(3-\lambda)(4-\lambda) - 2 = 0,$$

which simplifies to

$$\lambda^2 - 7\lambda + 10 = 0.$$

This is called the *characteristic equation* of $\mathbf{A}$.

Since $\lambda^2 - 7\lambda + 10 = (\lambda - 5)(\lambda - 2)$, we deduce that $\lambda = 5$ or $\lambda = 2$.

Thus it is only when $\lambda = 5$ or $\lambda = 2$ that Equation (2.3) has a non-zero solution $\mathbf{v}$, i.e. 5 and 2 are the only eigenvalues of $\mathbf{A}$.

In order to find the corresponding eigenvectors, we substitute each of these eigenvalues into Equations (2.4) and solve the resulting eigenvector equations, as follows.

$\boxed{\lambda = 5}$ The eigenvector equations (2.4) become $-2x + 2y = 0$ and $x - y = 0$, and both are equivalent to the single equation $y = x$. It follows that an eigenvector corresponding to $\lambda = 5$ is $[1 \quad 1]^T$.

The matrix $\mathbf{A} - \lambda\mathbf{I}$, i.e.

$$\begin{bmatrix} 3-\lambda & 2 \\ 1 & 4-\lambda \end{bmatrix},$$

is non-invertible, as stated above, so the equivalent eigenvector equations are linearly dependent — hence the *single* equation.

$\boxed{\lambda = 2}$ The eigenvector equations (2.4) become $x + 2y = 0$ and $x + 2y = 0$, and both are equivalent to the single equation $-2y = x$. It follows that an eigenvector corresponding to $\lambda = 2$ is $[-2 \quad 1]^T$.

Thus $[1 \quad 1]^T$ is an eigenvector of $\mathbf{A}$ with corresponding eigenvalue 5, and $[-2 \quad 1]^T$ is an eigenvector of $\mathbf{A}$ with corresponding eigenvalue 2.

In this case, the matrix $\mathbf{A}$ has two distinct eigenvalues, and these correspond to two linearly independent eigenvectors. ∎

In Example 2.2 we found an eigenvector $[1 \quad 1]^T$ corresponding to the eigenvalue 5, and an eigenvector $[-2 \quad 1]^T$ corresponding to the eigenvalue 2, but these vectors are not unique. We could have chosen $[2 \quad 2]^T$ as the eigenvector corresponding to the eigenvalue 5, and $[6 \quad -3]^T$ as the eigenvector corresponding to the eigenvalue 2. However, *all* the eigenvectors corresponding to 5 are multiples of $[1 \quad 1]^T$, and *all* the eigenvectors corresponding to 2 are multiples of $[-2 \quad 1]^T$. Thus, in a sense, $[1 \quad 1]^T$ and $[2 \quad 2]^T$ represent the 'same' eigenvector, as do $[-2 \quad 1]^T$ and $[6 \quad -3]^T$.

*Exercise 2.1 _____

Use the method in Example 2.2 to find the eigenvalues and corresponding eigenvectors of the matrix $\mathbf{A} = \begin{bmatrix} 5 & 2 \\ 2 & 5 \end{bmatrix}$.

_____

As we shall see shortly, there is a result involving the diagonal elements of a matrix that provides a useful check on calculations. To state this result succinctly, we shall need the following definition.

Definition

The sum of the elements on the leading diagonal of a square matrix $\mathbf{A}$ is known as the **trace** of $\mathbf{A}$ and is written as $\operatorname{tr}\mathbf{A}$.

In Example 2.2 we found the eigenvalues of the matrix

$$\mathbf{A} = \begin{bmatrix} 3 & 2 \\ 1 & 4 \end{bmatrix}$$

by solving the equation $\det(\mathbf{A} - \lambda\mathbf{I}) = 0$, i.e.

$$\begin{vmatrix} 3 - \lambda & 2 \\ 1 & 4 - \lambda \end{vmatrix} = 0,$$

which gives a quadratic equation in λ.

More generally, we find the eigenvalues of the 2×2 matrix

$$\mathbf{A} = \begin{bmatrix} a & b \\ c & d \end{bmatrix}$$

by solving the equation $\det(\mathbf{A} - \lambda\mathbf{I}) = 0$, i.e.

$$\begin{vmatrix} a - \lambda & b \\ c & d - \lambda \end{vmatrix} = 0,$$

for λ. Expanding this determinant gives

$$(a - \lambda)(d - \lambda) - bc = 0,$$

which simplifies to the quadratic equation

$$\lambda^2 - (a + d)\lambda + (ad - bc) = 0. \tag{2.7}$$

The roots of Equation (2.7), λ_1 and λ_2 say, are the eigenvalues of $\mathbf{A}$, and we see that

$$\lambda_1\lambda_2 = ad - bc = \det\mathbf{A} \quad \text{and} \quad \lambda_1 + \lambda_2 = a + d = \operatorname{tr}\mathbf{A}. \tag{2.8}$$

Equation (2.7) is called the **characteristic equation** of $\mathbf{A}$. It can have distinct real roots, a repeated real root or complex roots, depending on the values of a, b, c and d. We investigate these three possibilities in the next subsection.

Equation (2.7) can be written in the form
$$(\lambda - \lambda_1)(\lambda - \lambda_2) = 0,$$
so
$$\lambda^2 - (\lambda_1 + \lambda_2)\lambda + \lambda_1\lambda_2 = 0,$$
therefore
$$\lambda_1\lambda_2 = ad - bc,$$
$$\lambda_1 + \lambda_2 = a + d.$$

Using Example 2.2 and the above discussion as a model, we can now give the following procedures for determining the eigenvalues and eigenvectors of a given 2×2 matrix.

Procedure 2.1   Eigenvalues of a 2×2 matrix

Let $\mathbf{A} = \begin{bmatrix} a & b \\ c & d \end{bmatrix}$. To find the *eigenvalues* of $\mathbf{A}$, write down the *characteristic equation* $\det(\mathbf{A} - \lambda\mathbf{I}) = 0$. Expand this as

$$\begin{vmatrix} a - \lambda & b \\ c & d - \lambda \end{vmatrix} = \lambda^2 - (a + d)\lambda + (ad - bc) = 0. \tag{2.9}$$

Solve this quadratic equation for λ.

Using Equations (2.8) to determine the characteristic equation leads to the same quadratic equation.

Procedure 2.2   Eigenvectors of a 2×2 matrix

Let $\mathbf{A} = \begin{bmatrix} a & b \\ c & d \end{bmatrix}$. To find an *eigenvector* corresponding to the eigenvalue λ, write down the *eigenvector equations*

$$\begin{cases} (a - \lambda)x + by = 0, \\ cx + (d - \lambda)y = 0. \end{cases} \tag{2.10}$$

These equations reduce to a single equation of the form $py = qx$, with solution $x = p$, $y = q$, so $[p \quad q]^T$ is an eigenvector. Any non-zero multiple $[kp \quad kq]^T$ is also an eigenvector corresponding to the same eigenvalue.

Example 2.3

Find the eigenvalues and corresponding eigenvectors of the matrix

$$\mathbf{A} = \begin{bmatrix} 2 & 3 \\ 2 & 1 \end{bmatrix},$$

following Procedures 2.1 and 2.2.

Solution

The characteristic equation is

$$\begin{vmatrix} 2 - \lambda & 3 \\ 2 & 1 - \lambda \end{vmatrix} = (2 - \lambda)(1 - \lambda) - 6 = 0,$$

which simplifies to $\lambda^2 - 3\lambda - 4 = 0$. Using the formula for solving a quadratic equation, we deduce that the eigenvalues are $\lambda = 4$ and $\lambda = -1$.

Alternatively, you may have noticed that
$\lambda^2 - 3\lambda - 4 = (\lambda - 4)(\lambda + 1)$.

$\boxed{\lambda = 4}$ The eigenvector equations become $-2x + 3y = 0$ and $2x - 3y = 0$, which reduce to the single equation $3y = 2x$ (so $p = 3$ and $q = 2$ in Procedure 2.2). Thus an eigenvector corresponding to $\lambda = 4$ is $[3 \quad 2]^T$.

$\boxed{\lambda = -1}$ The eigenvector equations become $3x + 3y = 0$ and $2x + 2y = 0$, which reduce to the single equation $-y = x$ (so $p = -1$ and $q = 1$ in Procedure 2.2). Thus an eigenvector corresponding to $\lambda = -1$ is $[-1 \quad 1]^T$. ∎

In Example 2.3 we have two distinct real eigenvalues, and these correspond to two linearly independent eigenvectors.

*Exercise 2.2

Use Procedures 2.1 and 2.2 to find the eigenvalues and corresponding eigenvectors of each of the following matrices $\mathbf{A}$.

(a) $\mathbf{A} = \begin{bmatrix} 1 & 4 \\ 1 & -2 \end{bmatrix}$

(b) $\mathbf{A} = \begin{bmatrix} 8 & -5 \\ 10 & -7 \end{bmatrix}$

From Equations (2.8), the sum of the eigenvalues is $a + d = \operatorname{tr} \mathbf{A}$ and the product is $ad - bc = \det \mathbf{A}$. It is useful to check that these properties hold, whenever you have calculated the eigenvalues of a given matrix. If they do not hold, then you have made a mistake, which you should rectify before proceeding to calculate the eigenvectors.

Similar results are true for all square matrices, of any size.

Verify the properties in Equations (2.8) for the matrices in:

(a) Examples 2.2 and 2.3;   (b) Exercises 2.1 and 2.2.

2.2 Three types of eigenvalue

The characteristic equation of the matrix $\mathbf{A} = \begin{bmatrix} a & b \\ c & d \end{bmatrix}$ is a quadratic equa- See Equation (2.9).
tion, and this has distinct real, repeated real or distinct complex roots, depending on whether the discriminant of the quadratic equation is positive, zero or negative. We illustrate each of these three cases below.

Distinct real eigenvalues

In the following exercises, the eigenvalues are real and distinct.

Exercise 2.4

Calculate the eigenvalues and corresponding eigenvectors of the matrix $\mathbf{A} = \begin{bmatrix} p & 0 \\ 0 & q \end{bmatrix}$ with $p \neq q$. Check that your answers agree with those obtained by geometric considerations in Section 1 (see Table 1.1, page 60).

Exercise 2.5

Calculate the eigenvalues and corresponding eigenvectors of the matrix

$$\mathbf{A} = \begin{bmatrix} 0.9 & 0.2 \\ 0.1 & 0.8 \end{bmatrix}.$$

This matrix is associated with the migration problem discussed in the Introduction.

Notice that whenever we have two distinct real eigenvalues, we also have two linearly independent eigenvectors.

This is true in general, though we do not prove it here.

Repeated eigenvalue

In the following exercise, the eigenvalue is repeated.

Exercise 2.6

Calculate the eigenvalues and corresponding eigenvectors of the following matrices.

(a) $\begin{bmatrix} a & 0 \\ 0 & a \end{bmatrix}$, where $a \neq 0$.   (b) $\begin{bmatrix} a & 1 \\ 0 & a \end{bmatrix}$, where $a \neq 0$.

Complex eigenvalues

For 2×2 matrices, complex eigenvalues arise when there are no fixed directions under the corresponding linear transformation as, for example, in an anticlockwise rotation through $\frac{\pi}{4}$ about the origin (see Table 1.1 and the discussion beneath the table). They can occur for matrices of all sizes, but for real matrices they always occur in complex conjugate pairs (i.e. if $\lambda_1 = a + ib$ is an eigenvalue, then $\lambda_2 = a - ib$ is also an eigenvalue). The following example illustrates one of the simplest cases.

Although we discuss complex eigenvalues, in this course the elements of a matrix $\mathbf{A}$ will always be real, so that $\mathbf{A}$ is a *real* matrix.

Example 2.4

Calculate the eigenvalues and corresponding eigenvectors of the matrix

$$\mathbf{A} = \begin{bmatrix} 0 & -1 \\ 1 & 0 \end{bmatrix}.$$

Solution

The characteristic equation is $\lambda^2 + 1 = 0$. This equation has no real solutions, so there are no real eigenvalues. However, it has complex solutions

$$\lambda = i \quad \text{and} \quad \lambda = -i, \quad \text{where } i^2 = -1.$$

Thus the matrix $\mathbf{A}$ has the complex eigenvalues i and $-i$.

Check:
sum $= \operatorname{tr} \mathbf{A} = 0$;
product $= \det \mathbf{A} = 1.$

The eigenvector equations are $-\lambda x - y = 0$ and $x - \lambda y = 0$ (using Equations (2.10)).

$\boxed{\lambda = i}$ The eigenvector equations become $-ix - y = 0$ and $x - iy = 0$, which reduce to the single equation $y = -ix$ (so $p = 1$ and $q = -i$ in Procedure 2.2). Thus an eigenvector corresponding to the eigenvalue $\lambda = i$ is $\begin{bmatrix} 1 & -i \end{bmatrix}^T$.

The second equation is i times the first.

$\boxed{\lambda = -i}$ The eigenvector equations become $ix - y = 0$ and $x + iy = 0$, which reduce to the single equation $y = ix$ (so $p = 1$ and $q = i$ in Procedure 2.2). Thus an eigenvector corresponding to the eigenvalue $\lambda = -i$ is $\begin{bmatrix} 1 & i \end{bmatrix}^T$. ∎

The second equation is $-i$ times the first.

In Example 2.4 the eigenvectors are complex, but, nevertheless, are linearly independent. It remains true that any two eigenvectors corresponding to distinct eigenvalues, whether real or complex, are linearly independent.

*Exercise 2.7

Calculate the eigenvalues and corresponding eigenvectors of the matrix

$$\mathbf{A} = \begin{bmatrix} 3 & -1 \\ 2 & 1 \end{bmatrix}.$$

2.3   Some results on eigenvalues

In this subsection we list some general results that will be needed later. Although we introduce them in the context of 2×2 matrices, they hold for square matrices of any size.

We first consider the eigenvalues of various types of matrix: triangular, symmetric and non-invertible.

Triangular matrices

A matrix is *triangular* if all the entries above (or below) the leading diagonal are 0. Thus a 2×2 triangular matrix has one of the forms

See *Unit 9*.

$$\begin{bmatrix} a & b \\ 0 & d \end{bmatrix}, \qquad \begin{bmatrix} a & 0 \\ c & d \end{bmatrix}, \qquad \begin{bmatrix} a & 0 \\ 0 & d \end{bmatrix}.$$

(upper triangular)   (lower triangular)   (diagonal)

The above triangular matrices all have characteristic equation

$$(a - \lambda)(d - \lambda) = 0,$$

and eigenvalues $\lambda = a$ and $\lambda = d$.

Thus the eigenvalues of a triangular matrix are the diagonal entries.

Exercise 2.8 _____

Find the eigenvalues and corresponding eigenvectors of the upper triangular matrix $\begin{bmatrix} 1 & 3 \\ 0 & 2 \end{bmatrix}$.

Symmetric matrices

A matrix is *symmetric* if it is equal to its transpose — that is, if the entries are symmetric about the leading diagonal. Thus a 2×2 symmetric matrix has the form

$$\mathbf{A} = \begin{bmatrix} a & b \\ b & d \end{bmatrix}.$$

See *Unit 9*.

It has characteristic equation

$$\lambda^2 - (a + d)\lambda + (ad - b^2) = 0,$$

and eigenvalues

$$\lambda = \tfrac{1}{2} \left(a + d \pm \sqrt{(a + d)^2 - 4(ad - b^2)} \right).$$

In this course $\mathbf{A}$ is always a real matrix, so a, b and d are real numbers.

The discriminant is

$$(a + d)^2 - 4(ad - b^2) = (a^2 + 2ad + d^2) - 4ad + 4b^2 = (a - d)^2 + 4b^2,$$

which is the sum of two squares and therefore cannot be negative.

It follows that the eigenvalues of a symmetric matrix are real.

Exercise 2.9 _____

Under what circumstances can a symmetric matrix $\begin{bmatrix} a & b \\ b & d \end{bmatrix}$ have a repeated eigenvalue?

Non-invertible matrices

A matrix is *non-invertible* if and only if its determinant is 0. Thus a 2×2 non-invertible matrix has the form

$$\mathbf{A} = \begin{bmatrix} a & b \\ c & d \end{bmatrix} \quad \text{where } ad - bc = 0.$$

See *Unit 9*.

However, we know that if λ_1 and λ_2 are the eigenvalues of $\mathbf{A}$, then

$$\lambda_1 \lambda_2 = \det \mathbf{A} = 0.$$

See Equations (2.8).

It follows that a matrix is non-invertible if and only if at least one of its eigenvalues is 0. Also, a matrix is invertible if and only if all its eigenvalues are non-zero.

For example, if $\mathbf{A} = \begin{bmatrix} 2 & 1 \\ 4 & 2 \end{bmatrix}$, then $\det \mathbf{A} = 0$ and hence 0 is an eigenvalue of $\mathbf{A}$, as we saw on page 59 (below Exercise 1.2).

Since $\lambda_1 + \lambda_2 = \operatorname{tr} \mathbf{A} = 4$, the other eigenvalue is 4.

Non-invertible matrices

A square matrix $\mathbf{A}$ is non-invertible if and only if any of the following equivalent conditions holds:

- its determinant is zero;
- its rows are linearly dependent;
- its columns are linearly dependent;
- the equation $\mathbf{A}\mathbf{x} = \mathbf{0}$ has a non-zero solution;
- at least one of its eigenvalues is zero.

The third condition follows immediately from the second, since $\det \mathbf{A} = \det(\mathbf{A}^T)$.

Eigenvalues — summary

The eigenvalues of a triangular matrix are the diagonal entries.

The eigenvalues of a real symmetric matrix are real.

The sum of the eigenvalues of $\mathbf{A}$ is $\operatorname{tr} \mathbf{A}$.

The product of the eigenvalues of $\mathbf{A}$ is $\det \mathbf{A}$.

Exercise 2.10 _____

Without solving the characteristic equation, what can you say about the eigenvalues of each of the following matrices?

(a) $\mathbf{A} = \begin{bmatrix} 67 & 72 \\ 72 & -17 \end{bmatrix}$ (b) $\mathbf{A} = \begin{bmatrix} 67 & 72 \\ 0 & -17 \end{bmatrix}$ (c) $\mathbf{A} = \begin{bmatrix} 288 & 72 \\ 72 & 18 \end{bmatrix}$

2.4   Eigenvalues of related matrices

For the rest of this section, we compare the eigenvalues of a matrix $\mathbf{A}$ with the eigenvalues of some related matrices. The results of our investigations are needed in Section 4. The following exercise leads our discussion.

Exercise 2.11 _____

Let $\mathbf{A} = \begin{bmatrix} 3 & 2 \\ 1 & 4 \end{bmatrix}$. In Example 2.2 you saw that $[1 \quad 1]^T$ is an eigenvector of $\mathbf{A}$ corresponding to the eigenvalue 5, and that $[-2 \quad 1]^T$ is an eigenvector corresponding to the eigenvalue 2.

(a) Evaluate the following matrices. In each case, solve the characteristic equation, determine the eigenvalues, and compare these eigenvalues with the eigenvalues of $\mathbf{A}$.

  (i) $\mathbf{A}^2$ (ii) $\mathbf{A}^{-1}$ (iii) $\mathbf{A} + 2\mathbf{I}$ (iv) $(\mathbf{A} - 4\mathbf{I})^{-1}$ (v) $3\mathbf{A}$

(b) Verify that the given eigenvectors of $\mathbf{A}$ are also eigenvectors of the matrices in part (a).

Exercise 2.11 illustrates some general results.

- If $\mathbf{v}$ is an eigenvector of any matrix $\mathbf{A}$ with eigenvalue λ, then $\mathbf{A}\mathbf{v} = \lambda\mathbf{v}$. It follows that

$$\mathbf{A}^2\mathbf{v} = \mathbf{A}(\mathbf{A}\mathbf{v}) = \mathbf{A}(\lambda\mathbf{v}) = \lambda(\mathbf{A}\mathbf{v}) = \lambda(\lambda\mathbf{v}) = \lambda^2\mathbf{v},$$

which shows that $\mathbf{v}$ is an eigenvector of $\mathbf{A}^2$, with eigenvalue λ^2.

More generally, if $\mathbf{v}$ is an eigenvector of a matrix $\mathbf{A}$ with eigenvalue λ, then $\mathbf{v}$ is also an eigenvector of $\mathbf{A}^k$ (for any positive integer k), with eigenvalue λ^k.

- If $\mathbf{v}$ is an eigenvector of any matrix $\mathbf{A}$ with eigenvalue λ, then $\mathbf{A}\mathbf{v} = \lambda\mathbf{v}$. It follows that (provided that $\mathbf{A}$ is invertible, so $\mathbf{A}^{-1}$ exists)

$$\mathbf{A}^{-1}(\mathbf{A}\mathbf{v}) = \mathbf{A}^{-1}(\lambda\mathbf{v}) = \lambda\mathbf{A}^{-1}\mathbf{v},$$

so $\mathbf{v} = \lambda\mathbf{A}^{-1}\mathbf{v}$. Dividing by λ (which cannot be zero since $\mathbf{A}$ is invertible) gives

$$\mathbf{A}^{-1}\mathbf{v} = (1/\lambda)\mathbf{v},$$

which shows that $\mathbf{v}$ is an eigenvector of $\mathbf{A}^{-1}$, with eigenvalue $1/\lambda$.

- If $\mathbf{v}$ is an eigenvector of any matrix $\mathbf{A}$ with eigenvalue λ, then $\mathbf{A}\mathbf{v} = \lambda\mathbf{v}$. If p is any number, it follows that

$$(\mathbf{A} - p\mathbf{I})\mathbf{v} = \mathbf{A}\mathbf{v} - p\mathbf{I}\mathbf{v} = \lambda\mathbf{v} - p\mathbf{v} = (\lambda - p)\mathbf{v},$$

which shows that $\mathbf{v}$ is an eigenvector of $\mathbf{A} - p\mathbf{I}$, with eigenvalue $\lambda - p$.

If the number p is *not* an eigenvalue of $\mathbf{A}$, then the eigenvalues $\lambda - p$ of $\mathbf{A} - p\mathbf{I}$ are non-zero, so $\mathbf{A} - p\mathbf{I}$ is invertible. Therefore we can multiply both sides of the equation

$$(\mathbf{A} - p\mathbf{I})\mathbf{v} = (\lambda - p)\mathbf{v}$$

on the left by $(\mathbf{A} - p\mathbf{I})^{-1}$ to obtain

$$\mathbf{v} = (\mathbf{A} - p\mathbf{I})^{-1}(\lambda - p)\mathbf{v},$$

and, dividing by $\lambda - p$,

$$(\mathbf{A} - p\mathbf{I})^{-1}\mathbf{v} = (\lambda - p)^{-1}\mathbf{v}.$$

This shows that $\mathbf{v}$ is also an eigenvector of $(\mathbf{A} - p\mathbf{I})^{-1}$, with eigenvalue $(\lambda - p)^{-1}$.

- If $\mathbf{v}$ is an eigenvector of any matrix $\mathbf{A}$ with eigenvalue λ, then $\mathbf{A}\mathbf{v} = \lambda\mathbf{v}$. It follows that for any number p, $p(\mathbf{A}\mathbf{v}) = p\lambda\mathbf{v}$, so $(p\mathbf{A})\mathbf{v} = (p\lambda)\mathbf{v}$, which shows that $\mathbf{v}$ is an eigenvector of $p\mathbf{A}$ with eigenvalue $p\lambda$.

Eigenvalues and eigenvectors of associated matrices

If $\mathbf{A}$ is an arbitrary matrix and λ is one of its eigenvalues, then:

- λ^k is an eigenvalue of $\mathbf{A}^k$ for any positive integer k;
- if $\mathbf{A}$ is invertible, then λ^{-1} is an eigenvalue of $\mathbf{A}^{-1}$;
- $\lambda - p$ is an eigenvalue of $\mathbf{A} - p\mathbf{I}$, for any number p;
- $(\lambda - p)^{-1}$ is an eigenvalue of $(\mathbf{A} - p\mathbf{I})^{-1}$, for any number p that is not an eigenvalue of $\mathbf{A}$;
- $p\lambda$ is an eigenvalue of $p\mathbf{A}$ for any number p.

In each case, an eigenvector of the associated matrix is also an eigenvector of $\mathbf{A}$.

We shall need these results in Section 4 and in later units of the course.

*Exercise 2.12

(a) The eigenvalues of $\mathbf{A} = \begin{bmatrix} 2 & 3 \\ 2 & 1 \end{bmatrix}$ are 4 and -1. Write down the eigen-values of each of the following.

   (i) $\mathbf{A}^3$ (ii) $\mathbf{A}^{-1}$ (iii) $\mathbf{A} - 6\mathbf{I}$ (iv) $(\mathbf{A} + 3\mathbf{I})^{-1}$

(b) What can you say about the eigenvalues of $\mathbf{A} - 4\mathbf{I}$? What can you say about the inverse of $\mathbf{A} - 4\mathbf{I}$?

End-of-section Exercises

Exercise 2.13

(a) Find the eigenvalues and corresponding eigenvectors of the matrix $\mathbf{A} = \begin{bmatrix} 1 & 2 \\ 3 & -4 \end{bmatrix}$. Write down the eigenvalues and corresponding eigen-vectors of the matrix $\mathbf{A}^{10}$.

(b) Write down the eigenvalues and corresponding eigenvectors of the matrix $\begin{bmatrix} 3 & 2 \\ 3 & -2 \end{bmatrix}$.

   (*Hint*: Compare this matrix with the matrix $\mathbf{A}$ in part (a).)

Exercise 2.14

Let θ be an angle that is not an integer multiple of π. Calculate the eigen-values and eigenvectors of the matrix

$$\mathbf{A} = \begin{bmatrix} \cos\theta & -\sin\theta \\ \sin\theta & \cos\theta \end{bmatrix},$$

which represents an anticlockwise rotation through the angle θ.

3 Eigenvalues and eigenvectors of 3 × 3 matrices

In this section we extend the ideas of Section 2 to deal with 3×3 matrices. In fact it is possible to extend the treatment to $n \times n$ matrices, and with this in mind it is convenient to use the notation x_1, x_2 and x_3 (rather than x, y and z).

So we are interested in finding the eigenvalues and corresponding eigenvec-tors of a matrix such as

$$\begin{bmatrix} -2 & 1 & 0 \\ 1 & -2 & 1 \\ 0 & 1 & -2 \end{bmatrix}.$$

As in the case of 2×2 matrices, we can verify that a given vector is an eigenvector. For example, $\begin{bmatrix} 1 & 0 & -1 \end{bmatrix}^T$ is an eigenvector of the above matrix, since

$$\begin{bmatrix} -2 & 1 & 0 \\ 1 & -2 & 1 \\ 0 & 1 & -2 \end{bmatrix} \begin{bmatrix} 1 \\ 0 \\ -1 \end{bmatrix} = \begin{bmatrix} -2 \\ 0 \\ 2 \end{bmatrix} = -2 \begin{bmatrix} 1 \\ 0 \\ -1 \end{bmatrix},$$

and the corresponding eigenvalue is -2.

Exercise 3.1 _____

Verify that $\begin{bmatrix} 0 \\ 1 \\ 1 \end{bmatrix}$ and $\begin{bmatrix} 0 \\ 1 \\ -1 \end{bmatrix}$ are eigenvectors of $\mathbf{A} = \begin{bmatrix} 5 & 0 & 0 \\ 1 & 2 & 1 \\ 1 & 1 & 2 \end{bmatrix}$, and find the corresponding eigenvalues.

The above exercise should have convinced you that it is easy to *verify* that a given vector is an eigenvector, but how are we to *find* such eigenvectors? Moreover, how are we to deal with the more general case of an $n \times n$ matrix? This section examines these questions.

3.1   Basic method

In this subsection we look at a method for finding the eigenvalues and the corresponding eigenvectors of an arbitrary 3×3 matrix. Consider the following example.

Example 3.1

Find the eigenvalues and corresponding eigenvectors of the matrix

$$\mathbf{A} = \begin{bmatrix} 3 & 2 & 2 \\ 2 & 2 & 0 \\ 2 & 0 & 4 \end{bmatrix}.$$

Solution

We wish to find those non-zero vectors $\mathbf{v}$ that satisfy the equation

$$\mathbf{A}\mathbf{v} = \lambda\mathbf{v}$$

for some number λ. Writing $\mathbf{v} = [x_1 \quad x_2 \quad x_3]^T$, we have

$$\begin{bmatrix} 3 & 2 & 2 \\ 2 & 2 & 0 \\ 2 & 0 & 4 \end{bmatrix} \begin{bmatrix} x_1 \\ x_2 \\ x_3 \end{bmatrix} = \lambda \begin{bmatrix} x_1 \\ x_2 \\ x_3 \end{bmatrix},$$

which gives

$$\begin{cases} (3-\lambda)x_1 + 2x_2 + 2x_3 = 0, \\ 2x_1 + (2-\lambda)x_2 = 0, \\ 2x_1 + (4-\lambda)x_3 = 0, \end{cases} \qquad (3.1)$$

These are the *eigenvector equations.*

which can be written as $(\mathbf{A} - \lambda\mathbf{I})\mathbf{v} = \mathbf{0}$. We are interested in non-zero solutions of these equations (i.e. solutions in which x_1, x_2 and x_3 are not all 0). The condition for such solutions to exist is that the determinant of the coefficient matrix $\mathbf{A} - \lambda\mathbf{I}$ is 0, i.e.

$$\begin{vmatrix} 3-\lambda & 2 & 2 \\ 2 & 2-\lambda & 0 \\ 2 & 0 & 4-\lambda \end{vmatrix} = 0.$$

Expanding this determinant by the first row gives

See *Unit 9.*

$$(3-\lambda)\begin{vmatrix} 2-\lambda & 0 \\ 0 & 4-\lambda \end{vmatrix} - 2\begin{vmatrix} 2 & 0 \\ 2 & 4-\lambda \end{vmatrix} + 2\begin{vmatrix} 2 & 2-\lambda \\ 2 & 0 \end{vmatrix} = 0,$$

hence

$$(3-\lambda)(2-\lambda)(4-\lambda) - 2(8-2\lambda) - 2(4-2\lambda) = 0,$$

which simplifies to the cubic equation

$$\lambda^3 - 9\lambda^2 + 18\lambda = 0.$$

This is the *characteristic equation* of $\mathbf{A}$. For a 3×3 matrix $\mathbf{A}$, it will be a cubic equation.

We must now solve this equation. In general, it is difficult to solve a cubic equation algebraically, unless you use a computer algebra package. However, if you can spot one of the roots, then the task becomes considerably easier. In this case

$$\lambda^3 - 9\lambda^2 + 18\lambda = \lambda(\lambda^2 - 9\lambda + 18),$$

so $\lambda = 0$ is one of the roots. The others are obtained by solving the quadratic equation $\lambda^2 - 9\lambda + 18 = 0$ to give the roots 3 and 6. So the eigenvalues are 0, 3 and 6.

One way of solving the quadratic equation is to notice that
$\lambda^2 - 9\lambda + 18 = (\lambda - 3)(\lambda - 6)$.

In order to find the corresponding eigenvectors, we substitute each of these eigenvalues into the eigenvector equations (3.1) as follows.

$\boxed{\lambda = 6}$ The matrix form of the eigenvector equations (3.1) is

$$\begin{bmatrix} -3 & 2 & 2 \\ 2 & -4 & 0 \\ 2 & 0 & -2 \end{bmatrix} \begin{bmatrix} x_1 \\ x_2 \\ x_3 \end{bmatrix} = \mathbf{0}.$$

We saw in Subsection 2.3 that an equation of the form $\mathbf{Ax} = \mathbf{0}$ has a non-zero solution (and hence infinitely many solutions) if and only if the rows of $\mathbf{A}$ are linearly dependent. Here, this means that at least one of the following equations may be obtained from the other two:

$$\begin{cases} -3x_1 + 2x_2 + 2x_3 = 0, \\ 2x_1 - 4x_2 \phantom{{}+ 2x_3} = 0, \\ 2x_1 \phantom{{}- 4x_2} - 2x_3 = 0. \end{cases}$$

While it may appear that we have three equations in the three unknowns x_1, x_2 and x_3, only two of the equations are distinct. You may recall a similar occurrence in Exercise 1.7(c) of *Unit 9*.

So we can find our desired solution by considering just two of the equations. Using the second and third, we have $x_1 - 2x_2 = 0$ and $x_1 - x_3 = 0$. Putting $x_3 = k$ and solving for x_1 and x_2, we obtain $x_1 = k$, $x_2 = \frac{1}{2}k$. Choosing $k = 2$ gives an answer avoiding fractions: $x_1 = 2$, $x_2 = 1$, $x_3 = 2$. This means that $[2 \quad 1 \quad 2]^T$ is an eigenvector corresponding to the eigenvalue $\lambda = 6$.

We should check that these values satisfy the original equations.

Alternatively, we may solve the eigenvector equations by Gaussian elimination. In this case, we have the following augmented matrix.

$$\begin{bmatrix} -3 & 2 & 2 & | & 0 \\ 2 & -4 & 0 & | & 0 \\ 2 & 0 & -2 & | & 0 \end{bmatrix} \begin{matrix} \mathbf{R}_1 \\ \mathbf{R}_2 \\ \mathbf{R}_3 \end{matrix}$$

Gaussian elimination is a more cumbersome process than the previous method, but it is illuminating. At the final stage of the elimination process, the bottom row of the augmented matrix consists entirely of zeros — and this must be the case because the rows of $\mathbf{A} - \lambda \mathbf{I}$ are linearly dependent.

Stage 1(a)   We reduce to zero the elements below the leading diagonal in column 1.

$$\begin{matrix} \\ \mathbf{R}_2 + \frac{2}{3}\mathbf{R}_1 \\ \mathbf{R}_3 + \frac{2}{3}\mathbf{R}_1 \end{matrix} \begin{bmatrix} -3 & 2 & 2 & | & 0 \\ 0 & -\frac{8}{3} & \frac{4}{3} & | & 0 \\ 0 & \frac{4}{3} & -\frac{2}{3} & | & 0 \end{bmatrix} \begin{matrix} \mathbf{R}_1 \\ \mathbf{R}_{2a} \\ \mathbf{R}_{3a} \end{matrix}$$

Stage 1(b)   We reduce to zero the element below the leading diagonal in column 2.

$$\begin{matrix} \\ \\ \mathbf{R}_{3a} + \frac{1}{2}\mathbf{R}_{2a} \end{matrix} \begin{bmatrix} -3 & 2 & 2 & | & 0 \\ 0 & -\frac{8}{3} & \frac{4}{3} & | & 0 \\ 0 & 0 & 0 & | & 0 \end{bmatrix}$$

Stage 2   Back substitution gives $x_2 = \frac{1}{2}x_3$ and $x_1 = \frac{2}{3}(x_2 + x_3) = x_3$. We are free to choose x_3 as we please, so putting $x_3 = 2$, we find that $[2 \quad 1 \quad 2]^T$ is an eigenvector (as before).

The other cases, corresponding to $\lambda = 3$ and $\lambda = 0$, are dealt with in the same way.

$\boxed{\lambda = 3}$ Substituting $\lambda = 3$ into Equations (3.1), the eigenvector equations become $2x_2 + 2x_3 = 0$, $2x_1 - x_2 = 0$ and $2x_1 + x_3 = 0$. The first and second equations reduce to $x_3 = -x_2$ and $x_2 = 2x_1$. It follows that $[1 \quad 2 \quad -2]^T$ is an eigenvector corresponding to the eigenvalue 3.

Choose, for example, $x_1 = 1$, and use this to calculate x_2 and x_3.

$\boxed{\lambda = 0}$ Substituting $\lambda = 0$ into Equations (3.1), the eigenvector equations become $3x_1 + 2x_2 + 2x_3 = 0$, $2x_1 + 2x_2 = 0$ and $2x_1 + 4x_3 = 0$. These equations reduce to $x_2 = -x_1$ and $x_1 = -2x_3$. It follows that $[-2 \quad 2 \quad 1]^T$ is an eigenvector corresponding to the eigenvalue 0. ∎

Choose, for example, $x_3 = 1$, and use this to calculate x_1 and x_2.

In Example 3.1, we first found the eigenvalues by solving a cubic equation, then used these eigenvalues and the eigenvector equations to find the corresponding eigenvectors. We found the eigenvalues of the matrix

$$\mathbf{A} = \begin{bmatrix} 3 & 2 & 2 \\ 2 & 2 & 0 \\ 2 & 0 & 4 \end{bmatrix}$$

by solving the equation

$$\begin{vmatrix} 3 - \lambda & 2 & 2 \\ 2 & 2 - \lambda & 0 \\ 2 & 0 & 4 - \lambda \end{vmatrix} = 0.$$

Since the left-hand side of this equation is $\det(\mathbf{A} - \lambda\mathbf{I})$, it can be written in the form $\det(\mathbf{A} - \lambda\mathbf{I}) = 0$.

As in the case of a 2×2 matrix, the values of $\operatorname{tr}\mathbf{A}$ and $\det\mathbf{A}$ provide a useful check on the calculations. For Example 3.1, we see that $\operatorname{tr}\mathbf{A} = 3 + 2 + 4 = 9$ and the sum of the eigenvalues is also 9. Also, we have

$$\det\mathbf{A} = 3\begin{vmatrix} 2 & 0 \\ 0 & 4 \end{vmatrix} - 2\begin{vmatrix} 2 & 0 \\ 2 & 4 \end{vmatrix} + 2\begin{vmatrix} 2 & 2 \\ 2 & 0 \end{vmatrix} = 24 - 16 - 8 = 0$$

and the product of the eigenvalues is also 0.

Procedure 3.1   Eigenvalues and eigenvectors of an *n × n* matrix

To find the eigenvalues and eigenvectors of an $n \times n$ matrix $\mathbf{A}$:

(a) solve the characteristic equation

$$\det(\mathbf{A} - \lambda\mathbf{I}) = 0,$$

to determine the eigenvalues $\lambda_1, \lambda_2, \ldots, \lambda_n$;

(b) solve the corresponding eigenvector equations $(\mathbf{A} - \lambda_i\mathbf{I})\mathbf{v}_i = \mathbf{0}$ for each eigenvalue λ_i, to find a corresponding eigenvector $\mathbf{v}_i$.

The characteristic equation of an $n \times n$ matrix has n solutions (some of which may be repeated). If there are n distinct solutions, there will be n linearly independent eigenvectors (but there may be fewer if any of the eigenvalues is repeated).

This procedure extends Procedures 2.1 and 2.2 to $n \times n$ matrices.

Exercise 3.2

The eigenvalues of the matrix

$$\mathbf{A} = \begin{bmatrix} 1 & 0 & -1 \\ 1 & 2 & 1 \\ 2 & 2 & 3 \end{bmatrix}$$

are $\lambda = 1$, $\lambda = 2$ and $\lambda = 3$. Write down the eigenvector equations, and determine corresponding eigenvectors.

*Exercise 3.3

Determine the characteristic equation of the matrix $\mathbf{A} = \begin{bmatrix} 0 & 0 & 6 \\ \frac{1}{2} & 0 & 0 \\ 0 & \frac{1}{3} & 0 \end{bmatrix}$.

Verify that $\lambda = 1$ is an eigenvalue of $\mathbf{A}$, and find a corresponding eigenvector. (You do not need to find any other eigenvalues.)

3.2   Finding eigenvalues by hand

For the matrices that arise from real applications, it is rarely possible to calculate the eigenvalues and eigenvectors by hand, and we would generally use numerical techniques such as those discussed in the next section. However, finding eigenvalues and eigenvectors by hand is an important part of the learning process. In this course you can divide the exercises into two types: those for which it is easy to find the eigenvalues by hand, and the rest (for which you will probably need to use the computer algebra package for the course). The examples and exercises in this section have been carefully chosen to be of the former kind.

Example 3.2

Find the eigenvalues of the matrix

$$\mathbf{A} = \begin{bmatrix} 5 & 0 & 0 \\ 1 & 2 & 1 \\ 1 & 1 & 2 \end{bmatrix}.$$

Solution

The characteristic equation is

$$\begin{vmatrix} 5 - \lambda & 0 & 0 \\ 1 & 2 - \lambda & 1 \\ 1 & 1 & 2 - \lambda \end{vmatrix} = 0.$$

Expanding the determinant by the first row gives

$$(5 - \lambda) \begin{vmatrix} 2 - \lambda & 1 \\ 1 & 2 - \lambda \end{vmatrix} = 0,$$

hence $(5 - \lambda)(\lambda^2 - 4\lambda + 3) = 0$. So $5 - \lambda = 0$ or $\lambda^2 - 4\lambda + 3 = 0$. Hence one solution is $\lambda = 5$. The quadratic equation $\lambda^2 - 4\lambda + 3 = 0$ has roots 1 and 3. Thus the eigenvalues are $\lambda = 5$, $\lambda = 3$ and $\lambda = 1$. ∎

Exercise 3.4

Find the eigenvalues of each of the following matrices.

(a) $\mathbf{A} = \begin{bmatrix} 0 & 0 & 1 \\ 0 & 0 & 0 \\ 1 & 0 & 0 \end{bmatrix}$ (b) $\mathbf{A} = \begin{bmatrix} 1 & 0 & 0 \\ 6 & 2 & 0 \\ 5 & 4 & 3 \end{bmatrix}$

Often the most arduous part of such problems is the expansion of the determinant, but judicious interchanging of rows and/or taking the transpose can reduce the work, as the following example shows.

Example 3.3

Find the eigenvalues of the matrix $\mathbf{A} = \begin{bmatrix} 5 & 2 & 0 \\ 2 & 5 & 0 \\ -3 & 4 & 6 \end{bmatrix}$.

Solution

The characteristic equation is

$$\begin{vmatrix} 5-\lambda & 2 & 0 \\ 2 & 5-\lambda & 0 \\ -3 & 4 & 6-\lambda \end{vmatrix} = 0.$$

To make the calculation easier, we should like the third column to be the first row. Taking the transpose gives

$$\begin{vmatrix} 5-\lambda & 2 & -3 \\ 2 & 5-\lambda & 4 \\ 0 & 0 & 6-\lambda \end{vmatrix} = 0,$$

Recall from *Unit 9* that taking the transpose does not alter the value of the determinant.

and interchanging rows 1 and 3 gives

$$\begin{vmatrix} 0 & 0 & 6-\lambda \\ 2 & 5-\lambda & 4 \\ 5-\lambda & 2 & -3 \end{vmatrix} = 0.$$

This interchange changes the sign of the determinant, but this has no effect since we know that the value of the determinant is zero.

Expanding the determinant by the first row gives

$$(6-\lambda)\begin{vmatrix} 2 & 5-\lambda \\ 5-\lambda & 2 \end{vmatrix} = 0,$$

hence $(6-\lambda)(4-(5-\lambda)^2) = 0$. So $\lambda - 6 = 0$ or $4 - (5-\lambda)^2 = 0$. Hence one solution is $\lambda = 6$. The quadratic equation $4 - (5-\lambda)^2 = 0$ can be rewritten as $(5-\lambda)^2 = 4$, so $5 - \lambda = \pm 2$, and the two other solutions are $\lambda = 7$ and $\lambda = 3$. Thus the eigenvalues are $\lambda = 6$, $\lambda = 7$ and $\lambda = 3$. ∎

Exercise 3.5

Find the eigenvalues of the matrix $\mathbf{A} = \begin{bmatrix} 8 & 0 & -5 \\ 9 & 3 & -6 \\ 10 & 0 & -7 \end{bmatrix}$.

You will need the eigenvalues of this matrix in Exercise 3.7.

Exercise 3.6

Verify that the eigenvalues of the triangular matrices $\begin{bmatrix} a & 0 & 0 \\ d & b & 0 \\ e & f & c \end{bmatrix}$ and $\begin{bmatrix} a & d & e \\ 0 & b & f \\ 0 & 0 & c \end{bmatrix}$ are the diagonal entries a, b and c.

See Subsection 2.3.

Exercise 3.7

Verify that the sum of the eigenvalues is $\operatorname{tr}\mathbf{A}$ for the matrices $\mathbf{A}$ in:

(a) Examples 3.2 and 3.3;   (b) Exercises 3.2, 3.4 and 3.5.

In each case, write down the value of $\det \mathbf{A}$, and verify that this is the product of the eigenvalues.

The eigenvalues of a 3×3 matrix can be real and distinct (as in Exercise 3.2), or real and repeated (as in Exercise 3.5), or one may be real and the other two form a complex conjugate pair — as in the following example.

Repeated real eigenvalues may be repeated once,
$$\lambda_1 = \lambda_2 \neq \lambda_3,$$
or twice,
$$\lambda_1 = \lambda_2 = \lambda_3.$$

Example 3.4

Find the eigenvalues and corresponding eigenvectors of the matrix

$$\begin{bmatrix} 1 & 0 & 0 \\ 0 & 0 & 1 \\ 0 & -1 & 0 \end{bmatrix}.$$

Solution

The characteristic equation is

$$\begin{vmatrix} 1-\lambda & 0 & 0 \\ 0 & -\lambda & 1 \\ 0 & -1 & -\lambda \end{vmatrix} = 0.$$

Expanding the determinant by the first row gives

$$(1-\lambda) \begin{vmatrix} -\lambda & 1 \\ -1 & -\lambda \end{vmatrix} = (1-\lambda)(\lambda^2 + 1) = 0,$$

so $1 - \lambda = 0$ or $\lambda^2 + 1 = 0$. The quadratic equation $\lambda^2 + 1 = 0$ has roots $\lambda = i$ and $\lambda = -i$, where $i^2 = -1$. Thus the eigenvalues are $\lambda = 1$, $\lambda = i$ and $\lambda = -i$.

The eigenvector equations are

$$\begin{cases} (1-\lambda)x_1 & = 0, \\ -\lambda x_2 + x_3 = 0, \\ -x_2 - \lambda x_3 = 0. \end{cases}$$

$\boxed{\lambda = 1}$ The eigenvector equations become $0 = 0$, $-x_2 + x_3 = 0$ and $-x_2 - x_3 = 0$, which reduce to the equations $x_2 = 0$ and $x_3 = 0$. There is no constraint on the value of x_1, so we may choose it as we please. It follows that a corresponding eigenvector is $\begin{bmatrix} 1 & 0 & 0 \end{bmatrix}^T$.

$\boxed{\lambda = i}$ The eigenvector equations become $(1-i)x_1 = 0$, $-ix_2 + x_3 = 0$ and $-x_2 - ix_3 = 0$, which reduce to the equations $x_1 = 0$ and $ix_2 = x_3$. It follows that a corresponding eigenvector is $\begin{bmatrix} 0 & 1 & i \end{bmatrix}^T$.

$\boxed{\lambda = -i}$ The eigenvector equations become $(1+i)x_1 = 0$, $ix_2 + x_3 = 0$ and $-x_2 + ix_3 = 0$, which reduce to the equations $x_1 = 0$ and $-ix_2 = x_3$. It follows that a corresponding eigenvector is $\begin{bmatrix} 0 & 1 & -i \end{bmatrix}^T$.   ∎

In Example 3.4 we have three distinct eigenvalues and three distinct eigenvectors, but only the real eigenvalue $\lambda = 1$ gives rise to a real eigenvector.

Exercise 3.8

Calculate the eigenvalues and eigenvectors of the following matrices.

(a) $\begin{bmatrix} 0 & 0 & 1 \\ 0 & 1 & 0 \\ 1 & 0 & 0 \end{bmatrix}$ (b) $\begin{bmatrix} \frac{1}{\sqrt{2}} & 0 & \frac{1}{\sqrt{2}} \\ 0 & 1 & 0 \\ -\frac{1}{\sqrt{2}} & 0 & \frac{1}{\sqrt{2}} \end{bmatrix}$

We have dealt with 3×3 matrices for which the eigenvalues can be found easily, and it is reasonable to solve such problems by hand. Generally, the larger matrices that arise in practical problems are better dealt with in an entirely different fashion, as we shall see in the next section. However, our experience of finding the eigenvalues and eigenvectors of the simpler kinds of 2×2 and 3×3 matrices will not be wasted, for it will allow us to see what types of solution we may expect for larger matrices.

In each of the cases considered in this section, if a 3×3 matrix has three distinct eigenvalues, then the corresponding eigenvectors are linearly independent. More generally, any $n \times n$ matrix with n distinct eigenvalues has n linearly independent eigenvectors, although we shall not prove this here.

If eigenvalues are repeated, then the situation becomes more complicated. We shall leave that discussion to the next unit, when we return to this topic in the context of solving systems of differential equations.

End-of-section Exercise

Exercise 3.9

Find the eigenvalues and corresponding eigenvectors of the following matrices.

(a) $\begin{bmatrix} 2 & 1 & -1 \\ 0 & -3 & 2 \\ 0 & 0 & 4 \end{bmatrix}$ (b) $\begin{bmatrix} 0 & 2 & 0 \\ -2 & 0 & 0 \\ 0 & 0 & 1 \end{bmatrix}$

(c) $\begin{bmatrix} 1 & 0 & 0 \\ 0 & 1 & 2 \\ 0 & -2 & 5 \end{bmatrix}$ (d) $\begin{bmatrix} 1 & 0 & 0 \\ 0 & 1 & 0 \\ 1 & 1 & -2 \end{bmatrix}$

4 Iterative methods

Finding the eigenvalues and eigenvectors of a 3×3 matrix using the method of Section 3 can be quite a laborious process, and the calculations become progressively more difficult for larger matrices.

In this section we show how we can often find approximations to real eigenvectors and their corresponding eigenvalues by iteration — that is, by choosing a vector and applying the matrix repeatedly.

4.1 *Approximating eigenvectors*

In the Introduction we considered a migration problem in which the towns Exton and Wyeville have a regular interchange of population. We saw that if x_n and y_n denote the respective populations of Exton and Wyeville at the beginning of year n, then the corresponding populations at the beginning of year $n + 1$ are given by the matrix equation

$$\begin{bmatrix} x_{n+1} \\ y_{n+1} \end{bmatrix} = \begin{bmatrix} 0.9 & 0.2 \\ 0.1 & 0.8 \end{bmatrix} \begin{bmatrix} x_n \\ y_n \end{bmatrix}.$$

Using this equation, we saw that if the initial populations are $x_0 = 10\,000$ and $y_0 = 8000$, then the populations in successive years are

$$\begin{bmatrix} x_0 \\ y_0 \end{bmatrix} = \begin{bmatrix} 10\,000 \\ 8\,000 \end{bmatrix}, \quad \begin{bmatrix} x_1 \\ y_1 \end{bmatrix} = \begin{bmatrix} 10\,600 \\ 7\,400 \end{bmatrix}, \quad \begin{bmatrix} x_2 \\ y_2 \end{bmatrix} = \begin{bmatrix} 11\,020 \\ 6\,980 \end{bmatrix}, \quad \cdots$$

As n increases, the sequence of vectors $[x_n \ \ y_n]^T$ converges to the vector $[x \ \ y]^T = [12\,000 \ \ 6000]^T$, which is an eigenvector of the above 2×2 matrix.

More generally, suppose that we wish to find the eigenvectors of a given matrix $\mathbf{A}$, and that we have an initial estimate $\mathbf{e}_0$ for an eigenvector. It may happen that $\mathbf{e}_0$ is an eigenvector of $\mathbf{A}$ and $\mathbf{A}\mathbf{e}_0$ is in the same direction as $\mathbf{e}_0$, as in Figure 4.1. If, as usually happens, $\mathbf{e}_0$ is not an eigenvector, then we calculate the vector $\mathbf{e}_1 = \mathbf{A}\mathbf{e}_0$ and then another vector, $\mathbf{e}_2$, defined by $\mathbf{e}_2 = \mathbf{A}\mathbf{e}_1 = \mathbf{A}^2\mathbf{e}_0$. Continuing in this way, we obtain a sequence of vectors

$$\mathbf{e}_0, \quad \mathbf{e}_1 = \mathbf{A}\mathbf{e}_0, \quad \mathbf{e}_2 = \mathbf{A}^2\mathbf{e}_0, \quad \mathbf{e}_3 = \mathbf{A}^3\mathbf{e}_0, \quad \mathbf{e}_4 = \mathbf{A}^4\mathbf{e}_0, \quad \ldots,$$

as shown in Figure 4.2, where each vector in the sequence is obtained from the previous one by multiplying by the matrix $\mathbf{A}$. Often this simple method of repeatedly applying the matrix $\mathbf{A}$ produces a sequence of vectors that converges to an eigenvector.

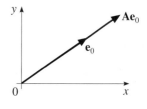

Figure 4.1

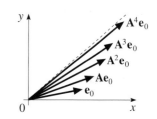

Figure 4.2

Exercise 4.1

Given

$$\mathbf{A} = \begin{bmatrix} 3 & 2 \\ 1 & 4 \end{bmatrix}, \quad \mathbf{e}_0 = \begin{bmatrix} 1 \\ 0 \end{bmatrix}, \quad \mathbf{e}_{n+1} = \mathbf{A}\mathbf{e}_n, \ n = 0, 1, 2, \ldots,$$

calculate $\mathbf{e}_1$, $\mathbf{e}_2$, $\mathbf{e}_3$ and $\mathbf{e}_4$.

From Example 2.2 we know that for $\mathbf{A} = \begin{bmatrix} 3 & 2 \\ 1 & 4 \end{bmatrix}$, $\mathbf{v}_1 = [1 \ \ 1]^T$ is an eigenvector corresponding to the eigenvalue 5, and $\mathbf{v}_2 = [-2 \ \ 1]^T$ is an eigenvector corresponding to the eigenvalue 2. We may suspect that the sequence $\mathbf{e}_1, \mathbf{e}_2, \mathbf{e}_3, \mathbf{e}_4, \ldots$ in Exercise 4.1 converges to a scalar multiple of the eigenvector $[1 \ \ 1]^T$, but how can we be sure that it does?

Suppose that we express our initial vector $\mathbf{e}_0 = [1 \ \ 0]^T$ as a linear combination of $\mathbf{v}_1$ and $\mathbf{v}_2$, so that $\mathbf{e}_0 = \alpha\mathbf{v}_1 + \beta\mathbf{v}_2$ for some numbers α and β. Then

> We can do this if there are two linearly independent eigenvectors (see Exercise 1.2 and the text following that exercise).

$$\mathbf{e}_0 = \begin{bmatrix} 1 \\ 0 \end{bmatrix} = \alpha \begin{bmatrix} 1 \\ 1 \end{bmatrix} + \beta \begin{bmatrix} -2 \\ 1 \end{bmatrix} = \begin{bmatrix} 1 & -2 \\ 1 & 1 \end{bmatrix} \begin{bmatrix} \alpha \\ \beta \end{bmatrix},$$

> α and β are known as the *components* of $\mathbf{v}_1$ and $\mathbf{v}_2$ in $\mathbf{e}_0$.

so

$$\begin{bmatrix} 1 & -2 \\ 1 & 1 \end{bmatrix} \begin{bmatrix} \alpha \\ \beta \end{bmatrix} = \begin{bmatrix} 1 \\ 0 \end{bmatrix}.$$

Multiplying both sides of this equation on the left by the inverse of the matrix on the left-hand side, we see that

> A matrix formed from linearly independent vectors in this way always has an inverse.

$$\begin{bmatrix} \alpha \\ \beta \end{bmatrix} = \tfrac{1}{3} \begin{bmatrix} 1 & 2 \\ -1 & 1 \end{bmatrix} \begin{bmatrix} 1 \\ 0 \end{bmatrix} = \begin{bmatrix} \tfrac{1}{3} \\ -\tfrac{1}{3} \end{bmatrix},$$

so $\alpha = \tfrac{1}{3}$, $\beta = -\tfrac{1}{3}$ and

$$\mathbf{e}_0 = \tfrac{1}{3}\mathbf{v}_1 - \tfrac{1}{3}\mathbf{v}_2.$$

We can now express $\mathbf{e}_1, \mathbf{e}_2, \ldots$ in terms of $\mathbf{v}_1$ and $\mathbf{v}_2$. Since $\mathbf{v}_1$ and $\mathbf{v}_2$ are eigenvectors, and we know that $\mathbf{A}\mathbf{v}_1 = 5\mathbf{v}_1$ and $\mathbf{A}\mathbf{v}_2 = 2\mathbf{v}_2$, we have

$$\mathbf{e}_1 = \mathbf{A}\mathbf{e}_0 = \tfrac{1}{3}\mathbf{A}\mathbf{v}_1 - \tfrac{1}{3}\mathbf{A}\mathbf{v}_2 = \tfrac{1}{3}(5\mathbf{v}_1) - \tfrac{1}{3}(2\mathbf{v}_2).$$

Applying $\mathbf{A}$ repeatedly gives

$$\mathbf{e}_2 = \mathbf{A}^2\mathbf{e}_0 = \tfrac{1}{3}(5\mathbf{A}\mathbf{v}_1) - \tfrac{1}{3}(2\mathbf{A}\mathbf{v}_2) = \tfrac{1}{3}(5^2\mathbf{v}_1) - \tfrac{1}{3}(2^2\mathbf{v}_2),$$

$$\mathbf{e}_3 = \mathbf{A}^3\mathbf{e}_0 = \tfrac{1}{3}(5^2\mathbf{A}\mathbf{v}_1) - \tfrac{1}{3}(2^2\mathbf{A}\mathbf{v}_2) = \tfrac{1}{3}(5^3\mathbf{v}_1) - \tfrac{1}{3}(2^3\mathbf{v}_2),$$

> $\mathbf{e}_2 = \mathbf{A}\mathbf{e}_1 = \mathbf{A}^2\mathbf{e}_0$

and so on.

In general, we can write
$$\mathbf{e}_n = \mathbf{A}^n \mathbf{e}_0 = \tfrac{1}{3}(5^n \mathbf{v}_1) - \tfrac{1}{3}(2^n \mathbf{v}_2).$$

For example,
$$\begin{aligned}
\mathbf{e}_{10} = \mathbf{A}^{10} \mathbf{e}_0 &= \tfrac{1}{3}(5^{10} \mathbf{v}_1) - \tfrac{1}{3}(2^{10} \mathbf{v}_2)\\
&\simeq 3\,255\,208 \mathbf{v}_1 - 341 \mathbf{v}_2\\
&\simeq 3\,255\,208(\mathbf{v}_1 - 0.000\,105 \mathbf{v}_2).
\end{aligned}$$

As you can see, the powers of 5 rapidly become much larger than the powers of 2, and for large values of n we can ignore the latter, to give the approximation
$$\mathbf{e}_n = \mathbf{A}^n \mathbf{e}_0 \simeq \tfrac{1}{3}(5^n \mathbf{v}_1).$$

This is a scalar multiple of an eigenvector that corresponds to the eigenvalue of larger magnitude.

Thus repeatedly applying $\mathbf{A}$ leads to an approximation of an eigenvector — an eigenvector corresponding to the eigenvalue of larger magnitude.

Taking another example, you can show that the matrix
$$\mathbf{A} = \begin{bmatrix} 4 & 2 \\ -7 & -5 \end{bmatrix}$$

has eigenvalues -3 and 2, and that the above method will give approximations to an eigenvector corresponding to the eigenvalue -3 because powers of -3 eventually dominate powers of 2.

Exercise 4.2 ———————————————————————————

Use
$$\mathbf{A} = \begin{bmatrix} 2 & 1 \\ 1 & 2 \end{bmatrix}, \qquad \mathbf{e}_0 = \begin{bmatrix} 1 \\ 0 \end{bmatrix}, \qquad \mathbf{e}_{n+1} = \mathbf{A}\mathbf{e}_n, \ n = 0, 1, 2, \ldots .$$

(a) Calculate $\mathbf{e}_1$, $\mathbf{e}_2$ and $\mathbf{e}_3$.

(b) Given $\mathbf{e}_{10} = [29\,525 \quad 29\,524]^T$, calculate $\mathbf{e}_{11}$.

(c) Use Procedures 2.1 and 2.2 to find the eigenvalues λ_1 and λ_2, and corresponding eigenvectors $\mathbf{v}_1$ and $\mathbf{v}_2$, of $\mathbf{A}$.

(d) Express $\mathbf{e}_0$ as a linear combination of $\mathbf{v}_1$ and $\mathbf{v}_2$.

(e) Express $\mathbf{e}_1$, $\mathbf{e}_2$, and hence $\mathbf{e}_n$, as linear combinations of $\mathbf{v}_1$ and $\mathbf{v}_2$.

(f) To which eigenvector does the sequence $\mathbf{e}_n$ provide an approximation?

The above technique provides us with increasingly accurate approximations to one of the eigenvectors of a 2×2 matrix. But the most significant aspect of the method is that it is possible to extend it to matrices of *any* size. However, there are difficulties, and you should be aware of them before we proceed. You may have noticed in the previous exercise that the components of an approximation to an eigenvector may be quite large and, had we attempted to calculate $\mathbf{e}_{20}$, we should have found that $\mathbf{e}_{20} = [1\,743\,392\,201 \quad 1\,743\,392\,200]^T$. For larger values of n, $\mathbf{e}_n$ involves even larger numbers. We shall see that this difficulty is easily overcome, but there are other difficulties. Table 4.1 shows five examples, each exhibiting a different problem.

Table 4.1

	Matrix	Eigenvalues	Corresponding eigenvectors	Initial vector and nth approximation
(a)	$\begin{bmatrix} 1 & 4 \\ 9 & 1 \end{bmatrix}$	7 -5	$\mathbf{v}_1 = [2 \quad 3]^T$ $\mathbf{v}_2 = [2 \quad -3]^T$	$\mathbf{e}_0 = [1 \quad 0]^T$ $\mathbf{e}_n = \frac{1}{4}(7)^n\mathbf{v}_1 + \frac{1}{4}(-5)^n\mathbf{v}_2$
(b)	$\begin{bmatrix} 2 & 0 \\ 0 & -2 \end{bmatrix}$	2 -2	$\mathbf{v}_1 = [1 \quad 0]^T$ $\mathbf{v}_2 = [0 \quad 1]^T$	$\mathbf{e}_0 = [1 \quad 1]^T$ $\mathbf{e}_n = 2^n\mathbf{v}_1 + (-2)^n\mathbf{v}_2$
(c)	$\begin{bmatrix} 1.2 & -0.2 \\ 0.3 & 0.7 \end{bmatrix}$	1 0.9	$\mathbf{v}_1 = [1 \quad 1]^T$ $\mathbf{v}_2 = [2 \quad 3]^T$	$\mathbf{e}_0 = [1 \quad 0]^T$ $\mathbf{e}_n = 3\mathbf{v}_1 - (0.9)^n\mathbf{v}_2$
(d)	$\begin{bmatrix} 0 & -1 \\ 1 & 0 \end{bmatrix}$	i $-i$	$\mathbf{v}_1 = [1 \quad -i]^T$ $\mathbf{v}_2 = [1 \quad i]^T$	$\mathbf{e}_0 = [1 \quad 0]^T$ $\mathbf{e}_n = \frac{1}{2}(i)^n\mathbf{v}_1 + \frac{1}{2}(-i)^n\mathbf{v}_2$
(e)	$\begin{bmatrix} 3 & 0 & 0 \\ 0 & 2 & 0 \\ 0 & 0 & 1 \end{bmatrix}$	3 2 1	$\mathbf{v}_1 = [1 \quad 0 \quad 0]^T$ $\mathbf{v}_2 = [0 \quad 1 \quad 0]^T$ $\mathbf{v}_3 = [0 \quad 0 \quad 1]^T$	$\mathbf{e}_0 = [0 \quad 1 \quad 1]^T$ $\mathbf{e}_n = 2^n\mathbf{v}_2 + \mathbf{v}_3$

> The $\mathbf{e}_0$ are normally chosen rather arbitrarily.

In row (a) of the table, the elements of $\mathbf{e}_n$ become very large: for example,

$$\mathbf{e}_5 = [6841 \quad 14\,949]^T$$

and

$$\mathbf{e}_{10} = [146\,120\,437 \quad 204\,532\,218]^T.$$

This may cause difficulties in the calculations. You may already suspect how this difficulty may be overcome. We are interested in only the *directions* of the vectors, and rescaling a vector does not change its direction. So, dividing both components of $\mathbf{e}_{10}$ by $204\,532\,218$, we obtain the vector $[0.7144 \quad 1]^T$ (to four decimal places) as the estimate of an eigenvector.

In (b) we have a rather more fundamental problem. The eigenvalues have the same magnitude, so, as n increases, neither the term involving $\mathbf{v}_1$ nor the term involving $\mathbf{v}_2$ becomes dominant, so the iteration does not converge.

The eigenvalues in (c) are certainly not equal, but they are similar in magnitude. This means that we need to choose a very large value of n in order to obtain a good approximation for $\mathbf{v}_1$ (the eigenvector corresponding to the eigenvalue of larger magnitude).

In (d) we have complex eigenvalues and, as you might expect, a sequence of real vectors cannot converge to a complex eigenvector.

> You always generate a real sequence (unless you start with a complex $\mathbf{e}_0$).

In (e) we see that the sequence $\mathbf{e}_n$ converges to the eigenvector $\mathbf{v}_2$, when we might expect it to converge to $\mathbf{v}_1$ (the eigenvector corresponding to the eigenvalue of largest magnitude). This is because the original estimate $\mathbf{e}_0$ contains no component of $\mathbf{v}_1$, so the same is true of all subsequent estimates.

> Such a difficulty is unlikely to arise in practice because rounding errors in the calculation of the iterates will normally ensure that the component of $\mathbf{v}_1$ is not exactly zero.

Exercise 4.3

In the migration problem first discussed in the Introduction, we have

$$\mathbf{A} = \begin{bmatrix} 0.9 & 0.2 \\ 0.1 & 0.8 \end{bmatrix}, \quad \mathbf{e}_0 = \begin{bmatrix} 10\,000 \\ 8\,000 \end{bmatrix}.$$

Eigenvectors of $\mathbf{A}$ are $\mathbf{v}_1 = [2 \quad 1]^T$ with corresponding eigenvalue 1, and $\mathbf{v}_2 = [1 \quad -1]^T$ with corresponding eigenvalue 0.7.

> You found these eigenvectors in Exercise 2.5.

(a) Write $\mathbf{e}_0$ as a linear combination of $\mathbf{v}_1$ and $\mathbf{v}_2$.

(b) Obtain an expression for $\mathbf{e}_n = \mathbf{A}^n\mathbf{e}_0$ as a linear combination of $\mathbf{v}_1$ and $\mathbf{v}_2$.

(c) Explain what happens as n becomes large.

4.2   Iterative techniques

Suppose that we are given a square matrix whose eigenvalues are known to be real and distinct in magnitude. Though we do not know their values, assume that the eigenvalues are listed in in decreasing order of magnitude. For example, eigenvalues 5, -1 and -4 would be listed in the order

$$\lambda_1 = 5, \quad \lambda_2 = -4, \quad \lambda_3 = -1. \qquad\qquad |5| > |-4| > |-1|$$

Using the ideas of the previous subsection, together with the results at the end of Section 2, we can approximate all the eigenvalues and corresponding eigenvectors. We start with the eigenvector corresponding to the eigenvalue of largest magnitude, then we show how the other eigenvectors and eigenvalues are approximated.

Eigenvalue of largest magnitude: direct iteration

In order to approximate an eigenvector corresponding to the eigenvalue λ_{max} of largest magnitude, we use the approach that we employed at the beginning of the previous subsection. We start with a vector $\mathbf{e}_0$, and successively calculate the new vectors

$$\mathbf{e}_1 = \mathbf{A}\mathbf{e}_0, \quad \mathbf{e}_2 = \mathbf{A}\mathbf{e}_1, \quad \mathbf{e}_3 = \mathbf{A}\mathbf{e}_2, \quad \ldots,$$

which is equivalent to writing $\mathbf{e}_n = \mathbf{A}^n\mathbf{e}_0$, $n = 1, 2, 3, \ldots.$

For example, if $\mathbf{A} = \begin{bmatrix} 3 & 2 \\ 1 & 4 \end{bmatrix}$ and $\mathbf{e}_0 = \begin{bmatrix} 1 \\ 0 \end{bmatrix}$, then, as you saw in Exercise 4.1,

$$\mathbf{e}_1 = \begin{bmatrix} 3 \\ 1 \end{bmatrix}, \quad \mathbf{e}_2 = \begin{bmatrix} 11 \\ 7 \end{bmatrix}, \quad \mathbf{e}_3 = \begin{bmatrix} 47 \\ 39 \end{bmatrix}, \quad \mathbf{e}_4 = \begin{bmatrix} 219 \\ 203 \end{bmatrix}, \quad \ldots.$$

The main difficulty with this method is that the components of $\mathbf{e}_n$ can rapidly become very large (or very small). But we can overcome this problem by setting α_n to be the component of largest magnitude in $\mathbf{e}_n$. Then dividing the vector $\mathbf{e}_n$ by α_n ensures that the vector $\mathbf{e}_n/\alpha_n$ has components that are less than, or equal to, one in magnitude. This process is called *scaling*, giving a *scaled vector*.

For the above vectors, $\alpha_1 = 3$, $\alpha_2 = 11$, $\alpha_3 = 47$ and $\alpha_4 = 219$, and we obtain the sequence of vectors

$$\begin{bmatrix} 1 \\ \frac{1}{3} \end{bmatrix}, \quad \begin{bmatrix} 1 \\ \frac{7}{11} \end{bmatrix}, \quad \begin{bmatrix} 1 \\ \frac{39}{47} \end{bmatrix}, \quad \begin{bmatrix} 1 \\ \frac{203}{219} \end{bmatrix}$$

(with the same directions as the sequence found in Exercise 4.1).

The components of our final answer will now be of reasonable size. If this scaling process is applied only at the final stage, we may still encounter very large components in the intermediate calculations. This difficulty is avoided by applying the scaling process at each step of the calculation, as in the following procedure.

Procedure 4.1   Direct iteration

For any square matrix $\mathbf{A}$ for which the eigenvalue $\lambda_{\max}$ of largest magnitude is real (and distinct in magnitude from any other eigenvalue), choose any vector $\mathbf{e}_0$.

For $n = 0, 1, 2, \ldots$:
(i)   calculate $\mathbf{z}_{n+1} = \mathbf{A}\mathbf{e}_n$;
(ii)   find α_{n+1}, the component of largest magnitude of $\mathbf{z}_{n+1}$;
(iii)   put $\mathbf{e}_{n+1} = \mathbf{z}_{n+1}/\alpha_{n+1}$.

For sufficiently large n, $\mathbf{e}_n$ will be a good approximation to an eigenvector corresponding to the eigenvalue of largest magnitude, provided that $\mathbf{e}_0$ has a non-zero component of the required eigenvector. If the sequence α_n converges, then it converges to $\lambda_{\max}$.

A matrix $\mathbf{A}$ with eigenvalues 3 and -3 would not qualify, because the eigenvalues are equal in magnitude.

If $\lambda_{\max}$ is complex, then its complex conjugate will also be an eigenvalue of the same magnitude, so the procedure works only when the eigenvalue of largest magnitude is real.

The final sentence of the above procedure can be deduced from the fact that at each stage of the calculation we have $\mathbf{A}\mathbf{e}_n = \mathbf{z}_{n+1} = \alpha_{n+1}\mathbf{e}_{n+1}$. If $\mathbf{e}_n$ converges to a vector $\mathbf{e}$ and α_n converges to a number α, then, in the limit, we have $\mathbf{A}\mathbf{e} = \alpha\mathbf{e}$, so $\mathbf{e}$ is an eigenvector corresponding to the eigenvalue α. But we know that $\mathbf{e}$ is an eigenvector corresponding to the eigenvalue of largest magnitude, so α must be this eigenvalue.

Example 4.1

Given $\mathbf{A} = \begin{bmatrix} 3 & 2 \\ 1 & 4 \end{bmatrix}$ and $\mathbf{e}_0 = \begin{bmatrix} 1 \\ 0 \end{bmatrix}$, use Procedure 4.1 to find $\mathbf{e}_1$, $\mathbf{e}_2$ and $\mathbf{e}_3$.

The eigenvalues of $\mathbf{A}$ are 5 and 2, with corresponding eigenvectors $\begin{bmatrix} 1 & 1 \end{bmatrix}^T$ and $\begin{bmatrix} -2 & 1 \end{bmatrix}^T$, respectively (see Example 2.2).

Solution

First iteration
(i) $\mathbf{z}_1 = \mathbf{A}\mathbf{e}_0 = \begin{bmatrix} 3 & 2 \\ 1 & 4 \end{bmatrix}\begin{bmatrix} 1 \\ 0 \end{bmatrix} = \begin{bmatrix} \boxed{3} \\ 1 \end{bmatrix}$
(ii) $\alpha_1 = 3$
(iii) $\mathbf{e}_1 = \dfrac{\mathbf{z}_1}{\alpha_1} = \frac{1}{3}\begin{bmatrix} 3 \\ 1 \end{bmatrix} = \begin{bmatrix} 1 \\ \frac{1}{3} \end{bmatrix}$

Second iteration
(i) $\mathbf{z}_2 = \mathbf{A}\mathbf{e}_1 = \begin{bmatrix} 3 & 2 \\ 1 & 4 \end{bmatrix}\begin{bmatrix} 1 \\ \frac{1}{3} \end{bmatrix} = \begin{bmatrix} \boxed{\frac{11}{3}} \\ \frac{7}{3} \end{bmatrix}$
(ii) $\alpha_2 = \frac{11}{3}$
(iii) $\mathbf{e}_2 = \dfrac{\mathbf{z}_2}{\alpha_2} = \frac{3}{11}\begin{bmatrix} \frac{11}{3} \\ \frac{7}{3} \end{bmatrix} = \begin{bmatrix} 1 \\ \frac{7}{11} \end{bmatrix}$

Third iteration
(i) $\mathbf{z}_3 = \mathbf{A}\mathbf{e}_2 = \begin{bmatrix} 3 & 2 \\ 1 & 4 \end{bmatrix}\begin{bmatrix} 1 \\ \frac{7}{11} \end{bmatrix} = \begin{bmatrix} \boxed{\frac{47}{11}} \\ \frac{39}{11} \end{bmatrix}$
(ii) $\alpha_3 = \frac{47}{11}$
(iii) $\mathbf{e}_3 = \dfrac{\mathbf{z}_3}{\alpha_3} = \frac{11}{47}\begin{bmatrix} \frac{47}{11} \\ \frac{39}{11} \end{bmatrix} = \begin{bmatrix} 1 \\ \frac{39}{47} \end{bmatrix}$ ∎

If we were to continue the process in Example 4.1, we should find that the sequence of vectors $\mathbf{e}_n$ converges to the eigenvector $\begin{bmatrix} 1 & 1 \end{bmatrix}^T$, and the sequence α_n converges to the corresponding eigenvalue 5.

*Exercise 4.4

Given $\mathbf{A} = \begin{bmatrix} 3 & 6 \\ 4 & 8 \end{bmatrix}$ and $\mathbf{e}_0 = \begin{bmatrix} 1 & 0 \end{bmatrix}^T$, use Procedure 4.1 to calculate $\mathbf{e}_1$, $\mathbf{e}_2$ and $\mathbf{e}_3$. What can you deduce about the eigenvalues and eigenvectors of $\mathbf{A}$?

Eigenvalue of smallest magnitude: inverse iteration

In order to approximate an eigenvector corresponding to the eigenvalue of *smallest* magnitude, we adapt the above method of direct iteration. Suppose again that the eigenvalues of an invertible matrix $\mathbf{A}$ are listed in decreasing order of magnitude. It follows that their reciprocals must appear in increasing order of magnitude. But, by the results of Subsection 2.4, the numbers λ^{-1} are the eigenvalues of the inverse matrix $\mathbf{A}^{-1}$ with the same eigenvectors as the matrix $\mathbf{A}$. So the problem of approximating the eigenvalue of smallest magnitude λ of $\mathbf{A}$ is the same as that of approximating the eigenvalue of largest magnitude λ^{-1} of $\mathbf{A}^{-1}$. It follows that repeatedly applying the matrix $\mathbf{A}^{-1}$ produces an eigenvector corresponding to the eigenvalue of smallest magnitude, assuming that it is real and distinct in magnitude from any other eigenvalue of $\mathbf{A}$.

We are assuming that the eigenvalues of $\mathbf{A}$ are real and distinct in magnitude.

If $\mathbf{A}$ is invertible, then $\mathbf{A}^{-1}$ exists and the eigenvalues are non-zero (see Subsection 2.3).

For any square matrix $\mathbf{A}$ with non-zero real eigenvalues, we find an eigenvector corresponding to an eigenvalue of smallest magnitude by choosing a vector $\mathbf{e}_0$ and successively calculating the vectors $\mathbf{e}_1, \mathbf{e}_2, \mathbf{e}_3, \ldots$ using the formula

$$\mathbf{e}_{n+1} = \mathbf{A}^{-1}\mathbf{e}_n, \quad n = 0, 1, 2, \ldots .$$

In practice, such calculations can suffer from the same difficulties as direct iteration. We solve the problem of very large or very small vectors as before, by scaling, writing

$$\mathbf{z}_{n+1} = \mathbf{A}^{-1}\mathbf{e}_n, \quad \mathbf{e}_{n+1} = \frac{\mathbf{z}_{n+1}}{\alpha_{n+1}}, \quad n = 0, 1, 2, \ldots,$$

where α_{n+1} is the component of largest magnitude of $\mathbf{z}_{n+1}$. However, there is a further complication — the calculation of the inverse matrix can be very time-consuming for large matrices. A more practical approach is based on solving the equations $\mathbf{A}\mathbf{z}_{n+1} = \mathbf{e}_n$ for $\mathbf{z}_{n+1}$ by Gaussian elimination and then putting $\mathbf{e}_{n+1} = \mathbf{z}_{n+1}/\alpha_{n+1}$.

Procedure 4.2   Inverse iteration

For any invertible (square) matrix $\mathbf{A}$ for which the eigenvalue $\lambda_{\min}$ of smallest magnitude is real and distinct in magnitude from any other eigenvalue, choose any vector $\mathbf{e}_0$.

The fact that $\mathbf{A}$ is invertible ensures that $\lambda_{\min} \neq 0$ and that $\mathbf{A}^{-1}$ exists.

(a) For $n = 0, 1, 2, \ldots$:
  (i)   calculate $\mathbf{z}_{n+1} = \mathbf{A}^{-1}\mathbf{e}_n$;
  (ii) find α_{n+1}, the component of largest magnitude of $\mathbf{z}_{n+1}$;
  (iii) put $\mathbf{e}_{n+1} = \mathbf{z}_{n+1}/\alpha_{n+1}$.

(b) The above method is inefficient for large matrices due to the difficulty of calculating $\mathbf{A}^{-1}$. In such cases, for $n = 0, 1, 2, \ldots$:
  (i)   calculate $\mathbf{z}_{n+1}$ by solving the equation $\mathbf{A}\mathbf{z}_{n+1} = \mathbf{e}_n$;
  (ii) find α_{n+1}, the component of largest magnitude of $\mathbf{z}_{n+1}$;
  (iii) put $\mathbf{e}_{n+1} = \mathbf{z}_{n+1}/\alpha_{n+1}$.

For sufficiently large n, $\mathbf{e}_n$ will be a good approximation to an eigenvector corresponding to the eigenvalue of smallest magnitude, provided that $\mathbf{e}_0$ has a non-zero component of the required eigenvector. If the sequence α_n converges, then it converges to $1/\lambda_{\min}$.

Example 4.2

Given the matrix $\mathbf{A} = \begin{bmatrix} 3 & 2 \\ 3 & 4 \end{bmatrix}$, calculate $\mathbf{A}^{-1}$. Given $\mathbf{e}_0 = [1 \quad 1]^T$, use Procedure 4.2(a) to calculate $\mathbf{e}_1$, $\mathbf{e}_2$ and $\mathbf{e}_3$.

Solution

We have
$$\mathbf{A}^{-1} = \tfrac{1}{6}\begin{bmatrix} 4 & -2 \\ -3 & 3 \end{bmatrix}.$$

First iteration

(i) $\quad \mathbf{z}_1 = \mathbf{A}^{-1}\mathbf{e}_0 = \tfrac{1}{6}\begin{bmatrix} 4 & -2 \\ -3 & 3 \end{bmatrix}\begin{bmatrix} 1 \\ 1 \end{bmatrix} = \begin{bmatrix} \tfrac{1}{3} \\ 0 \end{bmatrix}$

(ii) $\quad \alpha_1 = \tfrac{1}{3}$

(iii) $\quad \mathbf{e}_1 = \dfrac{\mathbf{z}_1}{\alpha_1} = 3\begin{bmatrix} \tfrac{1}{3} \\ 0 \end{bmatrix} = \begin{bmatrix} 1 \\ 0 \end{bmatrix}$

Second iteration

(i) $\quad \mathbf{z}_2 = \mathbf{A}^{-1}\mathbf{e}_1 = \tfrac{1}{6}\begin{bmatrix} 4 & -2 \\ -3 & 3 \end{bmatrix}\begin{bmatrix} 1 \\ 0 \end{bmatrix} = \begin{bmatrix} \tfrac{2}{3} \\ -\tfrac{1}{2} \end{bmatrix}$

(ii) $\quad \alpha_2 = \tfrac{2}{3}$

(iii) $\quad \mathbf{e}_2 = \dfrac{\mathbf{z}_2}{\alpha_2} = \tfrac{3}{2}\begin{bmatrix} \tfrac{2}{3} \\ -\tfrac{1}{2} \end{bmatrix} = \begin{bmatrix} 1 \\ -\tfrac{3}{4} \end{bmatrix}$

Third iteration

(i) $\quad \mathbf{z}_3 = \mathbf{A}^{-1}\mathbf{e}_2 = \tfrac{1}{6}\begin{bmatrix} 4 & -2 \\ -3 & 3 \end{bmatrix}\begin{bmatrix} 1 \\ -\tfrac{3}{4} \end{bmatrix} = \begin{bmatrix} \tfrac{11}{12} \\ -\tfrac{7}{8} \end{bmatrix}$

(ii) $\quad \alpha_3 = \tfrac{11}{12}$

(iii) $\quad \mathbf{e}_3 = \dfrac{\mathbf{z}_3}{\alpha_3} = \tfrac{12}{11}\begin{bmatrix} \tfrac{11}{12} \\ -\tfrac{7}{8} \end{bmatrix} = \begin{bmatrix} 1 \\ -\tfrac{21}{22} \end{bmatrix}$ ∎

If we were to continue the process in Example 4.2, we should find that the sequence of vectors $\mathbf{e}_n$ converges to the eigenvector $[1 \quad -1]^T$ and the sequence α_n converges to 1, corresponding to the eigenvalue $1/1 = 1$.

*Exercise 4.5

Use Procedure 4.2(a) with $\mathbf{A} = \begin{bmatrix} 7 & 3 \\ 8 & 5 \end{bmatrix}$ and $\mathbf{e}_0 = \begin{bmatrix} 1 \\ 1 \end{bmatrix}$ to obtain $\mathbf{e}_1$, $\mathbf{e}_2$ and $\mathbf{e}_3$. Hence find an approximation to the eigenvalue of $\mathbf{A}$ of smallest magnitude, and a corresponding eigenvector.

Specific eigenvalues: modified inverse iteration

The previous procedures are restricted to calculating the eigenvalue of largest or smallest magnitude. Sometimes we do not need either of these, but rather we need the eigenvalue closest to a given value. The following method will allow us to find it. We assume that there is just one eigenvalue of $\mathbf{A}$ closest to the given value p.

If λ is an eigenvalue of a matrix $\mathbf{A}$ (and p is not an eigenvalue of $\mathbf{A}$), then $(\lambda - p)^{-1}$ is an eigenvalue of the matrix $(\mathbf{A} - p\mathbf{I})^{-1}$, and the corresponding eigenvectors are unchanged. Suppose that λ_1 is the real eigenvalue closest to p. In other words, $|\lambda_1 - p|$ is the smallest of all possible choices of $|\lambda - p|$, thus $1/|\lambda_1 - p|$ is the largest of all possible choices of $1/|\lambda - p|$. It follows that repeatedly applying the matrix $(\mathbf{A} - p\mathbf{I})^{-1}$ to a chosen vector $\mathbf{e}_0$ produces an eigenvector corresponding to the eigenvalue closest to p. Thus the sequence $\mathbf{e}_{n+1} = (\mathbf{A} - p\mathbf{I})^{-1}\mathbf{e}_n$ $(n = 0, 1, 2, \ldots)$ should produce a sequence of approximations to the eigenvector.

See Subsection 2.4.

This method suffers from the deficiencies mentioned for inverse iteration, so we make similar refinements.

Procedure 4.3   Modified inverse iteration

Suppose that $\mathbf{A}$ is a square matrix for which one distinct real eigenvalue λ_1 is closest to a given real number p. To find an eigenvector corresponding to the eigenvalue closest to p, choose any vector $\mathbf{e}_0$.

(a) For $n = 0, 1, 2, \ldots$:

    (i)   calculate $\mathbf{z}_{n+1} = (\mathbf{A} - p\mathbf{I})^{-1}\mathbf{e}_n$;

    (ii) find α_{n+1}, the component of largest magnitude of $\mathbf{z}_{n+1}$;

    (iii) put $\mathbf{e}_{n+1} = \mathbf{z}_{n+1}/\alpha_{n+1}$.

(b) The above method is inefficient for large matrices due to the difficulty of calculating $(\mathbf{A} - p\mathbf{I})^{-1}$. In such cases, for $n = 0, 1, 2, \ldots$:

    (i)   calculate $\mathbf{z}_{n+1}$ by solving the equation $(\mathbf{A} - p\mathbf{I})\mathbf{z}_{n+1} = \mathbf{e}_n$;

    (ii) find α_{n+1}, the component of largest magnitude of $\mathbf{z}_{n+1}$;

    (iii) put $\mathbf{e}_{n+1} = \mathbf{z}_{n+1}/\alpha_{n+1}$.

For sufficiently large n, $\mathbf{e}_n$ will be a good approximation to an eigenvector corresponding to the eigenvalue closest to p, provided that $\mathbf{e}_0$ has a non-zero component of the required eigenvector. If the sequence α_n converges, then it converges to $1/(\lambda_1 - p)$.

The procedure breaks down if p is an eigenvalue.

In the following exercise, much of the work has been done for you.

*Exercise 4.6

We wish to obtain an approximation to an eigenvector corresponding to the eigenvalue closest to $p = -1$ for the matrix $\mathbf{A} = \begin{bmatrix} 1 & 2 & 3 \\ 2 & 3 & 4 \\ 3 & 4 & 6 \end{bmatrix}$.

We have

$$(\mathbf{A} - p\mathbf{I})^{-1} = (\mathbf{A} + \mathbf{I})^{-1} = \begin{bmatrix} \frac{3}{2} & -\frac{1}{4} & -\frac{1}{2} \\ -\frac{1}{4} & \frac{5}{8} & -\frac{1}{4} \\ -\frac{1}{2} & -\frac{1}{4} & \frac{1}{2} \end{bmatrix}.$$

This inverse was found using the computer algebra package for the course.

Applying Procedure 4.3(a) with $\mathbf{e}_0 = \begin{bmatrix} 1 & 0 & 0 \end{bmatrix}^T$ gives $\alpha_{20} = 1.725$ and $\mathbf{e}_{20} \simeq \begin{bmatrix} 1 & -0.141 & -0.379 \end{bmatrix}^T$.

Calculate $\mathbf{e}_{21}$ with the components given to three decimal places, and obtain an estimate for the corresponding eigenvalue to three decimal places.

Procedures 4.1, 4.2 and 4.3 can be used to find individual eigenvalues and eigenvectors of a matrix. If we require all the eigenvalues and/or eigenvectors, then there are more efficient methods that can be used, though we do not discuss them here.

The rate of convergence of each of the methods depends on the relative closeness in magnitude of the other eigenvalues of $\mathbf{A}$ (or $\mathbf{A}^{-1}$, or $(\mathbf{A} - p\mathbf{I})^{-1}$) to the required eigenvalue. For example, in Exercise 4.6 the eigenvalues are 10.187, -0.420 and 0.234, to three decimal places. The direct iteration method applied to this problem would converge very rapidly since the largest eigenvalue, 10.187, is much larger in magnitude than the other two. On the other hand, inverse iteration would be slower, since the eigenvalues of $\mathbf{A}^{-1}$ are 4.281, -2.379 and 0.098 (to 3 d.p.), and the second largest eigenvalue in magnitude, -2.379, is just over half the magnitude of the largest eigenvalue.

A judicious choice of p for the modified inverse iteration method can significantly increase the rate of convergence. For example, choosing $p = 0.2$ for the matrix in Exercise 4.6 gives the eigenvalues of $\mathbf{A} - p\mathbf{I}$ as 9.987, −0.620 and 0.034, so the eigenvalues of $(\mathbf{A} - p\mathbf{I})^{-1}$ are 29.781, −1.612 and 0.100. We expect that the modified inverse iteration method with this value of p would converge very rapidly to the eigenvalue 0.234 of the matrix $\mathbf{A}$.

Procedures 4.1 and 4.2 cannot be used to determine complex eigenvalues, since complex eigenvalues of real matrices occur in complex conjugate pairs, and a complex eigenvalue and its complex conjugate have the same magnitude. Both procedures fail to find the required eigenvalue when there is a second distinct eigenvalue of the same magnitude.

However, it is possible to use the modified inverse iteration method to find complex eigenvalues, provided that a complex value for p is chosen so that p is closer in magnitude to one of the complex eigenvalues than to any of the others.

End-of-section Exercises

Exercise 4.7

In this exercise $\mathbf{A} = \begin{bmatrix} 0.5 & 0.6 \\ 1.4 & -0.3 \end{bmatrix}$.

These calculations are intended to be done by hand (with the aid of a scientific calculator).

(a) Given $\mathbf{e}_0 = \begin{bmatrix} 1 & 0 \end{bmatrix}^T$, use direct iteration to calculate $\mathbf{e}_1$, $\mathbf{e}_2$ and $\mathbf{e}_3$.

(b) Use the methods of Section 2 to find the eigenvalues and corresponding eigenvectors of $\mathbf{A}$.

(c) To which eigenvector would you expect the sequence $\mathbf{e}_n$ of part (a) to converge?

(d) If $\mathbf{v}$ is an eigenvector of $\mathbf{A}$ corresponding to the eigenvalue λ, express $\mathbf{A}^8 \mathbf{v}$ in terms of λ and $\mathbf{v}$.

(e) Designate the eigenvectors found in part (b) as $\mathbf{v}_1$ and $\mathbf{v}_2$. Express $\mathbf{e}_0$ in terms of $\mathbf{v}_1$ and $\mathbf{v}_2$, then calculate $\mathbf{e}_8$. (If this seems like hard work, then look for an easier method.)

(f) Find $\mathbf{A}^{-1}$, then use inverse iteration to calculate $\mathbf{e}_1$, $\mathbf{e}_2$ and $\mathbf{e}_3$, given $\mathbf{e}_0 = \begin{bmatrix} -0.4 & 1 \end{bmatrix}^T$. To which eigenvector would you expect this sequence to converge?

(g) Comment on the rates of convergence for direct iteration and inverse iteration applied to this problem.

Exercise 4.8

Suppose that you wish to find all the eigenvalues of the matrix

$$\mathbf{A} = \begin{bmatrix} 1 & 2 & 3 \\ 2 & 3 & 4 \\ 3 & 4 & 6 \end{bmatrix}.$$

Before you start this exercise, consider how the third eigenvalue can be obtained from the other two eigenvalues. Applying this method will save excessive computation.

Further, suppose that you have used direct iteration to find an eigenvector

$$\mathbf{v}_1 \simeq \begin{bmatrix} 0.477 & 0.689 & 1 \end{bmatrix}^T,$$

and inverse iteration to find another eigenvector

$$\mathbf{v}_2 \simeq \begin{bmatrix} -0.102 & 1 & -0.641 \end{bmatrix}^T.$$

Use this information to find approximations to all three eigenvalues.

5 Using a computer to find eigenvalues and eigenvectors

In this section you are asked to use the three procedures in Section 4 on your computer to estimate some of the eigenvalues and eigenvectors of various matrices. This will enable you to gain experience in the use of these algorithms without doing excessive hand calculation.

The computer activities involve the following matrices.

(a) $\mathbf{P} = \begin{bmatrix} -2.86 & 4.16 & 14.56 & 3.64 \\ -0.34 & 3.58 & 11.62 & 0.68 \\ -0.20 & -0.80 & -2.54 & 0.40 \\ -1.82 & 4.16 & 14.56 & 2.60 \end{bmatrix}$

(b) $\mathbf{Q} = \begin{bmatrix} 3.179 & 0.107 & -3.310 & -1.183 & -0.587 \\ 0.636 & 3.576 & 2.054 & 0.486 & 0.263 \\ -3.308 & 5.588 & 2.591 & -0.595 & -2.492 \\ -0.719 & -0.401 & -4.406 & -0.040 & -0.803 \\ 0.600 & -0.732 & -0.622 & -2.992 & 4.695 \end{bmatrix}$

(c) $\mathbf{R} = \begin{bmatrix} 5.27 & -30.46 & 7.96 & -11.22 \\ -5.25 & 6.00 & -6.21 & -4.73 \\ 7.20 & -11.52 & -16.14 & -1.08 \\ -19.97 & -34.98 & 19.01 & 3.97 \end{bmatrix}$

(d) $\mathbf{S} = \begin{bmatrix} -3.65 & 4.16 & 14.56 & 3.64 \\ -0.34 & 2.79 & 11.62 & 0.68 \\ -0.20 & -0.80 & -3.33 & 0.40 \\ -1.82 & 4.16 & 14.56 & 1.81 \end{bmatrix}$

Use your computer to carry out the following activities.

PC

Activity 5.1

Find the eigenvalue of largest magnitude and a corresponding eigenvector using Procedure 4.1 (direct iteration) for the matrices $\mathbf{P}$, $\mathbf{Q}$, $\mathbf{R}$ and $\mathbf{S}$. Comment on the usefulness of this method applied to these matrices.

Activity 5.2

Find the eigenvalue of smallest magnitude and a corresponding eigenvector using Procedure 4.2 (inverse iteration) for the matrices $\mathbf{P}$, $\mathbf{Q}$, $\mathbf{R}$ and $\mathbf{S}$. Comment on the usefulness of this method applied to these matrices.

Activity 5.3

Use Procedure 4.3 (modified inverse iteration) to find more efficiently:
(i) the eigenvalues of largest and smallest magnitude of $\mathbf{R}$;
(ii) the eigenvalue of largest magnitude of $\mathbf{S}$.

Outcomes

After studying this unit you should be able to:

- explain the meaning of the terms eigenvector, eigenvalue and characteristic equation;
- calculate the eigenvalues of a given 2×2 matrix, and find the corresponding eigenvectors;
- calculate the eigenvalues and corresponding eigenvectors of a 3×3 matrix, where one of the eigenvalues is 'obvious';
- appreciate that an $n \times n$ matrix with n distinct eigenvalues gives rise to n linearly independent eigenvectors;
- appreciate that the eigenvalues of a matrix may be real and distinct, real and repeated, or complex;
- recall that the sum of the eigenvalues of an $n \times n$ matrix $\mathbf{A}$ is $\operatorname{tr} \mathbf{A}$ and that the product of the eigenvalues of $\mathbf{A}$ is $\det \mathbf{A}$, and use these properties as a check in hand calculations;
- write down the eigenvalues of a triangular matrix;
- write down the eigenvalues of the matrices $\mathbf{A}^k$, $\mathbf{A}^{-1}$, $\mathbf{A} + p\mathbf{I}$, $(\mathbf{A} - p\mathbf{I})^{-1}$ and $p\mathbf{A}$, given the eigenvalues of $\mathbf{A}$;
- appreciate the use of direct, inverse and modified inverse iteration in approximating individual eigenvalues and corresponding eigenvectors of a square matrix;
- use iterative methods and hand calculation to estimate an eigenvalue and corresponding eigenvector in simple cases;
- use the computer algebra package for the course to determine the eigenvalues and corresponding eigenvectors of a given square matrix.

Solutions to the exercises

Section 1

1.1 $\mathbf{Aw} = \begin{bmatrix} 3 & 2 \\ 1 & 4 \end{bmatrix} \begin{bmatrix} 3 \\ -1 \end{bmatrix} = \begin{bmatrix} 7 \\ -1 \end{bmatrix}$,

$\mathbf{Ax} = \begin{bmatrix} 3 & 2 \\ 1 & 4 \end{bmatrix} \begin{bmatrix} 1 \\ 1 \end{bmatrix} = \begin{bmatrix} 5 \\ 5 \end{bmatrix}$,

$\mathbf{Ay} = \begin{bmatrix} 3 & 2 \\ 1 & 4 \end{bmatrix} \begin{bmatrix} -2 \\ 1 \end{bmatrix} = \begin{bmatrix} -4 \\ 2 \end{bmatrix}$,

$\mathbf{Az} = \begin{bmatrix} 3 & 2 \\ 1 & 4 \end{bmatrix} \begin{bmatrix} 0 \\ 0 \end{bmatrix} = \begin{bmatrix} 0 \\ 0 \end{bmatrix}$.

1.2 If $[x \quad y]^T = \alpha[1 \quad 1]^T + \beta[-2 \quad 1]^T$, then
$$\begin{cases} \alpha - 2\beta = x, \\ \alpha + \beta = y. \end{cases}$$
Solving these equations, we obtain $\alpha = (2y + x)/3$ and $\beta = (y - x)/3$.

1.3 (a) $\begin{bmatrix} 2 & 3 \\ 2 & 1 \end{bmatrix} \begin{bmatrix} 3 \\ 2 \end{bmatrix} = \begin{bmatrix} 12 \\ 8 \end{bmatrix} = 4 \begin{bmatrix} 3 \\ 2 \end{bmatrix}$,

so $[3 \quad 2]^T$ is an eigenvector with eigenvalue 4.

(b) $\begin{bmatrix} 2 & 3 \\ 2 & 1 \end{bmatrix} \begin{bmatrix} 1 \\ -1 \end{bmatrix} = \begin{bmatrix} -1 \\ 1 \end{bmatrix} = (-1) \begin{bmatrix} 1 \\ -1 \end{bmatrix}$,

so $[1 \quad -1]^T$ is an eigenvector with eigenvalue -1.

(c) $\begin{bmatrix} 2 & 0 \\ 1 & 2 \end{bmatrix} \begin{bmatrix} 0 \\ 6 \end{bmatrix} = \begin{bmatrix} 0 \\ 12 \end{bmatrix} = 2 \begin{bmatrix} 0 \\ 6 \end{bmatrix}$,

so $[0 \quad 6]^T$ is an eigenvector with eigenvalue 2.

1.4 Since $\mathbf{v} = [12\,000 \quad 6000]^T$ is transformed to itself, this $\mathbf{v}$ is an eigenvector with eigenvalue 1.

You may have noticed that there are many other eigenvectors with the same eigenvalue, for example $[12 \quad 6]^T$.

There is another eigenvector $[1 \quad -1]^T$, with corresponding eigenvalue 0.7 (although we do not expect you to have found it).

1.5 The eigenvectors act along the line of reflection $y = x$ and perpendicular to it, so they are the scalar multiples of $[1 \quad 1]^T$ and $[1 \quad -1]^T$. The vector $[1 \quad 1]^T$ is scaled by a factor of 1 by the transformation, while for $[1 \quad -1]^T$ the scale factor is -1; these scale factors are the corresponding eigenvalues.

We may check our conclusion by evaluating
$$\begin{bmatrix} 0 & 1 \\ 1 & 0 \end{bmatrix} \begin{bmatrix} 1 \\ 1 \end{bmatrix} = \begin{bmatrix} 1 \\ 1 \end{bmatrix},$$
so $[1 \quad 1]^T$ corresponds to the eigenvalue 1, and
$$\begin{bmatrix} 0 & 1 \\ 1 & 0 \end{bmatrix} \begin{bmatrix} 1 \\ -1 \end{bmatrix} = \begin{bmatrix} -1 \\ 1 \end{bmatrix} = -1 \begin{bmatrix} 1 \\ -1 \end{bmatrix},$$
so $[1 \quad -1]^T$ corresponds to the eigenvalue -1.

1.6 $\begin{bmatrix} 1 & 4 \\ 9 & 1 \end{bmatrix} \begin{bmatrix} 2 \\ -3 \end{bmatrix} = \begin{bmatrix} -10 \\ 15 \end{bmatrix} = -5 \begin{bmatrix} 2 \\ -3 \end{bmatrix}$,

so $[2 \quad -3]^T$ is an eigenvector with eigenvalue -5. Also,
$$\begin{bmatrix} 1 & 4 \\ 9 & 1 \end{bmatrix} \begin{bmatrix} 2 \\ 3 \end{bmatrix} = \begin{bmatrix} 14 \\ 21 \end{bmatrix} = 7 \begin{bmatrix} 2 \\ 3 \end{bmatrix},$$
so $[2 \quad 3]^T$ is an eigenvector with eigenvalue 7.

1.7 $[0 \quad 1]^T$ is an eigenvector of $\mathbf{A}$ corresponding to the eigenvalue 1, and $[1 \quad 0]^T$ is an eigenvalue of $\mathbf{A}$ corresponding to the eigenvalue -1.

1.8 We have
$$\begin{bmatrix} a & b \\ c & d \end{bmatrix} \begin{bmatrix} 1 \\ 2 \end{bmatrix} = 2 \begin{bmatrix} 1 \\ 2 \end{bmatrix}, \quad \begin{bmatrix} a & b \\ c & d \end{bmatrix} \begin{bmatrix} 3 \\ 1 \end{bmatrix} = \begin{bmatrix} 3 \\ 1 \end{bmatrix},$$
from which we obtain the systems of equations
$$\begin{cases} a + 2b = 2, \\ 3a + b = 3, \end{cases} \quad \begin{cases} c + 2d = 4, \\ 3c + d = 1. \end{cases}$$
Solving these equations, we obtain $a = \frac{4}{5}$, $b = \frac{3}{5}$, $c = -\frac{2}{5}$ and $d = \frac{11}{5}$. So $\mathbf{A} = \begin{bmatrix} \frac{4}{5} & \frac{3}{5} \\ -\frac{2}{5} & \frac{11}{5} \end{bmatrix}$.

Section 2

2.1 The equation $\mathbf{Av} = \lambda\mathbf{v}$ becomes
$$\begin{bmatrix} 5 & 2 \\ 2 & 5 \end{bmatrix} \begin{bmatrix} x \\ y \end{bmatrix} = \lambda \begin{bmatrix} x \\ y \end{bmatrix}.$$
Thus x and y satisfy the simultaneous equations
$$\begin{cases} 5x + 2y = \lambda x, \\ 2x + 5y = \lambda y, \end{cases}$$
which can be rewritten as the eigenvector equations
$$\begin{cases} (5 - \lambda)x + 2y = 0, \\ 2x + (5 - \lambda)y = 0. \end{cases}$$
These equations have a non-zero solution only if
$$\begin{vmatrix} 5 - \lambda & 2 \\ 2 & 5 - \lambda \end{vmatrix} = 0.$$
So $(5 - \lambda)(5 - \lambda) - 4 = 0$, i.e. $5 - \lambda = \pm 2$, so the eigenvalues are $\lambda = 7$ and $\lambda = 3$.

$\boxed{\lambda = 7}$ The eigenvector equations become
$$\begin{cases} -2x + 2y = 0, \\ 2x - 2y = 0. \end{cases}$$
These equations reduce to the single equation $y = x$, so an eigenvector corresponding to $\lambda = 7$ is $[1 \quad 1]^T$.

$\boxed{\lambda = 3}$ The eigenvector equations become
$$\begin{cases} 2x + 2y = 0, \\ 2x + 2y = 0. \end{cases}$$
These equations reduce to the single equation $y = -x$, so an eigenvector corresponding to $\lambda = 3$ is $[1 \quad -1]^T$.

2.2 (a) The characteristic equation is
$$\begin{vmatrix} 1-\lambda & 4 \\ 1 & -2-\lambda \end{vmatrix} = 0.$$
Expanding gives $(1-\lambda)(-2-\lambda)-4=0$, which simplifies to $\lambda^2+\lambda-6=0$. (Alternatively, you could have calculated $a+d=-1$ and $ad-bc=-6$, and so obtained this equation directly.) So the eigenvalues are $\lambda=2$ and $\lambda=-3$.

The eigenvector equations are
$$\begin{cases} (1-\lambda)x+ & 4y=0, \\ x+(-2-\lambda)y=0. \end{cases}$$

$\boxed{\lambda=2}$ The eigenvector equations become
$$-x+4y=0 \quad\text{and}\quad x-4y=0,$$
which reduce to the single equation $4y=x$. So an eigenvector corresponding to $\lambda=2$ is $[4 \quad 1]^T$.

$\boxed{\lambda=-3}$ The eigenvector equations become
$$4x+4y=0 \quad\text{and}\quad x+y=0,$$
which reduce to the single equation $y=-x$. So an eigenvector corresponding to $\lambda=-3$ is $[1 \quad -1]^T$.

(b) The characteristic equation is
$$\begin{vmatrix} 8-\lambda & -5 \\ 10 & -7-\lambda \end{vmatrix} = 0.$$
Expanding this gives $(8-\lambda)(-7-\lambda)+50=0$, which simplifies to $\lambda^2-\lambda-6=0$. (Alternatively, you could have calculated $a+d=1$ and $ad-bc=-6$, and so obtained this equation directly.) So the eigenvalues are $\lambda=3$ and $\lambda=-2$.

$\boxed{\lambda=3}$ The eigenvector equations become
$$5x-5y=0 \quad\text{and}\quad 10x-10y=0,$$
which reduce to the single equation $y=x$. So an eigenvector corresponding to $\lambda=3$ is $[1 \quad 1]^T$.

$\boxed{\lambda=-2}$ The eigenvector equations become
$$10x-5y=0 \quad\text{and}\quad 10x-5y=0,$$
which reduce to the single equation $y=2x$. So an eigenvector corresponding to $\lambda=-2$ is $[1 \quad 2]^T$.

2.3 (a) Example 2.2:
sum of eigenvalues $=5+2=7$
and $\operatorname{tr}\mathbf{A}=3+4=7$;
product of eigenvalues $=5\times2=10$
and $\det\mathbf{A}=(3\times4)-(2\times1)=10$.

Example 2.3:
sum of eigenvalues $=4+(-1)=3$
and $\operatorname{tr}\mathbf{A}=2+1=3$;
product of eigenvalues $=4\times(-1)=-4$
and $\det\mathbf{A}=(2\times1)-(3\times2)=-4$.

(b) Exercise 2.1:
sum of eigenvalues $=7+3=10$
and $\operatorname{tr}\mathbf{A}=5+5=10$;
product of eigenvalues $=7\times3=21$
and $\det\mathbf{A}=(5\times5)-(2\times2)=21$.

Exercise 2.2(a):
sum of eigenvalues $=2+(-3)=-1$
and $\operatorname{tr}\mathbf{A}=1+(-2)=-1$;
product of eigenvalues $=2\times(-3)=-6$
and $\det\mathbf{A}=(1\times(-2))-(4\times1)=-6$.

Exercise 2.2(b):
sum of eigenvalues $=3+(-2)=1$
and $\operatorname{tr}\mathbf{A}=8+(-7)=1$;
product of eigenvalues $=3\times(-2)=-6$
and $\det\mathbf{A}=(8\times(-7))-((-5)\times10)=-6$.

2.4 The characteristic equation is
$$\begin{vmatrix} p-\lambda & 0 \\ 0 & q-\lambda \end{vmatrix} = (p-\lambda)(q-\lambda)=0.$$
Thus the eigenvalues are $\lambda=p$ and $\lambda=q$.
The eigenvector equations are
$$\begin{cases} (p-\lambda)x=0, \\ (q-\lambda)y=0. \end{cases}$$

$\boxed{\lambda=p}$ The eigenvector equations become
$$0=0 \quad\text{and}\quad (q-p)y=0,$$
which reduce to the single equation $y=0$ (since $p\neq q$), so a corresponding eigenvector is $[1 \quad 0]^T$.

$\boxed{\lambda=q}$ The eigenvector equations become
$$(p-q)x=0 \quad\text{and}\quad 0=0,$$
which reduce to the single equation $x=0$ (since $p\neq q$), so a corresponding eigenvector is $[0 \quad 1]^T$.

These agree with the eigenvectors found in Section 1.

2.5 The characteristic equation is
$$\lambda^2-1.7\lambda+0.7=0.$$
The eigenvalues are $\lambda=1$ and $\lambda=0.7$.
The eigenvector equations are
$$\begin{cases} (0.9-\lambda)x+ & 0.2y=0, \\ 0.1x+(0.8-\lambda)y=0. \end{cases}$$

$\boxed{\lambda=1}$ The eigenvector equations become
$$-0.1x+0.2y=0 \quad\text{and}\quad 0.1x-0.2y=0,$$
which reduce to the single equation $2y=x$, so a corresponding eigenvector is $[2 \quad 1]^T$.

(In the migration problem, where the total population was $18\,000$, an eigenvector corresponding to $\lambda=1$ was found to be $[12\,000 \quad 6000]^T$. This is a multiple of $[2 \quad 1]^T$, as expected, giving stable populations of $12\,000$ in Exton and 6000 in Wyeville.)

$\boxed{\lambda=0.7}$ The eigenvector equations become
$$0.2x+0.2y=0 \quad\text{and}\quad 0.1x+0.1y=0,$$
which reduce to the single equation $y=-x$, so a corresponding eigenvector is $[1 \quad -1]^T$.

(Since populations cannot be negative, this solution has no relevance for the migration problem.)

2.6 (a) The characteristic equation is

$$\begin{vmatrix} a - \lambda & 0 \\ 0 & a - \lambda \end{vmatrix} = (a - \lambda)^2 = 0,$$

for which $\lambda = a$ is a repeated root.

The eigenvector equations are

$$\begin{cases} (a - \lambda)x = 0, \\ (a - \lambda)y = 0, \end{cases}$$

which for $\lambda = a$ become

$$0 = 0 \quad \text{and} \quad 0 = 0,$$

which are satisfied by all values of x and y, so the eigenvectors are all the non-zero vectors of the form $\begin{bmatrix} k & l \end{bmatrix}^T$.

(Any non-zero vector is an eigenvector, but it is possible to choose two eigenvectors that are linearly independent, for example, $\begin{bmatrix} 1 & 0 \end{bmatrix}^T$ and $\begin{bmatrix} 0 & 1 \end{bmatrix}^T$.)

(b) The characteristic equation is

$$\begin{vmatrix} a - \lambda & 1 \\ 0 & a - \lambda \end{vmatrix} = (a - \lambda)^2 = 0,$$

for which $\lambda = a$ is a repeated root.

The eigenvector equations are

$$\begin{cases} y = 0, \\ 0 = 0, \end{cases}$$

so we have a single equation $y = 0$, and a corresponding eigenvector is $\begin{bmatrix} 1 & 0 \end{bmatrix}^T$.

(In this case, there is only one linearly independent eigenvector.)

2.7 The characteristic equation is $\lambda^2 - 4\lambda + 5 = 0$. The eigenvalues are

$$\lambda = \tfrac{1}{2}\left(4 \pm \sqrt{16 - 20}\right) = \tfrac{1}{2}(4 \pm 2i) = 2 \pm i.$$

i.e. $\lambda = 2 + i$ and $\lambda = 2 - i$.

The eigenvector equations are

$$\begin{cases} (3 - \lambda)x - \quad\quad y = 0, \\ \quad 2x + (1 - \lambda)y = 0. \end{cases}$$

$\boxed{\lambda = 2 + i}$ The eigenvector equations become

$$(1 - i)x - y = 0 \quad \text{and} \quad 2x - (1 + i)y = 0,$$

which reduce to the single equation $y = (1 - i)x$ (since $(1 + i)(1 - i) = 2$), so a corresponding eigenvector is $\begin{bmatrix} 1 & 1 - i \end{bmatrix}^T$.

$\boxed{\lambda = 2 - i}$ The eigenvector equations become

$$(1 + i)x - y = 0 \quad \text{and} \quad 2x - (1 - i)y = 0,$$

which reduce to the single equation $y = (1 + i)x$, so a corresponding eigenvector is $\begin{bmatrix} 1 & 1 + i \end{bmatrix}^T$.

2.8 The eigenvalues are 1 and 2.

$\boxed{\lambda = 1}$ The eigenvector equations become

$$3y = 0 \quad \text{and} \quad y = 0,$$

which reduce to the single equation $y = 0$, so $\begin{bmatrix} 1 & 0 \end{bmatrix}^T$ is a corresponding eigenvector.

$\boxed{\lambda = 2}$ The eigenvector equations become

$$-x + 3y = 0 \quad \text{and} \quad 0 = 0,$$

which reduce to the single equation $3y = x$, so $\begin{bmatrix} 3 & 1 \end{bmatrix}^T$ is a corresponding eigenvector.

2.9 For the eigenvalue to be repeated, we require $\sqrt{(a + d)^2 - 4(ad - b^2)} = 0$, i.e. $(a - d)^2 + 4b^2 = 0$. This is true only if $a = d$ and $b = 0$, so the only symmetric 2×2 matrices with a repeated eigenvalue are of the form $\begin{bmatrix} a & 0 \\ 0 & a \end{bmatrix}$.

2.10 (a) The eigenvalues are real, since $\mathbf{A}$ is real and symmetric. One is positive and the other negative, since $\lambda_1 \lambda_2 = \det \mathbf{A} < 0$. Also, $\lambda_1 + \lambda_2 = \operatorname{tr} \mathbf{A} = 50$.

(b) The eigenvalues are the diagonal entries 67 and -17, since $\mathbf{A}$ is triangular.

(c) The eigenvalues are real, since $\mathbf{A}$ is real and symmetric. In fact, $\mathbf{A}$ is non-invertible, since $\det \mathbf{A} = 0$. Thus one eigenvalue is 0. Hence the other is 306, since $0 + \lambda_2 = \operatorname{tr} \mathbf{A} = 306$.

2.11 (a) (i) $\mathbf{A}^2 = \begin{bmatrix} 3 & 2 \\ 1 & 4 \end{bmatrix}\begin{bmatrix} 3 & 2 \\ 1 & 4 \end{bmatrix} = \begin{bmatrix} 11 & 14 \\ 7 & 18 \end{bmatrix}$.

The characteristic equation of $\mathbf{A}^2$ is

$$\lambda^2 - 29\lambda + 100 = 0.$$

So the eigenvalues of $\mathbf{A}^2$ are $\lambda = 25$ and $\lambda = 4$. These are the squares of the eigenvalues of $\mathbf{A}$.

(ii) $\mathbf{A}^{-1} = \tfrac{1}{10}\begin{bmatrix} 4 & -2 \\ -1 & 3 \end{bmatrix} = \begin{bmatrix} 0.4 & -0.2 \\ -0.1 & 0.3 \end{bmatrix}$.

The characteristic equation of $\mathbf{A}^{-1}$ is

$$\lambda^2 - 0.7\lambda + 0.1 = 0.$$

So the eigenvalues of $\mathbf{A}^{-1}$ are $\lambda = 0.5$ and $\lambda = 0.2$. These are the reciprocals of the eigenvalues of $\mathbf{A}$.

(iii) $\mathbf{A} + 2\mathbf{I} = \begin{bmatrix} 3 & 2 \\ 1 & 4 \end{bmatrix} + \begin{bmatrix} 2 & 0 \\ 0 & 2 \end{bmatrix} = \begin{bmatrix} 5 & 2 \\ 1 & 6 \end{bmatrix}$.

The characteristic equation of $\mathbf{A} + 2\mathbf{I}$ is

$$\lambda^2 - 11\lambda + 28 = 0.$$

So the eigenvalues of $\mathbf{A} + 2\mathbf{I}$ are $\lambda = 7$ and $\lambda = 4$. These can be obtained by adding 2 to the eigenvalues of $\mathbf{A}$.

(iv) $(\mathbf{A} - 4\mathbf{I})^{-1} = \begin{bmatrix} -1 & 2 \\ 1 & 0 \end{bmatrix}^{-1}$

$$= \frac{1}{(-2)}\begin{bmatrix} 0 & -2 \\ -1 & -1 \end{bmatrix} = \begin{bmatrix} 0 & 1 \\ 0.5 & 0.5 \end{bmatrix}.$$

The characteristic equation of $(\mathbf{A} - 4\mathbf{I})^{-1}$ is

$$\lambda^2 - 0.5\lambda - 0.5 = 0.$$

So the eigenvalues of $(\mathbf{A} - 4\mathbf{I})^{-1}$ are $\lambda = 1$ and $\lambda = -0.5$. These can be obtained by subtracting 4 from the eigenvalues of $\mathbf{A}$ and then finding the reciprocals.

(v) $3\mathbf{A} = \begin{bmatrix} 9 & 6 \\ 3 & 12 \end{bmatrix}$, and the characteristic equation of $3\mathbf{A}$ is $(9 - \lambda)(12 - \lambda) - 18 = 0$, which simplifies to $\lambda^2 - 21\lambda + 90 = 0$. Thus the eigenvalues of $3\mathbf{A}$ are $\lambda = 15$ and $\lambda = 6$, which are three times those of $\mathbf{A}$.

(b) (i) $\mathbf{A}^2 \begin{bmatrix} 1 \\ 1 \end{bmatrix} = \begin{bmatrix} 11 & 14 \\ 7 & 18 \end{bmatrix}\begin{bmatrix} 1 \\ 1 \end{bmatrix} = \begin{bmatrix} 25 \\ 25 \end{bmatrix} = 25\begin{bmatrix} 1 \\ 1 \end{bmatrix}$,

$$\mathbf{A}^2 \begin{bmatrix} -2 \\ 1 \end{bmatrix} = \begin{bmatrix} 11 & 14 \\ 7 & 18 \end{bmatrix}\begin{bmatrix} -2 \\ 1 \end{bmatrix} = \begin{bmatrix} -8 \\ 4 \end{bmatrix} = 4\begin{bmatrix} -2 \\ 1 \end{bmatrix},$$

so the eigenvectors of $\mathbf{A}$ are also eigenvectors of $\mathbf{A}^2$.

(ii) $\mathbf{A}^{-1}\begin{bmatrix}1\\1\end{bmatrix} = \begin{bmatrix}0.4 & -0.2\\-0.1 & 0.3\end{bmatrix}\begin{bmatrix}1\\1\end{bmatrix}$

$\qquad = \begin{bmatrix}0.2\\0.2\end{bmatrix} = 0.2\begin{bmatrix}1\\1\end{bmatrix}$,

$\mathbf{A}^{-1}\begin{bmatrix}-2\\1\end{bmatrix} = \begin{bmatrix}0.4 & -0.2\\-0.1 & 0.3\end{bmatrix}\begin{bmatrix}-2\\1\end{bmatrix}$

$\qquad = \begin{bmatrix}-1\\0.5\end{bmatrix} = 0.5\begin{bmatrix}-2\\1\end{bmatrix}$,

so the eigenvectors of $\mathbf{A}$ are also eigenvectors of $\mathbf{A}^{-1}$.

(iii) $(\mathbf{A} + 2\mathbf{I})\begin{bmatrix}1\\1\end{bmatrix} = \begin{bmatrix}5 & 2\\1 & 6\end{bmatrix}\begin{bmatrix}1\\1\end{bmatrix} = \begin{bmatrix}7\\7\end{bmatrix} = 7\begin{bmatrix}1\\1\end{bmatrix}$,

$(\mathbf{A} + 2\mathbf{I})\begin{bmatrix}-2\\1\end{bmatrix} = \begin{bmatrix}5 & 2\\1 & 6\end{bmatrix}\begin{bmatrix}-2\\1\end{bmatrix}$

$\qquad = \begin{bmatrix}-8\\4\end{bmatrix} = 4\begin{bmatrix}-2\\1\end{bmatrix}$,

so the eigenvectors of $\mathbf{A}$ are also eigenvectors of $\mathbf{A} + 2\mathbf{I}$.

(iv) $(\mathbf{A} - 4\mathbf{I})^{-1}\begin{bmatrix}1\\1\end{bmatrix} = \begin{bmatrix}0 & 1\\0.5 & 0.5\end{bmatrix}\begin{bmatrix}1\\1\end{bmatrix} = \begin{bmatrix}1\\1\end{bmatrix}$,

$(\mathbf{A} - 4\mathbf{I})^{-1}\begin{bmatrix}-2\\1\end{bmatrix} = \begin{bmatrix}0 & 1\\0.5 & 0.5\end{bmatrix}\begin{bmatrix}-2\\1\end{bmatrix}$

$\qquad = \begin{bmatrix}1\\-0.5\end{bmatrix} = -0.5\begin{bmatrix}-2\\1\end{bmatrix}$,

so the eigenvectors of $\mathbf{A}$ are also eigenvectors of $(\mathbf{A} - 4\mathbf{I})^{-1}$.

(v) $3\mathbf{A}\begin{bmatrix}1\\1\end{bmatrix} = \begin{bmatrix}9 & 6\\3 & 12\end{bmatrix}\begin{bmatrix}1\\1\end{bmatrix} = \begin{bmatrix}15\\15\end{bmatrix} = 15\begin{bmatrix}1\\1\end{bmatrix}$,

$3\mathbf{A}\begin{bmatrix}-2\\1\end{bmatrix} = \begin{bmatrix}9 & 6\\3 & 12\end{bmatrix}\begin{bmatrix}-2\\1\end{bmatrix} = \begin{bmatrix}-12\\6\end{bmatrix} = 6\begin{bmatrix}-2\\1\end{bmatrix}$,

so the eigenvectors of $\mathbf{A}$ are also eigenvectors of $3\mathbf{A}$.

2.12 (a) (i) 4^3 and $(-1)^3$, i.e. 64 and -1.

(ii) 4^{-1} and $(-1)^{-1}$, i.e. $\frac{1}{4}$ and -1.

(iii) $4 - 6$ and $(-1) - 6$, i.e. -2 and -7.

(iv) $(4 + 3)^{-1}$ and $((-1) + 3)^{-1}$, i.e. $\frac{1}{7}$ and $\frac{1}{2}$.

(b) The eigenvalues of $\mathbf{A} - 4\mathbf{I}$ are $4 - 4 = 0$ and $-1 - 4 = -5$. The matrix $\mathbf{A} - 4\mathbf{I}$ is non-invertible because one of the eigenvalues is 0, so the inverse does not exist.

2.13 (a) Using Procedure 2.1, we solve the characteristic equation $\det(\mathbf{A} - \lambda\mathbf{I}) = 0$, which can be written as

$$\begin{vmatrix}1 - \lambda & 2\\3 & -4 - \lambda\end{vmatrix} = \lambda^2 + 3\lambda - 10 = 0.$$

The eigenvalues are $\lambda = -5$ and $\lambda = 2$. Solving the eigenvector equations for each eigenvalue, we obtain corresponding eigenvectors $[1 \quad -3]^T$ and $[2 \quad 1]^T$, respectively.

The eigenvalues of $\mathbf{A}^{10}$ are $(-5)^{10}$ and 2^{10}, corresponding to eigenvectors $[1 \quad -3]^T$ and $[2 \quad 1]^T$, respectively.

(b) $\begin{bmatrix}3 & 2\\3 & -2\end{bmatrix} = \mathbf{A} + 2\mathbf{I}$, where $\mathbf{A}$ is the matrix of part (a).

So the eigenvalues are $-5 + 2 = -3$ and $2 + 2 = 4$, with corresponding eigenvectors $[1 \quad -3]^T$ and $[2 \quad 1]^T$, respectively.

2.14 The characteristic equation is

$$\lambda^2 - (2\cos\theta)\lambda + 1 = 0,$$

since $\sin^2\theta + \cos^2\theta = 1$. Using the quadratic equation formula, the eigenvalues are

$$\lambda = \tfrac{1}{2}\left(2\cos\theta \pm \sqrt{4\cos^2\theta - 4}\right)$$

$$= \tfrac{1}{2}\left(2\cos\theta \pm \sqrt{(-4\sin^2\theta)}\right) = \cos\theta \pm i\sin\theta.$$

So the eigenvalues are $\cos\theta + i\sin\theta$ and $\cos\theta - i\sin\theta$. The eigenvector equations are

$$\begin{cases}(\cos\theta - \lambda)x - (\sin\theta)y = 0,\\(\sin\theta)x + (\cos\theta - \lambda)y = 0.\end{cases}$$

$\boxed{\lambda = \cos\theta + i\sin\theta}$ The eigenvector equations become $-(i\sin\theta)x - (\sin\theta)y = 0$ and $(\sin\theta)x - (i\sin\theta)y = 0$, which reduce to the single equation $iy = x$ (since $\sin\theta \neq 0$ as θ is not an integer multiple of π), so a corresponding eigenvector is $[i \quad 1]^T$.

$\boxed{\lambda = \cos\theta - i\sin\theta}$ The eigenvector equations become $(i\sin\theta)x - (\sin\theta)y = 0$ and $(\sin\theta)x + (i\sin\theta)y = 0$, which reduce to the single equation $-iy = x$ (since $\sin\theta \neq 0$), so a corresponding eigenvector is $[-i \quad 1]^T$.

Section 3

3.1 $\begin{bmatrix}5 & 0 & 0\\1 & 2 & 1\\1 & 1 & 2\end{bmatrix}\begin{bmatrix}0\\1\\1\end{bmatrix} = \begin{bmatrix}0\\3\\3\end{bmatrix} = 3\begin{bmatrix}0\\1\\1\end{bmatrix}$;

the corresponding eigenvalue is 3.

$\begin{bmatrix}5 & 0 & 0\\1 & 2 & 1\\1 & 1 & 2\end{bmatrix}\begin{bmatrix}0\\1\\-1\end{bmatrix} = \begin{bmatrix}0\\1\\-1\end{bmatrix}$;

the corresponding eigenvalue is 1.

3.2 The eigenvector equations are

$$\begin{cases}(1 - \lambda)x_1 - x_3 = 0,\\x_1 + (2 - \lambda)x_2 + x_3 = 0,\\2x_1 + 2x_2 + (3 - \lambda)x_3 = 0.\end{cases}$$

$\boxed{\lambda = 1}$ The eigenvector equations become

$$-x_3 = 0, \quad x_1 + x_2 + x_3 = 0, \quad 2x_1 + 2x_2 + 2x_3 = 0,$$

which reduce to the equations $x_3 = 0$ and $x_2 = -x_1$, so a corresponding eigenvector is $[1 \quad -1 \quad 0]^T$.

$\boxed{\lambda = 2}$ The eigenvector equations become

$$-x_1 - x_3 = 0, \quad x_1 + x_3 = 0, \quad 2x_1 + 2x_2 + x_3 = 0,$$

which reduce to the equations $-x_3 = x_1$ and $-2x_2 = x_1$, so a corresponding eigenvector is $[-2 \quad 1 \quad 2]^T$.

$\boxed{\lambda = 3}$ The eigenvector equations become

$$-2x_1 - x_3 = 0, \quad x_1 - x_2 + x_3 = 0, \quad 2x_1 + 2x_2 = 0,$$

which reduce to the equations $x_3 = -2x_1$ and $x_2 = -x_1$, so a corresponding eigenvector is $[1 \quad -1 \quad -2]^T$.

3.3 The characteristic equation is

$$\begin{vmatrix} -\lambda & 0 & 6 \\ \frac{1}{2} & -\lambda & 0 \\ 0 & \frac{1}{3} & -\lambda \end{vmatrix} = 0.$$

Expanding the determinant gives

$$-\lambda \begin{vmatrix} -\lambda & 0 \\ \frac{1}{3} & -\lambda \end{vmatrix} + 6 \begin{vmatrix} \frac{1}{2} & -\lambda \\ 0 & \frac{1}{3} \end{vmatrix} = 0,$$

which simplifies to $\lambda^3 - 1 = 0$. Since $\lambda = 1$ satisfies this equation, it is an eigenvalue of $\mathbf{A}$. (The other two eigenvalues are complex numbers.)

For $\lambda = 1$, the eigenvector equations become

$$-x_1 + 6x_3 = 0, \quad \tfrac{1}{2}x_1 - x_2 = 0, \quad \tfrac{1}{3}x_2 - x_3 = 0,$$

which reduce to the equations $x_1 = 6x_3$ and $x_2 = 3x_3$, so an eigenvector is $[6 \ \ 3 \ \ 1]^T$.

3.4 (a) The characteristic equation is

$$\begin{vmatrix} -\lambda & 0 & 1 \\ 0 & -\lambda & 0 \\ 1 & 0 & -\lambda \end{vmatrix} = 0.$$

Expanding the determinant gives

$$-\lambda \begin{vmatrix} -\lambda & 0 \\ 0 & -\lambda \end{vmatrix} + 1 \begin{vmatrix} 0 & -\lambda \\ 1 & 0 \end{vmatrix} = 0,$$

which simplifies to $-\lambda^3 + \lambda = 0$, or $\lambda(\lambda^2 - 1) = 0$, so the eigenvalues are $\lambda = 0$, $\lambda = -1$ and $\lambda = 1$.

(b) The matrix is triangular, so, from Subsection 2.3, the eigenvalues are $\lambda = 1$, $\lambda = 2$ and $\lambda = 3$.

3.5 The characteristic equation is

$$\begin{vmatrix} 8 - \lambda & 0 & -5 \\ 9 & 3 - \lambda & -6 \\ 10 & 0 & -7 - \lambda \end{vmatrix} = 0.$$

Taking the transpose gives

$$\begin{vmatrix} 8 - \lambda & 9 & 10 \\ 0 & 3 - \lambda & 0 \\ -5 & -6 & -7 - \lambda \end{vmatrix} = 0,$$

then interchanging rows 1 and 2 gives

$$\begin{vmatrix} 0 & 3 - \lambda & 0 \\ 8 - \lambda & 9 & 10 \\ -5 & -6 & -7 - \lambda \end{vmatrix} = 0.$$

Expanding by the first row gives

$$-(3 - \lambda) \begin{vmatrix} 8 - \lambda & 10 \\ -5 & -7 - \lambda \end{vmatrix} = 0,$$

so $\lambda = 3$ or $(8 - \lambda)(-7 - \lambda) + 50 = 0$. This quadratic equation simplifies to $\lambda^2 - \lambda - 6 = 0$, which has roots $\lambda = 3$ and $\lambda = -2$.

Thus the eigenvalues are $\lambda = 3$ (repeated) and $\lambda = -2$.

3.6 The characteristic equation of the first matrix is

$$\begin{vmatrix} a - \lambda & 0 & 0 \\ d & b - \lambda & 0 \\ e & f & c - \lambda \end{vmatrix} = 0.$$

Expanding by the top row gives

$$(a - \lambda) \begin{vmatrix} b - \lambda & 0 \\ f & c - \lambda \end{vmatrix} = 0,$$

so $(a - \lambda)(b - \lambda)(c - \lambda) = 0$.

Thus the eigenvalues are $\lambda = a$, $\lambda = b$ and $\lambda = c$.

The second matrix is the transpose of the first, so it has the same eigenvalues.

3.7 (a) Example 3.2:
sum of eigenvalues $= 5 + 3 + 1 = 9$
and tr $\mathbf{A} = 5 + 2 + 2 = 9$;
det $\mathbf{A} = 5 \times 3 \times 1 = 15$.

Example 3.3:
sum of eigenvalues $= 6 + 7 + 3 = 16$
and tr $\mathbf{A} = 5 + 5 + 6 = 16$;
det $\mathbf{A} = 6 \times 7 \times 3 = 126$.

(b) Exercise 3.2:
sum of eigenvalues $= 1 + 2 + 3 = 6$
and tr $\mathbf{A} = 1 + 2 + 3 = 6$;
det $\mathbf{A} = 1 \times 2 \times 3 = 6$.

Exercise 3.4(a):
sum of eigenvalues $= 0 + (-1) + 1 = 0$
and tr $\mathbf{A} = 0 + 0 + 0 = 0$;
det $\mathbf{A} = 0 \times (-1) \times 1 = 0$.

Exercise 3.4(b):
sum of eigenvalues $= 1 + 2 + 3 = 6$
and tr $\mathbf{A} = 1 + 2 + 3 = 6$;
det $\mathbf{A} = 1 \times 2 \times 3 = 6$.

Exercise 3.5:
sum of eigenvalues $= 3 + 3 + (-2) = 4$
and tr $\mathbf{A} = 8 + 3 + (-7) = 4$;
det $\mathbf{A} = 3 \times 3 \times (-2) = -18$.

3.8 (a) The characteristic equation is

$$\begin{vmatrix} -\lambda & 0 & 1 \\ 0 & 1 - \lambda & 0 \\ 1 & 0 & -\lambda \end{vmatrix} = 0.$$

Interchanging rows 1 and 2 gives

$$\begin{vmatrix} 0 & 1 - \lambda & 0 \\ -\lambda & 0 & 1 \\ 1 & 0 & -\lambda \end{vmatrix} = 0.$$

Expanding by the first row gives

$$-(1 - \lambda) \begin{vmatrix} -\lambda & 1 \\ 1 & -\lambda \end{vmatrix} = 0,$$

so $\lambda = 1$ or $\lambda^2 - 1 = 0$.

Since $\lambda^2 - 1 = (\lambda - 1)(\lambda + 1)$, the eigenvalues are $\lambda = 1$ (repeated) and $\lambda = -1$.

The eigenvector equations are

$$\begin{cases} -\lambda x_1 & + x_3 = 0, \\ (1 - \lambda)x_2 & = 0, \\ x_1 & - \lambda x_3 = 0. \end{cases}$$

$\boxed{\lambda = 1}$ The eigenvector equations become

$$-x_1 + x_3 = 0, \quad 0 = 0, \quad x_1 - x_3 = 0,$$

which reduce to the single equation $x_3 = x_1$.

Since x_2 can take any value, two linearly independent eigenvectors are $[0 \ \ 1 \ \ 0]^T$ and $[1 \ \ 0 \ \ 1]^T$.

$\boxed{\lambda = -1}$ The eigenvector equations become

$$x_1 + x_3 = 0, \quad 2x_2 = 0, \quad x_1 + x_3 = 0,$$

which reduce to the equations $x_3 = -x_1$ and $x_2 = 0$, so an eigenvector is $[1 \ \ 0 \ \ -1]^T$.

(b) The characteristic equation is

$$\begin{vmatrix} \frac{1}{\sqrt{2}} - \lambda & 0 & \frac{1}{\sqrt{2}} \\ 0 & 1-\lambda & 0 \\ -\frac{1}{\sqrt{2}} & 0 & \frac{1}{\sqrt{2}} - \lambda \end{vmatrix} = 0,$$

which, after interchanging the first and second rows, simplifies to

$$(\lambda - 1)(\lambda^2 - \sqrt{2}\lambda + 1) = 0.$$

The quadratic equation $\lambda^2 - \sqrt{2}\lambda + 1 = 0$ has roots $\lambda = \frac{1}{\sqrt{2}}(1+i)$ and $\lambda = \frac{1}{\sqrt{2}}(1-i)$.

Thus the eigenvalues are $\lambda = 1$, $\lambda = \frac{1}{\sqrt{2}}(1+i)$ and $\lambda = \frac{1}{\sqrt{2}}(1-i)$.

The eigenvector equations are

$$\begin{cases} \left(\frac{1}{\sqrt{2}} - \lambda\right)x_1 & + & \frac{1}{\sqrt{2}}x_3 = 0, \\ & (1-\lambda)x_2 & = 0, \\ -\frac{1}{\sqrt{2}}x_1 & + & \left(\frac{1}{\sqrt{2}} - \lambda\right)x_3 = 0. \end{cases}$$

$\boxed{\lambda = 1}$ The eigenvector equations become

$$\left(\frac{1}{\sqrt{2}} - 1\right)x_1 + \frac{1}{\sqrt{2}}x_3 = 0, \quad 0 = 0,$$

$$-\frac{1}{\sqrt{2}}x_1 + \left(\frac{1}{\sqrt{2}} - 1\right)x_3 = 0,$$

which reduce to the equations $x_1 = 0$ and $x_3 = 0$, so a corresponding eigenvector is $[0 \ \ 1 \ \ 0]^T$.

$\boxed{\lambda = \frac{1}{\sqrt{2}}(1+i)}$ The eigenvector equations become

$$-\frac{1}{\sqrt{2}}ix_1 + \frac{1}{\sqrt{2}}x_3 = 0, \quad \frac{1}{\sqrt{2}}(\sqrt{2} - 1 - i)x_2 = 0,$$

$$-\frac{1}{\sqrt{2}}x_1 - \frac{1}{\sqrt{2}}ix_3 = 0,$$

which reduce to the equations $x_3 = ix_1$ and $x_2 = 0$, so a corresponding eigenvector is $[1 \ \ 0 \ \ i]^T$.

$\boxed{\lambda = \frac{1}{\sqrt{2}}(1-i)}$ The eigenvector equations become

$$\frac{1}{\sqrt{2}}ix_1 + \frac{1}{\sqrt{2}}x_3 = 0, \quad \frac{1}{\sqrt{2}}(\sqrt{2} - 1 + i)x_2 = 0,$$

$$-\frac{1}{\sqrt{2}}x_1 + \frac{1}{\sqrt{2}}ix_3 = 0,$$

which reduce to the equations $x_3 = -ix_1$ and $x_2 = 0$, so a corresponding eigenvector is $[1 \ \ 0 \ \ -i]^T$.

(The eigenvalue $\frac{1}{\sqrt{2}}(1-i)$ and eigenvector $[1 \ \ 0 \ \ -i]^T$ can be obtained from $\frac{1}{\sqrt{2}}(1+i)$ and $[1 \ \ 0 \ \ i]^T$, respectively, by replacing i by $-i$. That is, the second complex eigenvalue and corresponding eigenvector are the complex conjugates of the first complex eigenvalue and corresponding eigenvector.)

3.9 **(a)** The matrix is upper triangular, so the eigenvalues are 2, −3 and 4.

$\boxed{\lambda = 2}$ The eigenvector equations become

$$x_2 - x_3 = 0, \quad -5x_2 + 2x_3 = 0, \quad 2x_3 = 0,$$

which reduce to $x_2 = x_3 = 0$, so a corresponding eigenvector is $[1 \ \ 0 \ \ 0]^T$.

$\boxed{\lambda = -3}$ The eigenvector equations become

$$5x_1 + x_2 - x_3 = 0, \quad 2x_3 = 0, \quad 7x_3 = 0,$$

which reduce to $5x_1 + x_2 = 0$ and $x_3 = 0$, so a corresponding eigenvector is $[1 \ \ -5 \ \ 0]^T$.

$\boxed{\lambda = 4}$ The eigenvector equations become

$$-2x_1 + x_2 - x_3 = 0, \quad -7x_2 + 2x_3 = 0, \quad 0 = 0.$$

Choosing $x_3 = 14$ keeps the numbers simple, and a corresponding eigenvector is $[-5 \ \ 4 \ \ 14]^T$.

(b) The characteristic equation is

$$\begin{vmatrix} -\lambda & 2 & 0 \\ -2 & -\lambda & 0 \\ 0 & 0 & 1-\lambda \end{vmatrix} = 0,$$

and (after interchanging the first and third rows) this gives $(1-\lambda)(\lambda^2 + 4) = 0$, so the eigenvalues are 1, $2i$ and $-2i$.

$\boxed{\lambda = 1}$ The eigenvector equations become

$$-x_1 + 2x_2 = 0, \quad -2x_1 - x_2 = 0, \quad 0 = 0,$$

so a corresponding eigenvector is $[0 \ \ 0 \ \ 1]^T$.

$\boxed{\lambda = 2i}$ The eigenvector equations become

$$-2ix_1 + 2x_2 = 0, \quad -2x_1 - 2ix_2 = 0, \quad (1 - 2i)x_3 = 0,$$

which reduce to $x_2 = ix_1$ and $x_3 = 0$, so a corresponding eigenvector is $[1 \ \ i \ \ 0]^T$.

$\boxed{\lambda = -2i}$ Similarly, an eigenvector corresponding to $\lambda = -2i$ is $[1 \ \ -i \ \ 0]^T$.

(c) The characteristic equation is

$$\begin{vmatrix} 1-\lambda & 0 & 0 \\ 0 & 1-\lambda & 2 \\ 0 & -2 & 5-\lambda \end{vmatrix} = 0,$$

which gives $(1-\lambda)((1-\lambda)(5-\lambda) + 4) = 0$. This simplifies to $(1-\lambda)(\lambda - 3)^2 = 0$, so the eigenvalues are $\lambda = 1$ and $\lambda = 3$ (repeated).

$\boxed{\lambda = 1}$ The eigenvector equations become

$$0 = 0, \quad 2x_3 = 0, \quad -2x_2 + 4x_3 = 0,$$

which reduce to $x_2 = x_3 = 0$, so $[1 \ \ 0 \ \ 0]^T$ is a corresponding eigenvector.

$\boxed{\lambda = 3}$ The eigenvector equations become

$$-2x_1 = 0, \quad -2x_2 + 2x_3 = 0,$$

which reduce to $x_1 = 0$ and $x_2 = x_3$, so a corresponding eigenvector is $[0 \ \ 1 \ \ 1]^T$. In this case, the repeated eigenvalue $\lambda = 3$ has only one linearly independent eigenvector.

(d) The matrix is lower triangular, so the eigenvalues are −2 and 1 (repeated).

$\boxed{\lambda = -2}$ The eigenvector equations become

$$3x_1 = 0, \quad 3x_2 = 0, \quad x_1 + x_2 = 0,$$

which reduce to $x_1 = x_2 = 0$, so $[0 \ \ 0 \ \ 1]^T$ is a corresponding eigenvector.

$\boxed{\lambda = 1}$ The eigenvector equations become

$$0 = 0, \quad x_1 + x_2 - 3x_3 = 0.$$

These equations are satisfied if $x_1 = 3x_3 - x_2$ (whatever values we choose for x_2 and x_3). Two linearly independent eigenvectors can be found. For example, setting $x_2 = 1$ and $x_3 = 0$ gives $[-1 \ \ 1 \ \ 0]^T$, and setting $x_2 = 0$ and $x_3 = 1$ gives $[3 \ \ 0 \ \ 1]^T$.

Section 4

4.1 $\mathbf{e}_1 = \mathbf{A}\mathbf{e}_0 = \begin{bmatrix} 3 & 2 \\ 1 & 4 \end{bmatrix}\begin{bmatrix} 1 \\ 0 \end{bmatrix} = \begin{bmatrix} 3 \\ 1 \end{bmatrix}$,

$\mathbf{e}_2 = \mathbf{A}\mathbf{e}_1 = \begin{bmatrix} 3 & 2 \\ 1 & 4 \end{bmatrix}\begin{bmatrix} 3 \\ 1 \end{bmatrix} = \begin{bmatrix} 11 \\ 7 \end{bmatrix}$,

$\mathbf{e}_3 = \mathbf{A}\mathbf{e}_2 = \begin{bmatrix} 3 & 2 \\ 1 & 4 \end{bmatrix}\begin{bmatrix} 11 \\ 7 \end{bmatrix} = \begin{bmatrix} 47 \\ 39 \end{bmatrix}$,

$\mathbf{e}_4 = \mathbf{A}\mathbf{e}_3 = \begin{bmatrix} 3 & 2 \\ 1 & 4 \end{bmatrix}\begin{bmatrix} 47 \\ 39 \end{bmatrix} = \begin{bmatrix} 219 \\ 203 \end{bmatrix}$.

4.2 (a) $\mathbf{e}_1 = \mathbf{A}\mathbf{e}_0 = \begin{bmatrix} 2 & 1 \\ 1 & 2 \end{bmatrix}\begin{bmatrix} 1 \\ 0 \end{bmatrix} = \begin{bmatrix} 2 \\ 1 \end{bmatrix}$,

$\mathbf{e}_2 = \mathbf{A}\mathbf{e}_1 = \begin{bmatrix} 2 & 1 \\ 1 & 2 \end{bmatrix}\begin{bmatrix} 2 \\ 1 \end{bmatrix} = \begin{bmatrix} 5 \\ 4 \end{bmatrix}$,

$\mathbf{e}_3 = \mathbf{A}\mathbf{e}_2 = \begin{bmatrix} 2 & 1 \\ 1 & 2 \end{bmatrix}\begin{bmatrix} 5 \\ 4 \end{bmatrix} = \begin{bmatrix} 14 \\ 13 \end{bmatrix}$.

(b) $\mathbf{e}_{11} = \mathbf{A}\mathbf{e}_{10} = [88\,574 \quad 88\,573]^T$.

(c) The characteristic equation is $(2 - \lambda)^2 - 1 = 0$, so $2 - \lambda = \pm 1$, thus $\lambda_1 = 3$ and $\lambda_2 = 1$. Corresponding eigenvectors are $\mathbf{v}_1 = [1 \quad 1]^T$ and $\mathbf{v}_2 = [1 \quad -1]^T$.

(d) We need to determine constants α and β so that $\mathbf{e}_0 = \alpha\mathbf{v}_1 + \beta\mathbf{v}_2$, i.e.

$\begin{bmatrix} 1 & 1 \\ 1 & -1 \end{bmatrix}\begin{bmatrix} \alpha \\ \beta \end{bmatrix} = \begin{bmatrix} 1 \\ 0 \end{bmatrix}$.

Solving this equation for α and β gives $\alpha = \frac{1}{2}$ and $\beta = \frac{1}{2}$. Thus we have

$\mathbf{e}_0 = \frac{1}{2}\mathbf{v}_1 + \frac{1}{2}\mathbf{v}_2$.

(e) $\mathbf{e}_1 = \mathbf{A}\mathbf{e}_0 = \mathbf{A}(\frac{1}{2}\mathbf{v}_1 + \frac{1}{2}\mathbf{v}_2)$
$= \frac{1}{2}\mathbf{A}\mathbf{v}_1 + \frac{1}{2}\mathbf{A}\mathbf{v}_2$
$= \frac{3}{2}\mathbf{v}_1 + \frac{1}{2}\mathbf{v}_2$,

$\mathbf{e}_2 = \mathbf{A}\mathbf{e}_1 = \mathbf{A}(\frac{3}{2}\mathbf{v}_1 + \frac{1}{2}\mathbf{v}_2)$
$= \frac{3}{2}\mathbf{A}\mathbf{v}_1 + \frac{1}{2}\mathbf{A}\mathbf{v}_2$
$= \frac{9}{2}\mathbf{v}_1 + \frac{1}{2}\mathbf{v}_2$.

Similarly,

$\mathbf{e}_n = \frac{1}{2}(3^n\mathbf{v}_1 + \mathbf{v}_2)$.

(f) The coefficient of $\mathbf{v}_1$, i.e. $\frac{1}{2} \times 3^n$, dominates the expression for $\mathbf{e}_n$, so we obtain approximations to $\mathbf{v}_1$ (an eigenvector corresponding to the eigenvalue of larger magnitude).

4.3 (a) If $\mathbf{e}_0 = \alpha\mathbf{v}_1 + \beta\mathbf{v}_2$, then

$\begin{bmatrix} 10000 \\ 8000 \end{bmatrix} = \alpha\begin{bmatrix} 2 \\ 1 \end{bmatrix} + \beta\begin{bmatrix} 1 \\ -1 \end{bmatrix}$,

so α and β satisfy the simultaneous equations

$\begin{cases} 2\alpha + \beta = 10\,000, \\ \alpha - \beta = 8000. \end{cases}$

Solving these equations gives $\alpha = 6000$, $\beta = -2000$, so

$\mathbf{e}_0 = 6000\mathbf{v}_1 - 2000\mathbf{v}_2$.

(b) Since $\mathbf{A}\mathbf{v}_1 = \mathbf{v}_1$ and $\mathbf{A}\mathbf{v}_2 = 0.7\mathbf{v}_2$, we have

$\mathbf{e}_1 = \mathbf{A}\mathbf{e}_0 = 6000\mathbf{A}\mathbf{v}_1 - 2000\mathbf{A}\mathbf{v}_2$
$= 6000\mathbf{v}_1 - 2000(0.7)\mathbf{v}_2$,

$\mathbf{e}_2 = \mathbf{A}\mathbf{e}_1 = 6000\mathbf{A}\mathbf{v}_1 - 2000(0.7)\mathbf{A}\mathbf{v}_2$
$= 6000\mathbf{v}_1 - 2000(0.7)^2\mathbf{v}_2$.

Continuing in this way, we obtain

$\mathbf{e}_n = 6000\mathbf{v}_1 - 2000(0.7)^n\mathbf{v}_2$.

(c) As n becomes large, $(0.7)^n$ becomes small and the term in $\mathbf{v}_2$ can be ignored in comparison with the term in $\mathbf{v}_1$. Thus

$\mathbf{e}_n \simeq 6000\mathbf{v}_1 = [12\,000 \quad 6000]^T$,

which agrees with our observations in the Introduction.

4.4 First iteration:

$\mathbf{z}_1 = \begin{bmatrix} 3 & 6 \\ 4 & 8 \end{bmatrix}\begin{bmatrix} 1 \\ 0 \end{bmatrix} = \begin{bmatrix} 3 \\ \boxed{4} \end{bmatrix}$,

$\alpha_1 = 4$,

$\mathbf{e}_1 = \dfrac{\mathbf{z}_1}{\alpha_1} = \frac{1}{4}\begin{bmatrix} 3 \\ 4 \end{bmatrix} = \begin{bmatrix} \frac{3}{4} \\ 1 \end{bmatrix}$.

Second iteration:

$\mathbf{z}_2 = \begin{bmatrix} 3 & 6 \\ 4 & 8 \end{bmatrix}\begin{bmatrix} \frac{3}{4} \\ 1 \end{bmatrix} = \begin{bmatrix} \frac{33}{4} \\ \boxed{11} \end{bmatrix}$,

$\alpha_2 = 11$,

$\mathbf{e}_2 = \dfrac{\mathbf{z}_2}{\alpha_2} = \frac{1}{11}\begin{bmatrix} \frac{33}{4} \\ 11 \end{bmatrix} = \begin{bmatrix} \frac{3}{4} \\ 1 \end{bmatrix}$.

Since $\mathbf{e}_2 = \mathbf{e}_1$, the third iteration will be identical to the second, and $\mathbf{e}_3$ is also $[\frac{3}{4} \quad 1]^T$.

So $[\frac{3}{4} \quad 1]^T$ is an eigenvector. We have

$\begin{bmatrix} 3 & 6 \\ 4 & 8 \end{bmatrix}\begin{bmatrix} \frac{3}{4} \\ 1 \end{bmatrix} = \begin{bmatrix} \frac{33}{4} \\ 11 \end{bmatrix} = 11\begin{bmatrix} \frac{3}{4} \\ 1 \end{bmatrix}$,

so the corresponding eigenvalue is 11. Since $\operatorname{tr}\mathbf{A} = 11$, the other eigenvalue is 0, which explains why the iteration converges so rapidly.

(This is a very special case; generally, we would not expect $\mathbf{e}_n$ to be *equal* to an eigenvector for any value of n, unless we start with an eigenvector.)

4.5 We have $\mathbf{A}^{-1} = \frac{1}{11}\begin{bmatrix} 5 & -3 \\ -8 & 7 \end{bmatrix}$.

First iteration:

$\mathbf{z}_1 = \frac{1}{11}\begin{bmatrix} 5 & -3 \\ -8 & 7 \end{bmatrix}\begin{bmatrix} 1 \\ 1 \end{bmatrix} = \begin{bmatrix} \boxed{\frac{2}{11}} \\ -\frac{1}{11} \end{bmatrix}$,

therefore $\alpha_1 = \frac{2}{11}$ and $\mathbf{e}_1 = [1 \quad -\frac{1}{2}]^T$.

Second iteration:

$\mathbf{z}_2 = \frac{1}{11}\begin{bmatrix} 5 & -3 \\ -8 & 7 \end{bmatrix}\begin{bmatrix} 1 \\ -\frac{1}{2} \end{bmatrix} = \begin{bmatrix} \frac{13}{22} \\ \boxed{-\frac{23}{22}} \end{bmatrix}$,

therefore $\alpha_2 = -\frac{23}{22}$ and $\mathbf{e}_2 = [-\frac{13}{23} \quad 1]^T$.

Third iteration:

$\mathbf{z}_3 = \frac{1}{11}\begin{bmatrix} 5 & -3 \\ -8 & 7 \end{bmatrix}\begin{bmatrix} -\frac{13}{23} \\ 1 \end{bmatrix} = \begin{bmatrix} -\frac{134}{253} \\ \boxed{\frac{265}{253}} \end{bmatrix}$,

therefore $\alpha_3 = \frac{265}{253}$ and $\mathbf{e}_3 = [-\frac{134}{265} \quad 1]^T$.

Taking $\mathbf{e}_3 = [-\frac{134}{265} \quad 1]^T \simeq [-0.506 \quad 1]^T$ as our approximation to the eigenvector, the estimate for the corresponding eigenvalue of $\mathbf{A}$ of smallest magnitude is $1/\alpha_3 = \frac{253}{265} \simeq 0.955$. (The exact eigenvector is $[-0.5 \quad 1]^T$, corresponding to the eigenvalue 1.)

4.6 We follow Procedure 4.3(a).

Twenty-first iteration:

$$\mathbf{z}_{21} = (\mathbf{A} + \mathbf{I})^{-1}\mathbf{e}_{20}$$
$$= \begin{bmatrix} \frac{3}{2} & -\frac{1}{4} & -\frac{1}{2} \\ -\frac{1}{4} & \frac{5}{8} & -\frac{1}{4} \\ -\frac{1}{2} & -\frac{1}{4} & \frac{1}{2} \end{bmatrix} \begin{bmatrix} 1 \\ -0.141 \\ -0.379 \end{bmatrix} = \begin{bmatrix} \boxed{1.725} \\ -0.243 \\ -0.654 \end{bmatrix},$$

$\alpha_{21} = 1.725$,

$$\mathbf{e}_{21} = \frac{\mathbf{z}_{21}}{\alpha_{21}} \simeq [1 \quad -0.141 \quad -0.379]^T.$$

The sequence α_n appears to have converged to 1.725, and a corresponding eigenvector is approximately $[1 \quad -0.141 \quad -0.379]^T$.

Since α_n converges to $1/(\lambda_1 - p) = 1/(\lambda_1 + 1) = 1.725$, we have $\lambda_1 = \frac{1}{1.725} - 1 \simeq -0.420$.

4.7 **(a)** We follow Procedure 4.1.

First iteration:

$$\mathbf{z}_1 = \mathbf{A}\mathbf{e}_0 = \begin{bmatrix} 0.5 & 0.6 \\ 1.4 & -0.3 \end{bmatrix} \begin{bmatrix} 1 \\ 0 \end{bmatrix} = \begin{bmatrix} 0.5 \\ \boxed{1.4} \end{bmatrix},$$

$\alpha_1 = 1.4$,

$$\mathbf{e}_1 = \frac{\mathbf{z}_1}{\alpha_1} = \frac{1}{1.4}\begin{bmatrix} 0.5 \\ 1.4 \end{bmatrix} = \begin{bmatrix} 0.357143 \\ 1 \end{bmatrix}.$$

Second iteration: $\mathbf{e}_2 = [1 \quad 0.256881]^T$.

Third iteration: $\mathbf{e}_3 = [0.494452 \quad 1]^T$.

(b) We follow Procedure 2.1.

The characteristic equation is

$$\lambda^2 - 0.2\lambda - 0.99 = 0,$$

so the eigenvalues are $\lambda_1 = -0.9$ and $\lambda_2 = 1.1$.

$\boxed{\lambda_1 = -0.9}$ The eigenvector equations both become

$$1.4x + 0.6y = 0, \quad \text{i.e.} \quad 3y = -7x,$$

so a corresponding eigenvector is $[3 \quad -7]^T$.

$\boxed{\lambda_2 = 1.1}$ The eigenvector equations become

$$-0.6x + 0.6y = 0, \quad 1.4x - 1.4y = 0,$$

which reduce to $x = y$, so a corresponding eigenvector is $[1 \quad 1]^T$.

(c) The sequence $\mathbf{e}_n$ will converge to an eigenvector corresponding to the eigenvalue of larger magnitude, i.e. to $[1 \quad 1]^T$.

(d) $\mathbf{A}^8\mathbf{v} = \lambda^8\mathbf{v}$.

(e) We express $\mathbf{e}_0$ in terms of the eigenvectors as $\mathbf{e}_0 = \alpha\mathbf{v}_1 + \beta\mathbf{v}_2$, so

$$\mathbf{e}_0 = \begin{bmatrix} 1 \\ 0 \end{bmatrix} = \alpha\begin{bmatrix} 3 \\ -7 \end{bmatrix} + \beta\begin{bmatrix} 1 \\ 1 \end{bmatrix},$$

giving $\alpha = 0.1$ and $\beta = 0.7$.

In general, $\mathbf{e}_n = \mathbf{A}^n\mathbf{e}_0$, so we calculate

$$\mathbf{A}^8\mathbf{e}_0 = \mathbf{A}^8(0.1\mathbf{v}_1 + 0.7\mathbf{v}_2)$$
$$= 0.1(\mathbf{A}^8\mathbf{v}_1) + 0.7(\mathbf{A}^8\mathbf{v}_2)$$
$$= (0.1)(-0.9)^8\mathbf{v}_1 + (0.7)(1.1)^8\mathbf{v}_2$$
$$\simeq 0.043047\mathbf{v}_1 + 1.500512\mathbf{v}_2$$
$$= [0.129140 \quad -0.301327]^T$$
$$\quad + [1.500512 \quad 1.500512]^T$$
$$= [1.629652 \quad 1.199185]^T.$$

Dividing by 1.629652, we obtain $\mathbf{e}_8 = [1 \quad 0.735853]^T$.

(f) $\mathbf{A}^{-1} = \begin{bmatrix} 0.303030 & 0.606060 \\ 1.414141 & -0.505050 \end{bmatrix}.$

We follow Procedure 4.2(a).

First iteration:

$$\mathbf{z}_1 = \mathbf{A}^{-1}\mathbf{e}_0 = \begin{bmatrix} 0.484848 \\ \boxed{-1.070707} \end{bmatrix},$$

$\alpha_1 = -1.070707$,

$$\mathbf{e}_1 = \frac{\mathbf{z}_1}{\alpha_1} = -\frac{1}{1.070707}\begin{bmatrix} 0.484845 \\ -1.070707 \end{bmatrix}$$
$$= \begin{bmatrix} -0.452830 \\ 1 \end{bmatrix}.$$

Second iteration:

$$\alpha_2 = -1.145416, \quad \mathbf{e}_2 = [-0.409318 \quad 1]^T.$$

Third iteration:

$$\alpha_3 = -1.083884, \quad \mathbf{e}_3 = [-0.444720 \quad 1]^T.$$

This sequence of vectors is converging to $[-\frac{3}{7} \quad 1]^T \simeq [-0.428571 \quad 1]^T$, an eigenvector corresponding to the eigenvalue of smallest magnitude, $\lambda = -0.9$.

(g) Convergence will be slow for direct iteration, since the two eigenvalues of $\mathbf{A}$ are -0.9 and 1.1, which are relatively close in magnitude. Similarly, inverse iteration will also be slow to converge, since the eigenvalues of $\mathbf{A}^{-1}$ are -1.1111 and 0.9091, to four decimal places, and these are relatively close in magnitude.

4.8 We could use Procedure 4.3 to find the third eigenvector, but without a computer this could be very hard work. Alternatively, we could find two of the eigenvalues from the given eigenvectors, and we could then find the third eigenvalue very easily because the sum of the eigenvalues is $\text{tr}\,\mathbf{A}$.

We know that $\mathbf{v}_1$ is an eigenvector, so $\mathbf{A}\mathbf{v}_1 = \lambda_1\mathbf{v}_1$. Calculating just the third components, we have

$$(3 \times 0.477) + (4 \times 0.689) + (6 \times 1) = \lambda_1 \times 1,$$

so $\lambda_1 \simeq 10.187$.

Similarly, using the second components of $\mathbf{A}\mathbf{v}_2 = \lambda_2\mathbf{v}_2$, we have

$$(2 \times (-0.102)) + (3 \times 1) + (4 \times (-0.641)) = \lambda_2 \times 1,$$

so $\lambda_2 \simeq 0.232$.

Since $\text{tr}\,\mathbf{A} = 1 + 3 + 6 = 10$,

$$\lambda_3 = 10 - \lambda_1 - \lambda_2 \simeq -0.419.$$

UNIT 11   Systems of differential equations

Study guide for Unit 11

Before reading this unit, you will need to be familiar with the main ideas of *Units 2* and *3* on differential equations. You will also need to be familiar with the properties of matrices and determinants, as described in *Unit 9*, and with the material on eigenvalues and eigenvectors in *Unit 10*. The material in this unit will be needed for later units in the course — in particular, *Unit 13*.

Section 1 is intended to show you how systems of differential equations arise from modelling. It should not take you very long to study, since there are no exercises.

Section 2 is the most important part of the unit, and depends heavily on *Unit 10*. In particular, you should make sure that you understand Subsection 2.1 before proceeding.

Subsection 3.1 of Section 3 is more theoretical, and you should make sure that you understand the statements of the two theorems. In Subsection 3.2, you should concentrate on the first part of the subsection rather than the exceptional cases that come later.

Section 4 is a straightforward section in which the ideas from previous sections are applied to a different type of problem.

Section 5 involves use of the computer algebra package for the course.

Introduction

You have already met several types of linear differential equation in this course. For example, in *Unit 2* you met linear first-order differential equations of the form

$$\frac{dy}{dx} + g(x)y = h(x),$$

where $g(x)$ and $h(x)$ are given functions, and in *Unit 3* you met linear constant-coefficient second-order differential equations of the form

$$a\frac{d^2y}{dx^2} + b\frac{dy}{dx} + cy = f(x),$$

where a, b and c are constants, and $f(x)$ is a given function.

We now turn our attention to systems of linear differential equations relating two or more functions and their derivatives. A simple example of such a system is

$$\begin{cases} \dot{x} = 3x + 2y, \\ \dot{y} = x + 4y, \end{cases}$$

Recall that $\dot{x}$ means dx/dt and $\dot{y}$ means dy/dt.

where $x(t)$ and $y(t)$ are both functions of the independent variable t. You can think of $(\dot{x}, \dot{y}) = (\dot{x}(t), \dot{y}(t))$ as the velocity at time t of a particle at position $(x, y) = (x(t), y(t))$. If we are given the above system and an initial condition for the position of the particle at time $t = 0$, then solving the differential equations will give us the position $(x(t), y(t))$ of the particle at any subsequent time t.

In Subsection 2.1 you will see that we can solve these differential equations by writing the second as $x = \dot{y} - 4y$ and substituting this expression into the first to give a single second-order differential equation in y. However, this method does not extend easily to more complicated systems, such as those involving three differential equations in three unknowns. In this unit we develop techniques for solving such systems of linear differential equations with constant coefficients. We shall see that such systems can be written in matrix form, and that we can solve them by calculating the eigenvalues and eigenvectors of the resulting coefficient matrix.

Conversely, we can always write a single second-order differential equation as a pair of first-order equations: for example, writing $y = \dot{x}$, we can replace $\ddot{x} - 3\dot{x} - 2x = 0$ by the system

$$\begin{cases} \dot{x} = y, \\ \dot{y} = 2x + 3y. \end{cases}$$

We also examine systems of equations involving second derivatives, such as

$$\begin{cases} \ddot{x} = x + 4y, \\ \ddot{y} = x - 2y, \end{cases}$$

where you can think of $(\ddot{x}, \ddot{y}) = (\ddot{x}(t), \ddot{y}(t))$ as the acceleration at time t of a particle at position $(x, y) = (x(t), y(t))$.

In Section 1 we show how various situations can be modelled by a system of linear differential equations. In Section 2 we show how such a system can be written in matrix form, and use eigenvalues and eigenvectors to solve it when the equations are homogeneous with constant coefficients. This discussion spills over into Section 3, where we discuss the inhomogeneous case, and into Section 4, where we show how similar techniques can be used to solve certain systems of *second-order* differential equations. In Section 5 we use the computer to apply many of the techniques of this unit to various situations.

Although many of the problems that we consider in this unit may appear to be rather restricted in scope, the type of system discussed here arises surprisingly often in practice. In particular, systems of linear constant-coefficient differential equations occur frequently in modelling situations, especially when we need to make simplifying assumptions about the situations involved. In *Unit 13*, we shall consider certain types of *non-linear* systems.

1 Systems of differential equations as models

In this short motivational section, you will see how systems of linear differential equations arise in the process of modelling three rather different types of situation.

We shall not give here full details of the modelling process which is required in each case, since the aim is to give a fairly rapid impression of where systems of differential equations might occur in practice. You should not spend too much time dwelling on the details.

1.1 Conflicts

Consider a situation in which two different groups are in direct competition for survival. In a military context, the individual members of these groups might be humans (soldiers, say) or they might be tanks, ships or aircraft. In the absence of any external means of stopping the conflict, a battle unfolds by a process of attrition, in which individual members of the two groups are in one way or another rendered inactive (in the case of humans, killed or severely wounded). The battle terminates when one side or the other has lost all of its active members.

The model described in this subsection was first published by F. W. Lanchester in 1914.

What factors affect who will 'win' such a conflict? Other things being equal, we would expect a larger group to prevail over a smaller one, so the size of each group is important. However, it is often the case that one side is more effective per member than the other. Militarily, this effectiveness is determined by the choice and design of the weaponry used, and a recognized measure of this effectiveness is the abhorrent term *kill rate*, that is, the rate at which single members of one group can, on average, render members of the other group inactive.

For two groups of equal initial size, the more effective group will, on average, win a battle. But what will occur when group X is numerically larger than group Y but has inferior weaponry? We shall describe a simple model which is capable of providing a first answer to this question.

The model is a continuous one: it approximates the actual situation, in which the active group size at any time is an integer, by assuming that the group size is capable of continuous variation. This is a very reasonable approximation if each group has a large number of members.

Let the active sizes of groups X and Y be denoted by x and y, respectively. These sizes vary with time t, so $x(t)$ represents the active size of group X at time t, and similarly for $y(t)$. Suppose that the constant kill rates of the two groups are α for group X, and β for group Y, where α and β are both positive.

We suppose that the rate of reduction of each group is proportional to the size of the other, so

$$\frac{dx}{dt} = -\beta y \quad \text{and} \quad \frac{dy}{dt} = -\alpha x.$$

This pair of equations can be written alternatively as

$$\begin{cases} \dot{x} = -\beta y, \\ \dot{y} = -\alpha x, \end{cases} \tag{1.1}$$

which is a system of two first-order differential equations. Neither of these equations is soluble directly by the methods of *Unit 2*, because they are *coupled*; that is, the equation which features the derivative of one of the variables x also includes the other variable y on the right-hand side, and vice versa. In order to solve the first equation for x, we need to know explicitly what the function $y(t)$ is, and similarly for the second equation.

You will appreciate in Section 2 that this system of equations may be solved in terms of the eigenvalues and eigenvectors of the matrix

$$\begin{bmatrix} 0 & -\beta \\ -\alpha & 0 \end{bmatrix},$$

which arises from expressing Equations (1.1) in the matrix form

$$\begin{bmatrix} \dot{x} \\ \dot{y} \end{bmatrix} = \begin{bmatrix} 0 & -\beta \\ -\alpha & 0 \end{bmatrix} \begin{bmatrix} x \\ y \end{bmatrix}.$$

There are also other methods of solution. However, without solving this system of differential equations, it is possible to deduce an interesting conclusion about such conflicts. Suppose that we multiply both sides of the first equation of (1.1) by αx, then both sides of the second equation by βy, and finally subtract the resulting equations. This produces

$$\alpha x \dot{x} - \beta y \dot{y} = 0,$$

which, by the Chain Rule, can also be expressed as

$$\tfrac{1}{2}\alpha \frac{d}{dt}(x^2) - \tfrac{1}{2}\beta \frac{d}{dt}(y^2) = 0.$$

Integration with respect to time then gives

$$\alpha x^2 - \beta y^2 = c,$$

where c is a constant. If the initial sizes of the two groups (at time $t = 0$) are respectively x_0 and y_0, then the value of c is $\alpha x_0^2 - \beta y_0^2$, and we have

$$\alpha x^2 - \beta y^2 = \alpha x_0^2 - \beta y_0^2 \tag{1.2}$$

throughout the conflict.

This relationship allows us to predict when two sides are equally matched in a conflict. Neither side wins if both have their size reduced to zero at the same time, that is, if $x = 0$ when $y = 0$. In this case, we must have $\alpha x^2 - \beta y^2 = 0$ throughout the conflict, so at the start $\alpha x_0^2 = \beta y_0^2$. This reasoning led Lanchester to define the *fighting strength* of a force as 'the square of its size multiplied by the kill rate of its individual units'.

According to this definition, a force which outnumbers an adversarial force by only half as much again is more than twice as strong, assuming equal effectiveness on both sides. For any potential conflict, the initial fighting strengths of the two sides can be estimated, and according to Equation (1.2) any difference in these strengths remains constant throughout the conflict. At the end, the size and therefore the strength of the loser is zero, so this difference is equal to the remaining strength of the winning side. From this, the number of survivors can be predicted.

The model is of course very simple, and will not be applicable in exact form for any particular conflict. Nevertheless, the rule of thumb which it provides is an informative one, and is taken into account by, for example, military strategists.

Lanchester applied this model to the situation at the Battle of Trafalgar (1805), and was able to demonstrate why Nelson's tactic of splitting the opposition fleet into two parts might have been expected to succeed, even with a smaller total number of ships.

1.2   Two-compartment drug model

The administration of clinical drugs is a complex task. The doctor must ensure that the concentration of the drug in the patient's blood remains between certain upper and lower limits. One model that has been developed to assist in understanding the process is given by the following differential equation, in which $c(t)$ represents the concentration of drug in the patient's blood (as a function of time):

$$\frac{dc}{dt} = \frac{q}{V} - \lambda c.$$

Here the drug enters the bloodstream at a constant rate q, V is the 'apparent volume of distribution', and λ is a constant (which may be interpreted as the proportionate rate at which the kidneys excrete the drug). You are not expected to understand how this equation is derived.

Such a constant rate q of drug input to the bloodstream may be achieved by intravenous infusion, but this requires the patient to be connected to certain apparatus and is consequently inconvenient. A modern alternative is to use slow-release capsules which are taken orally. These capsules gradually dissolve within the stomach and by so doing raise the drug concentration there. The drug reaches the bloodstream from the stomach by a process which may be represented as passing through a membrane which separates the stomach 'compartment' from the bloodstream 'compartment'. Later on the drug is excreted from the kidneys, as before. The whole process is indicated diagrammatically in Figure 1.1.

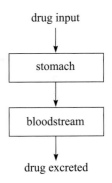

Figure 1.1

We shall now indicate briefly how to model such a two-compartment situation. We make the following assumptions.

(a) The slow-release capsule has the effect of providing a constant rate of input of the drug to the stomach, until the capsule is completely dissolved.

(b) The concentrations of drug within the stomach compartment and within the bloodstream compartment are each uniform at any instant of time.

(c) The rate at which the drug passes from the stomach to the bloodstream is proportional to the difference in concentrations between them.

(d) The rate of excretion from the bloodstream via the kidneys is (as in the earlier model) proportional to the concentration in the bloodstream.

Suppose that the drug concentrations in the stomach and bloodstream at time t are denoted by $x(t)$ and $y(t)$, respectively, and consider the period after the slow-release capsule has been swallowed but before it has completely dissolved.

Assumption (c) is based upon *Fick's law*, which is an empirical result stating that 'the amount of material passing through a membrane is proportional to the difference in concentration between the two sides of the membrane'.

The drug concentration in the stomach will be raised at a constant rate, k_1 say, by Assumption (a), but simultaneously lowered at a rate $k_2(x - y)$, where k_2 is a constant, by Assumption (c). Hence we have

$$\frac{dx}{dt} = k_1 - k_2(x - y).$$

The drug concentration in the blood will be raised at a rate $k_3(x - y)$, by Assumption (c), but also lowered at a rate k_4y, by Assumption (d) (where k_3 and k_4 are constants). This gives

$$\frac{dy}{dt} = k_3(x - y) - k_4y.$$

We might expect that $k_2 = k_3$ if all the drug leaving the stomach enters the bloodstream, but this is not one of our assumptions.

The drug concentrations in the two compartments are therefore governed within the model by the pair of differential equations

$$\begin{cases} \dot{x} = -k_2x + k_2y + k_1, \\ \dot{y} = k_3x - (k_3 + k_4)y, \end{cases} \quad (1.3)$$

which can be written in matrix form as

$$\begin{bmatrix} \dot{x} \\ \dot{y} \end{bmatrix} = \begin{bmatrix} -k_2 & k_2 \\ k_3 & -(k_3 + k_4) \end{bmatrix} \begin{bmatrix} x \\ y \end{bmatrix} + \begin{bmatrix} k_1 \\ 0 \end{bmatrix}.$$

Figure 1.2 sketches the type of behaviour which this model predicts for the drug concentration $y(t)$ in the bloodstream. It is characterized by an absorption phase followed by a steady decline as the drug is eliminated. The graph for the drug concentration $x(t)$ in the stomach is of similar shape. The drug concentrations do not approach zero for large values of t so long as k_1 is non-zero. In reality, a slow-release capsule will eventually dissolve completely, and then the patient must swallow another capsule in order to prevent the drug concentration from falling below some predetermined level.

Figure 1.2

The eigenvalues and eigenvectors of the matrix of coefficients

$$\begin{bmatrix} -k_2 & k_2 \\ k_3 & -(k_3 + k_4) \end{bmatrix}$$

provide a starting point for solving the system of equations (1.3). However, the form of this system differs from that which was derived in the previous subsection. The presence of the term k_1 on the right-hand side of the first equation, which is non-zero and does not depend upon x or y, makes this system *inhomogeneous*, whereas system (1.1) in Subsection 1.1 is *homogeneous*, since it has no such term present. You will see shortly that, as with ordinary differential equations, the solution of an inhomogeneous system is related to, but slightly more complicated than, that of a homogeneous system.

You will study methods of solution in the following two sections.

However, system (1.3) will become homogeneous if the slow-release capsule dissolves completely and is not replaced. This corresponds to putting $k_1 = 0$.

1.3 Motion of a ball-bearing in a bowl

The previous examples each led to a system of two first-order linear differential equations, homogeneous in the case of the conflict model, and inhomogeneous for the two-compartment drug model. We now look at an example where the system which arises involves *second-order* linear differential equations.

When a ball-bearing (that is, a small metallic ball) is placed in a bowl and set in motion, it tends to roll along the surface of the bowl for some considerable time before coming to rest. We shall now indicate how this motion might be modelled for a generalized 'bowl'.

To simplify matters, we model the ball-bearing as a particle (so that the rolling aspect of the motion is ignored), and assume that the surface of the bowl is frictionless and that there is no air resistance. To describe the surface, suppose that a three-dimensional Cartesian coordinate system is chosen with the (x, y)-plane horizontal, the z-axis vertical, and the lowest point of the bowl's surface at the origin, $(0, 0, 0)$. We assume further that in the vicinity of the origin, the surface may be described by an equation of the form

$$z = \tfrac{1}{2}ax^2 + bxy + \tfrac{1}{2}cy^2, \tag{1.4}$$

where the constants a, b, c satisfy the conditions $ac - b^2 > 0$ and $a > 0$. The first condition here ensures that the surface under consideration is a *paraboloid*, for which any vertical cross-section through the origin is a parabola, while the second condition means that these cross-sectional parabolas are all concave upwards rather than downwards. The surface is sketched in Figure 1.3.

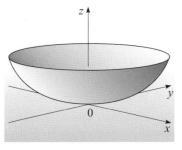

Figure 1.3

It may seem restrictive to specify the particular form of surface given by Equation (1.4). However, it turns out that many other functions $z = f(x, y)$ with a minimum value $z = 0$ at $(0, 0)$ can be approximated satisfactorily by a function of the form (1.4) near to the origin.

You will be able to appreciate this point more fully after studying the topic of two-variable Taylor polynomial approximations in *Unit 12*.

Since the surface is assumed to be frictionless and there is no air resistance, the only forces which act upon the particle are its weight $\mathbf{W} = -mg\mathbf{k}$ (where m is its mass and g is the acceleration due to gravity) and the normal reaction $\mathbf{N}$ from the surface. In order to describe the latter, we need to be able to write down a vector which is normal to the surface given by Equation (1.4) at any point (x, y, z) on the surface. One such vector, pointing inwards, is

$$-(ax + by)\mathbf{i} - (bx + cy)\mathbf{j} + \mathbf{k}.$$

We ask you to take this on trust.

Hence the normal reaction is

$$\mathbf{N} = C(-(ax + by)\mathbf{i} - (bx + cy)\mathbf{j} + \mathbf{k}),$$

where C is some positive quantity. Newton's second law then gives

$$m\ddot{\mathbf{r}} = \mathbf{N} + \mathbf{W}$$
$$= -C(ax + by)\mathbf{i} - C(bx + cy)\mathbf{j} + (C - mg)\mathbf{k},$$

where $\mathbf{r} = x\mathbf{i} + y\mathbf{j} + z\mathbf{k}$ is a position vector of a point on the surface, relative to the origin. Resolving in the $\mathbf{i}$-, $\mathbf{j}$- and $\mathbf{k}$-directions, we obtain

$$m\ddot{x} = -C(ax + by),$$
$$m\ddot{y} = -C(bx + cy),$$
$$m\ddot{z} = C - mg.$$

On eliminating the quantity C between these equations, and dividing through by m, we have

$$\ddot{x} = -(ax + by)(g + \ddot{z}) \quad \text{and} \quad \ddot{y} = -(bx + cy)(g + \ddot{z}).$$

For motions which do not move too far from the lowest point of the bowl, the vertical component of acceleration, $\ddot{z}$, will be small in magnitude compared with g, so to a good approximation the horizontal motion of the particle is governed by the pair of equations

$$\begin{cases} \ddot{x} = -g(ax + by), \\ \ddot{y} = -g(bx + cy). \end{cases}$$

This motion is what would be observed if you looked down onto the surface from some distance above it, as indicated in Figure 1.4.

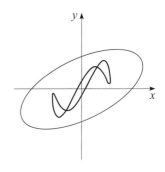

Figure 1.4

For example, if the surface is given by

$$z = 0.25x^2 - 0.4xy + 0.25y^2,$$

then the corresponding equations for horizontal motion (taking $10\,\text{m}\,\text{s}^{-2}$ as an approximation to g) are

$$\begin{cases} \ddot{x} = -5x + 4y, \\ \ddot{y} = 4x - 5y. \end{cases} \tag{1.5}$$

These differential equations are linear, constant-coefficient, homogeneous and second-order. You will see them solved, and the possible motions interpreted, in Subsection 4.2. As you will see, their solutions can be expressed in terms of the eigenvalues and eigenvectors of the matrix

$$\begin{bmatrix} -5 & 4 \\ 4 & -5 \end{bmatrix},$$

which arises from expressing the pair of equations (1.5) in matrix form as

$$\begin{bmatrix} \ddot{x} \\ \ddot{y} \end{bmatrix} = \begin{bmatrix} -5 & 4 \\ 4 & -5 \end{bmatrix} \begin{bmatrix} x \\ y \end{bmatrix}.$$

2 First-order homogeneous systems

In this unit we discuss systems of equations involving either two functions of time $x(t)$ and $y(t)$, or three functions of time $x(t)$, $y(t)$, $z(t)$ (which we abbreviate to x, y and z). For larger systems it is often convenient to denote the functions by subscripts, for example $x_1, x_2, \ldots, x_n$, but we shall not use this notation here because we wish to use subscripts later for another purpose. Throughout, we write

$$\mathbf{x} = \begin{bmatrix} x \\ y \end{bmatrix}, \quad \mathbf{x} = \begin{bmatrix} x \\ y \\ z \end{bmatrix} \quad \text{or} \quad \mathbf{x} = \begin{bmatrix} x_1 \\ x_2 \\ \vdots \\ x_n \end{bmatrix},$$

as appropriate.

In *Unit 9* you saw that any system of linear equations can be written in matrix form. For example, the equations

$$\begin{cases} 3x + 2y = 5, \\ x + 4y = 5, \end{cases}$$

can be written in matrix form as $\begin{bmatrix} 3 & 2 \\ 1 & 4 \end{bmatrix} \begin{bmatrix} x \\ y \end{bmatrix} = \begin{bmatrix} 5 \\ 5 \end{bmatrix}$, that is, as $\mathbf{Ax} = \mathbf{b}$,

where $\mathbf{A} = \begin{bmatrix} 3 & 2 \\ 1 & 4 \end{bmatrix}$, $\mathbf{x} = \begin{bmatrix} x \\ y \end{bmatrix}$ and $\mathbf{b} = \begin{bmatrix} 5 \\ 5 \end{bmatrix}$.

In a similar way, we can write systems of linear differential equations in matrix form. To see what is involved, consider the system

$$\begin{cases} \dot{x} = 3x + 2y + 5t, \\ \dot{y} = x + 4y + 5, \end{cases} \tag{2.1}$$

Here x and y are functions of t.

which can be written in matrix form as

$$\begin{bmatrix} \dot{x} \\ \dot{y} \end{bmatrix} = \begin{bmatrix} 3 & 2 \\ 1 & 4 \end{bmatrix} \begin{bmatrix} x \\ y \end{bmatrix} + \begin{bmatrix} 5t \\ 5 \end{bmatrix},$$

that is, as $\dot{\mathbf{x}} = \mathbf{Ax} + \mathbf{h}$, where $\mathbf{A} = \begin{bmatrix} 3 & 2 \\ 1 & 4 \end{bmatrix}$, $\mathbf{x} = \begin{bmatrix} x \\ y \end{bmatrix}$ and $\mathbf{h} = \begin{bmatrix} 5t \\ 5 \end{bmatrix}$.

Here $\mathbf{h}$ is generally a function of t, but $\mathbf{A}$ is constant.

Note that $\dot{\mathbf{x}} = [\dot{x} \quad \dot{y}]^T$.

We can similarly represent systems of three, or more, linear differential equations in matrix form. For example, the system

$$\begin{cases} \dot{x} = 3x + 2y + 2z + \;e^t, \\ \dot{y} = 2x + 2y \quad\;\; + 2e^t, \\ \dot{z} = 2x \quad\quad + 4z, \end{cases}$$

can be written in matrix form as $\dot{\mathbf{x}} = \mathbf{A}\mathbf{x} + \mathbf{h}$, where

$$\mathbf{A} = \begin{bmatrix} 3 & 2 & 2 \\ 2 & 2 & 0 \\ 2 & 0 & 4 \end{bmatrix}, \quad \mathbf{x} = \begin{bmatrix} x \\ y \\ z \end{bmatrix} \quad \text{and} \quad \mathbf{h} = \begin{bmatrix} e^t \\ 2e^t \\ 0 \end{bmatrix} = \begin{bmatrix} 1 \\ 2 \\ 0 \end{bmatrix} e^t. \quad (2.2)$$

Note that here $\dot{\mathbf{x}} = [\dot{x} \;\; \dot{y} \;\; \dot{z}]^T$.

Definition

A matrix equation of the form $\dot{\mathbf{x}} = \mathbf{A}\mathbf{x} + \mathbf{h}$ is said to be **homogeneous** if $\mathbf{h} = \mathbf{0}$, and **inhomogeneous** otherwise.

Note that in an inhomogeneous system, some, *but not all*, of the components of $\mathbf{h}$ may be 0.

For example, the system

$$\begin{bmatrix} \dot{x} \\ \dot{y} \end{bmatrix} = \begin{bmatrix} 2 & 3 \\ 2 & 1 \end{bmatrix} \begin{bmatrix} x \\ y \end{bmatrix}$$

is homogeneous, whereas systems (2.1) and (2.2) are inhomogeneous.

*Exercise 2.1

Write each of the following systems in matrix form, and classify it as homogeneous or inhomogeneous.

(a) $\begin{cases} \dot{x} = 2x + y + 1 \\ \dot{y} = \;\;x \quad\quad - 2 \end{cases}$ (b) $\begin{cases} \dot{x} = y \\ \dot{y} = t \end{cases}$ (c) $\begin{cases} \dot{x} = 5x \\ \dot{y} = \;\;x + 2y + \;\;z \\ \dot{z} = \;\;x + \;\;y + 2z \end{cases}$

In this section we present an algebraic method for solving homogeneous systems of linear first-order differential equations with constant coefficients. In Section 3 we show how this method can be adapted to inhomogeneous systems.

2.1 The eigenvalue method

Our intention is to develop a method for finding the general solution of any homogeneous system $\dot{\mathbf{x}} = \mathbf{A}\mathbf{x}$, however large, but we shall start with a 2×2 matrix $\mathbf{A}$. We begin by solving a system of differential equations using a non-matrix method, then we look at the same example again, but this time the emphasis is on the links to matrices.

Suppose that we wish to find a solution of the system

$$\begin{cases} \dot{x} = 3x + 2y, & (2.3) \\ \dot{y} = \;\;x + 4y. & (2.4) \end{cases}$$

Equation (2.4) gives $x = \dot{y} - 4y$, so $\dot{x} = \ddot{y} - 4\dot{y}$. Substituting into (2.3), we obtain

$$\ddot{y} - 4\dot{y} = 3(\dot{y} - 4y) + 2y,$$

which simplifies to give

$$\ddot{y} - 7\dot{y} + 10y = 0.$$

Using the methods of *Unit 3*, we see that the auxiliary equation is

$$\lambda^2 - 7\lambda + 10 = 0,$$

with roots $\lambda = 5$ and $\lambda = 2$, from which we have $y = \alpha e^{5t} + \beta e^{2t}$ (for arbitrary constants α and β). Having found y, we can substitute for y and $\dot{y}$ in Equation (2.4) and obtain $x = \alpha e^{5t} - 2\beta e^{2t}$, so the solution is

$$x = \alpha e^{5t} - 2\beta e^{2t} \quad \text{and} \quad y = \alpha e^{5t} + \beta e^{2t}.$$

Thus we have found the general solution of our original system of two equations, and this solution contains two arbitrary constants, as expected (one for each derivative).

Definitions

(a) The **general solution** of a system of n linear constant-coefficient first-order differential equations is a collection of all possible solutions of the system of equations.

(b) A **particular solution** of a system of n linear constant-coefficient first-order differential equations is a solution containing no arbitrary constants and satisfying given conditions.

Compare the definitions for the single equation cases in *Unit 2*, Section 1.

Usually, the general solution of a system of n first-order differential equations contains n arbitrary constants.

The above method does not extend very well to larger systems. However, notice that the above general solution is a linear combination of exponential terms of the form $e^{\lambda_1 t}$ and $e^{\lambda_2 t}$ (where in the above case $\lambda_1 = 5$ and $\lambda_2 = 2$). This suggests an alternative approach to solving such systems of equations. In the above case we have a solution $x = e^{5t}$, $y = e^{5t}$ corresponding to choosing $\alpha = 1$ and $\beta = 0$, and another solution $x = -2e^{2t}$, $y = e^{2t}$ corresponding to choosing $\alpha = 0$ and $\beta = 1$. Thus the general solution is a linear combination of much simpler solutions, and this suggests that we might be able to solve such systems by looking for these simpler solutions. So the idea is to search for solutions of the form $x = Ce^{\lambda t}$, $y = De^{\lambda t}$, and then form linear combinations of such solutions in order to find the general solution. There is only one minor problem — we have to convince ourselves that a linear combination of two solutions is itself a solution.

Suppose that $\mathbf{x}_1$ and $\mathbf{x}_2$ are solutions of the matrix equation $\dot{\mathbf{x}} = \mathbf{A}\mathbf{x}$; then $\dot{\mathbf{x}}_1 = \mathbf{A}\mathbf{x}_1$ and $\dot{\mathbf{x}}_2 = \mathbf{A}\mathbf{x}_2$. If α and β are arbitrary constants, then

$$\frac{d}{dt}(\alpha\mathbf{x}_1 + \beta\mathbf{x}_2) = \alpha\dot{\mathbf{x}}_1 + \beta\dot{\mathbf{x}}_2 = \alpha\mathbf{A}\mathbf{x}_1 + \beta\mathbf{A}\mathbf{x}_2 = \mathbf{A}(\alpha\mathbf{x}_1 + \beta\mathbf{x}_2),$$

so $\alpha\mathbf{x}_1 + \beta\mathbf{x}_2$ is indeed a solution. This is a particular case of a more general result known as the *principle of superposition* that you will meet later (in Theorem 3.1).

You met the principle of superposition in the case of second-order differential equations in *Unit 3*.

We apply the above technique in the following example.

Example 2.1

(a) For the following pair of equations, find a solution of the form $x = Ce^{\lambda t}$, $y = De^{\lambda t}$, and hence find the general solution:

$$\begin{cases} \dot{x} = 3x + 2y, \\ \dot{y} = x + 4y. \end{cases} \tag{2.5}$$

(b) Find the particular solution for which $x(0) = 1$ and $y(0) = 4$.

Solution

(a) We investigate possible solutions of the form

$$x = Ce^{\lambda t}, \quad y = De^{\lambda t},$$

where C and D are constants. Since $\dot{x} = C\lambda e^{\lambda t}$ and $\dot{y} = D\lambda e^{\lambda t}$, substituting the expressions for x and y into Equations (2.5) gives

$$\begin{cases} C\lambda e^{\lambda t} = 3Ce^{\lambda t} + 2De^{\lambda t}, \\ D\lambda e^{\lambda t} = Ce^{\lambda t} + 4De^{\lambda t}. \end{cases}$$

Cancelling the $e^{\lambda t}$ terms, we obtain the simultaneous linear equations

$$\begin{cases} C\lambda = 3C + 2D, \\ D\lambda = C + 4D, \end{cases}$$

which can be rearranged to give

$$\begin{cases} (3 - \lambda)C + 2D = 0, \\ C + (4 - \lambda)D = 0. \end{cases} \tag{2.6}$$

$e^{\lambda t}$ can never be zero.

This system of linear equations has non-zero solutions for C and D only if the determinant of the coefficient matrix is 0, that is, if

$$\begin{vmatrix} 3 - \lambda & 2 \\ 1 & 4 - \lambda \end{vmatrix} = 0.$$

See the summary of results for non-invertible matrices in *Unit 10*.

Expanding this determinant gives $(3 - \lambda)(4 - \lambda) - 2 = 0$, which simplifies to $\lambda^2 - 7\lambda + 10 = 0$, and we deduce that $\lambda = 5$ or $\lambda = 2$. We now substitute these values of λ in turn into Equations (2.6).

$\boxed{\lambda = 5}$ Equations (2.6) become

$$\begin{cases} -2C + 2D = 0, \\ C - D = 0, \end{cases}$$

which reduce to the single equation $C = D$. Choosing $C = D = 1$ provides us with the solution $x = e^{5t}$, $y = e^{5t}$.

You will see later that choosing any non-zero value will work.

$\boxed{\lambda = 2}$ Equations (2.6) become

$$\begin{cases} C + 2D = 0, \\ C + 2D = 0, \end{cases}$$

which reduce to the single equation $C = -2D$. Choosing $C = -2$ and $D = 1$ provides us with another solution, $x = -2e^{2t}$, $y = e^{2t}$.

In vector form, these solutions are

$$\mathbf{x}_1 = \begin{bmatrix} 1 \\ 1 \end{bmatrix} e^{5t} \quad \text{and} \quad \mathbf{x}_2 = \begin{bmatrix} -2 \\ 1 \end{bmatrix} e^{2t}.$$

(Notice that these solution vectors are linearly independent.)

Linear independence of vectors is defined in *Unit 10*.

Thus the general solution can be written in the form

$$\begin{bmatrix} x \\ y \end{bmatrix} = \alpha \begin{bmatrix} 1 \\ 1 \end{bmatrix} e^{5t} + \beta \begin{bmatrix} -2 \\ 1 \end{bmatrix} e^{2t}. \tag{2.7}$$

Here we are using the principle of superposition.

The fact that $\mathbf{x}_1$ and $\mathbf{x}_2$ are linearly independent ensures that this expression contains *two* arbitrary constants (in other words, one term cannot be absorbed into the other).

We shall not prove that this is the case.

(b) We seek the solution for which $x = 1$ and $y = 4$ when $t = 0$. Substituting these values into Equation (2.7) gives the simultaneous linear equations

$$\begin{cases} 1 = \alpha - 2\beta, \\ 4 = \alpha + \beta. \end{cases}$$

Solving these equations gives $\alpha = 3$, $\beta = 1$, so the required particular solution is $\begin{bmatrix} x \\ y \end{bmatrix} = \begin{bmatrix} 3 \\ 3 \end{bmatrix} e^{5t} + \begin{bmatrix} -2 \\ 1 \end{bmatrix} e^{2t}.$ ∎

You may have noticed that the method in Example 2.1(a) is similar to that used for calculating eigenvalues and eigenvectors in *Unit 10*. This similarity is not coincidental. Indeed, if we write the system of differential equations (2.5) in matrix form $\dot{\mathbf{x}} = \mathbf{A}\mathbf{x}$, that is,

$$\begin{bmatrix} \dot{x} \\ \dot{y} \end{bmatrix} = \begin{bmatrix} 3 & 2 \\ 1 & 4 \end{bmatrix} \begin{bmatrix} x \\ y \end{bmatrix},$$

then the numbers $\lambda = 5$ and $\lambda = 2$ arising in the general solution (2.7) turn out to be the *eigenvalues* of the coefficient matrix

$$\mathbf{A} = \begin{bmatrix} 3 & 2 \\ 1 & 4 \end{bmatrix},$$

and the vectors $[1 \ \ 1]^T$ and $[-2 \ \ 1]^T$ appearing in the general solution are corresponding *eigenvectors*.

You may like to check that

$$\mathbf{A}\begin{bmatrix} 1 \\ 1 \end{bmatrix} = 5 \begin{bmatrix} 1 \\ 1 \end{bmatrix}$$

and

$$\mathbf{A}\begin{bmatrix} -2 \\ 1 \end{bmatrix} = 2 \begin{bmatrix} -2 \\ 1 \end{bmatrix}.$$

To see why this happens, consider a general system of homogeneous linear constant-coefficient first-order differential equations $\dot{\mathbf{x}} = \mathbf{A}\mathbf{x}$, of any size. Suppose that there is a solution of the form $\mathbf{x} = \mathbf{v}e^{\lambda t}$, where $\mathbf{v}$ is a constant column vector. Then $\dot{\mathbf{x}} = \mathbf{v}\lambda e^{\lambda t}$, and the system of differential equations becomes $\mathbf{v}\lambda e^{\lambda t} = \mathbf{A}\mathbf{v}e^{\lambda t}$. Dividing the latter equation by $e^{\lambda t}$ (which is never 0) and rearranging, we have

$$\mathbf{A}\mathbf{v} = \lambda \mathbf{v}.$$

Thus $\mathbf{v}$ is an eigenvector of $\mathbf{A}$, and λ is the corresponding eigenvalue.

Conversely, we have the following result.

Theorem 2.1

If λ is an eigenvalue of the matrix $\mathbf{A}$ corresponding to an eigenvector $\mathbf{v}$, then $\mathbf{x} = \mathbf{v}e^{\lambda t}$ is a solution of the system of differential equations $\dot{\mathbf{x}} = \mathbf{A}\mathbf{x}$.

This theorem holds because if $\mathbf{x} = \mathbf{v}e^{\lambda t}$, then
$\dot{\mathbf{x}} = \lambda \mathbf{v}e^{\lambda t} = \mathbf{A}\mathbf{v}e^{\lambda t} = \mathbf{A}\mathbf{x}$.

Example 2.2

A particle moves in the (x, y)-plane in such a way that its position (x, y) at any time t satisfies the simultaneous differential equations

$$\begin{cases} \dot{x} = x + 4y, \\ \dot{y} = x - 2y. \end{cases}$$

Find the position (x, y) at time t if $x(0) = 2$ and $y(0) = 3$.

Solution

The matrix of coefficients is $\mathbf{A} = \begin{bmatrix} 1 & 4 \\ 1 & -2 \end{bmatrix}$. The eigenvectors of $\mathbf{A}$ are $[4 \ \ 1]^T$ with corresponding eigenvalue 2, and $[1 \ \ -1]^T$ with corresponding eigenvalue -3. The general solution is therefore

These eigenvectors and eigenvalues were found in *Unit 10*, Exercise 2.2(a).

$$\begin{bmatrix} x \\ y \end{bmatrix} = \alpha \begin{bmatrix} 4 \\ 1 \end{bmatrix} e^{2t} + \beta \begin{bmatrix} 1 \\ -1 \end{bmatrix} e^{-3t},$$

where α and β are arbitrary constants.

Since $x(0) = 2$ and $y(0) = 3$, we have, on putting $t = 0$,

$$\begin{cases} 2 = 4\alpha + \beta, \\ 3 = \ \ \alpha - \beta. \end{cases}$$

Solving these equations gives $\alpha = 1$, $\beta = -2$, so the required particular solution is

$$\begin{bmatrix} x \\ y \end{bmatrix} = \begin{bmatrix} 4 \\ 1 \end{bmatrix} e^{2t} + \begin{bmatrix} -2 \\ 2 \end{bmatrix} e^{-3t}. \quad \blacksquare$$

In the above example the particle starts at the point $(2, 3)$ when $t = 0$, and follows a certain path as t increases. The ultimate direction of this path is easy to determine, because e^{-3t} is small when t is large, so we have $[x \quad y]^T \simeq [4 \quad 1]^T e^{2t}$, that is, $x \simeq 4e^{2t}$, $y \simeq e^{2t}$, so $x \simeq 4y$ and $y \simeq 0.25x$. Thus the solution approaches the line $y = 0.25x$ as t increases.

*Exercise 2.2

Use the above method to solve the system of differential equations

$$\begin{cases} \dot{x} = 5x + 2y, \\ \dot{y} = 2x + 5y, \end{cases}$$

given that $x = 4$ and $y = 0$ when $t = 0$.

The eigenvalues of $\begin{bmatrix} 5 & 2 \\ 2 & 5 \end{bmatrix}$ are 7 and 3, corresponding to eigenvectors $[1 \quad 1]^T$ and $[1 \quad -1]^T$, respectively.

The above method works equally well for larger systems. For example, consider the following example of a system of three differential equations.

Example 2.3

Find the general solution of the system of differential equations

$$\begin{cases} \dot{x} = 3x + 2y + 2z, \\ \dot{y} = 2x + 2y, \\ \dot{z} = 2x \qquad + 4z. \end{cases}$$

Solution

The matrix of coefficients is $\mathbf{A} = \begin{bmatrix} 3 & 2 & 2 \\ 2 & 2 & 0 \\ 2 & 0 & 4 \end{bmatrix}$. The eigenvectors of $\mathbf{A}$ are $[2 \quad 1 \quad 2]^T$, $[1 \quad 2 \quad -2]^T$ and $[-2 \quad 2 \quad 1]^T$, corresponding to the eigenvalues $\lambda_1 = 6$, $\lambda_2 = 3$ and $\lambda_3 = 0$, respectively. The general solution is therefore

These eigenvectors and eigenvalues were found in *Unit 10*, Example 3.1.

$$\begin{bmatrix} x \\ y \\ z \end{bmatrix} = \alpha \begin{bmatrix} 2 \\ 1 \\ 2 \end{bmatrix} e^{6t} + \beta \begin{bmatrix} 1 \\ 2 \\ -2 \end{bmatrix} e^{3t} + \gamma \begin{bmatrix} -2 \\ 2 \\ 1 \end{bmatrix},$$

where α, β and γ are arbitrary constants. $\quad \blacksquare$

Note that the last term on the right-hand side corresponds to the term in $e^{\lambda_3 t} = e^{0t} = 1$.

*Exercise 2.3

A particle moves in three-dimensional space in such a way that its position (x, y, z) at any time t satisfies the simultaneous differential equations

$$\begin{cases} \dot{x} = 5x, \\ \dot{y} = x + 2y + z, \\ \dot{z} = x + y + 2z. \end{cases}$$

Find the position (x, y, z) at time t if $x(0) = 4$, $y(0) = 6$ and $z(0) = 0$.

The eigenvectors of $\begin{bmatrix} 5 & 0 & 0 \\ 1 & 2 & 1 \\ 1 & 1 & 2 \end{bmatrix}$ are $[2 \quad 1 \quad 1]^T$, $[0 \quad 1 \quad 1]^T$ and $[0 \quad 1 \quad -1]^T$, corresponding to eigenvalues 5, 3 and 1, respectively.

The above method can be used to solve any system $\dot{\mathbf{x}} = \mathbf{A}\mathbf{x}$ of linear constant-coefficient first-order differential equations for which the matrix $\mathbf{A}$ has distinct real eigenvalues. We summarize the procedure as follows.

Procedure 2.1   Distinct real eigenvalues

To solve a system of linear constant-coefficient first-order differential equations $\dot{\mathbf{x}} = \mathbf{A}\mathbf{x}$, where $\mathbf{A}$ is an $n \times n$ matrix with distinct real eigenvalues:

(a) find the eigenvalues $\lambda_1, \lambda_2, \ldots, \lambda_n$ and a corresponding set of eigenvectors $\mathbf{v}_1, \mathbf{v}_2, \ldots, \mathbf{v}_n$;

(b) write down the general solution in the form

$$\mathbf{x} = C_1 \mathbf{v}_1 e^{\lambda_1 t} + C_2 \mathbf{v}_2 e^{\lambda_2 t} + \cdots + C_n \mathbf{v}_n e^{\lambda_n t},$$

where $C_1, C_2, \ldots, C_n$ are arbitrary constants.

In the next subsection we investigate what happens when the eigenvalues of the matrix $\mathbf{A}$ are not distinct, or when they are complex numbers.

2.2   Two variations

The above method relies on the fact that eigenvectors corresponding to distinct eigenvalues are linearly independent, which ensures that the solution given in Procedure 2.1(b) contains n arbitrary constants and so is the required general solution. If the eigenvalues are not distinct, then we may not be able to write down n linearly independent eigenvectors, so when we attempt to construct the solution for $\mathbf{x}$ given in Procedure 2.1(b), we shall find that it contains too few constants. In the following example we are able to find a sufficient number of eigenvectors in spite of the fact that an eigenvalue is repeated.

This result is not obvious; we ask you to take it on trust.

Example 2.4

Find the general solution of the system of differential equations

$$\begin{cases} \dot{x} = 5x + 3z, \\ \dot{y} = 3x + 2y + 3z, \\ \dot{z} = -6x - 4z. \end{cases}$$

Solution

The matrix of coefficients is $\mathbf{A} = \begin{bmatrix} 5 & 0 & 3 \\ 3 & 2 & 3 \\ -6 & 0 & -4 \end{bmatrix}$. Using the techniques of *Unit 10*, we can calculate the eigenvalues of $\mathbf{A}$. They are $\lambda = -1$ and $\lambda = 2$ (repeated), corresponding to eigenvectors $[1 \quad 1 \quad -2]^T$ and $[0 \quad 1 \quad 0]^T$, respectively.

You need to understand what goes wrong before we show you how to put it right, so suppose that we try to follow Procedure 2.1(b), and let

$$\mathbf{x} = C_1 [1 \quad 1 \quad -2]^T e^{-t} + C_2 [0 \quad 1 \quad 0]^T e^{2t}.$$

This is certainly a solution, but it is not the general solution because it contains only two arbitrary constants and we require three.

The answer to our difficulty lies in our method of calculating the eigenvectors when the eigenvalue is repeated. The eigenvector equations are

$$\begin{cases} (5 - \lambda)x + 3z = 0, \\ 3x + (2 - \lambda)y + 3z = 0, \\ -6x + (-4 - \lambda)z = 0. \end{cases}$$

$\boxed{\lambda = 2}$ The eigenvector equations become

$$3x + 3z = 0, \quad 3x + 3z = 0 \quad \text{and} \quad -6x - 6z = 0.$$

All three equations give $z = -x$, but there is no restriction on y. It follows that any vector of the form $[k \quad l \quad -k]^T$ is an eigenvector corresponding to $\lambda = 2$. (In particular, the vector $[0 \quad 1 \quad 0]^T$ mentioned above is an eigenvector corresponding to $\lambda = 2$.)

Here k and l are any real numbers, not both zero.

Remember that we need to find three linearly independent eigenvectors, and it might appear that we have found only two, namely $[1 \quad 1 \quad -2]^T$ corresponding to $\lambda = -1$ and $[k \quad l \quad -k]^T$ corresponding to $\lambda = 2$. However, the numbers k and l are arbitrary, so there are infinitely many vectors in the second category; our task is to choose two that are linearly independent. If we write

$$[k \quad l \quad -k]^T = k[1 \quad 0 \quad -1]^T + l[0 \quad 1 \quad 0]^T,$$

then we see at once that $[1 \quad 0 \quad -1]^T$ and $[0 \quad 1 \quad 0]^T$ are suitable candidates.

Thus

$$\begin{bmatrix} x \\ y \\ z \end{bmatrix} = C_1 \begin{bmatrix} 1 \\ 1 \\ -2 \end{bmatrix} e^{-t} + \left(C_2 \begin{bmatrix} 1 \\ 0 \\ -1 \end{bmatrix} + C_3 \begin{bmatrix} 0 \\ 1 \\ 0 \end{bmatrix} \right) e^{2t},$$

where C_1, C_2 and C_3 are arbitrary constants, is a solution, by Theorem 2.1 and the principle of superposition. The fact that the three eigenvectors are linearly independent ensures that there are three arbitrary constants, and hence that this is the general solution.   ∎

Exercise 2.4

A particle moves in three-dimensional space in such a way that its position (x, y, z) at any time t satisfies the simultaneous differential equations

$$\begin{cases} \dot{x} = z, \\ \dot{y} = y, \\ \dot{z} = x. \end{cases}$$

Find the position (x, y, z) at time t if $x(0) = 7$, $y(0) = 5$ and $z(0) = 1$.

The eigenvalues of
$$\begin{bmatrix} 0 & 0 & 1 \\ 0 & 1 & 0 \\ 1 & 0 & 0 \end{bmatrix}$$
are $\lambda = -1$, corresponding to an eigenvector $[1 \quad 0 \quad -1]^T$, and $\lambda = 1$ (repeated), corresponding to an eigenvector $[k \quad l \quad k]^T$.

In Example 2.4 we were able to determine the general solution even though there were only two distinct eigenvalues. This is because we were able to find three linearly independent eigenvectors. We now consider a situation in which there are too few linearly independent eigenvectors.

Suppose that we try to apply the above method to find the general solution of the system of differential equations

$$\begin{cases} \dot{x} = x, \\ \dot{y} = x + y. \end{cases}$$

The matrix of coefficients is

$$\mathbf{A} = \begin{bmatrix} 1 & 0 \\ 1 & 1 \end{bmatrix},$$

Since $\mathbf{A}$ is a triangular matrix, the eigenvalues are simply the diagonal entries.

and the eigenvalues are $\lambda = 1$ (repeated). We now substitute this eigenvalue into the eigenvector equations

$$(1 - \lambda)x = 0$$

and

$$x + (1 - \lambda)y = 0.$$

$\boxed{\lambda = 1}$ The eigenvector equations become $0 = 0$ and $x = 0$. The first equation tells us nothing; the second equation gives $x = 0$, but imposes no restriction on y. It follows that $[0 \quad k]^T$ is an eigenvector corresponding to $\lambda = 1$, for any non-zero value of k. Thus, choosing $k = 1$, we have the solution

$$\begin{bmatrix} x \\ y \end{bmatrix} = C \begin{bmatrix} 0 \\ 1 \end{bmatrix} e^t.$$

But this is clearly not the general solution, since it has only one arbitrary constant instead of two; the procedure has failed.

Before extending our matrix procedure to cover the above case, it is illuminating to solve the given system of differential equations directly. The first equation, $\dot{x} = x$, has solution $x = De^t$, where D is an arbitrary constant. Substituting this solution into the second equation gives $\dot{y} = y + De^t$, which can be solved by the integrating factor method of *Unit 2* to give $y = Ce^t + Dte^t$. Thus the solution for which we are searching is

$$\begin{bmatrix} x \\ y \end{bmatrix} = C \underbrace{\begin{bmatrix} 0 \\ 1 \end{bmatrix} e^t}_{\text{eigenvector}} + D \underbrace{\begin{bmatrix} 1 \\ t \end{bmatrix} e^t}_{\text{notice the } t \text{ here}},$$

There are *two* arbitrary constants since $[0 \quad 1]^T$ and $[1 \quad t]^T$ are linearly independent.

and this is the general solution since it contains two arbitrary constants.

The above solution provides a clue to a general method. The origins of the first term on the right-hand side are clear — it corresponds to an eigenvector — but let us look more closely at the second term on the right-hand side. We have

$$D \begin{bmatrix} 1 \\ t \end{bmatrix} e^t = D \underbrace{\begin{bmatrix} 0 \\ 1 \end{bmatrix}}_{\text{eigenvector}} te^t + D \begin{bmatrix} 1 \\ 0 \end{bmatrix} e^t = D \left(\begin{bmatrix} 0 \\ 1 \end{bmatrix} t + \begin{bmatrix} 1 \\ 0 \end{bmatrix} \right) e^t.$$

This suggests that if we wish to solve the system $\dot{\mathbf{x}} = \mathbf{A}\mathbf{x}$ for which $\mathbf{A}$ has a repeated eigenvalue λ, giving rise to too few eigenvectors, it may be helpful to search for solutions of the form

$$\mathbf{x} = (\mathbf{v}t + \mathbf{b})e^{\lambda t},$$

where $\mathbf{v}$ is an eigenvector corresponding to λ, and $\mathbf{b}$ is to be determined.

Let us suppose that our system has a solution of this form, and examine the consequences. Substituting this proposed solution into $\dot{\mathbf{x}} = \mathbf{A}\mathbf{x}$ gives

$$\lambda(\mathbf{v}t + \mathbf{b})e^{\lambda t} + \mathbf{v}e^{\lambda t} = \mathbf{A}(\mathbf{v}t + \mathbf{b})e^{\lambda t},$$

or, on division by $e^{\lambda t}$ and rearranging,

$$(\mathbf{A}\mathbf{v} - \lambda\mathbf{v})t + (\mathbf{A}\mathbf{b} - \lambda\mathbf{b}) = \mathbf{v}.$$

The first term disappears, because $\mathbf{v}$ is an eigenvector of $\mathbf{A}$ corresponding to the eigenvalue λ (so $\mathbf{A}\mathbf{v} = \lambda\mathbf{v}$), and we are left with $(\mathbf{A} - \lambda\mathbf{I})\mathbf{b} = \mathbf{v}$. If this equation can be solved for $\mathbf{b}$, then we shall have found a solution of the required form.

For example, in the above case we had $\mathbf{A} = \begin{bmatrix} 1 & 0 \\ 1 & 1 \end{bmatrix}$ and $\lambda = 1$, so

$$\mathbf{A} - \lambda\mathbf{I} = \mathbf{A} - \mathbf{I} = \begin{bmatrix} 0 & 0 \\ 1 & 0 \end{bmatrix} \quad \text{and} \quad \mathbf{v} = \begin{bmatrix} 0 \\ 1 \end{bmatrix}.$$

Thus, if $\mathbf{b} = [b_1 \quad b_2]^T$, the equation $(\mathbf{A} - \lambda\mathbf{I})\mathbf{b} = \mathbf{v}$ becomes

$$\begin{bmatrix} 0 & 0 \\ 1 & 0 \end{bmatrix} \begin{bmatrix} b_1 \\ b_2 \end{bmatrix} = \begin{bmatrix} 0 \\ 1 \end{bmatrix}.$$

Any solution of this equation for b_1 and b_2 is acceptable. In fact, this equation gives just $b_1 = 1$ (with no condition on b_2), and we can take $\mathbf{b}$ to be $[1 \quad 0]^T$, giving the solution $\left(\begin{bmatrix} 0 \\ 1 \end{bmatrix} t + \begin{bmatrix} 1 \\ 0 \end{bmatrix} \right) e^t = \begin{bmatrix} 1 \\ t \end{bmatrix} e^t$.

The value of b_2 is irrelevant, since it is absorbed into the arbitrary constant C.

Now we have two linearly independent solutions of our system of differential equations, namely $[0 \quad 1]^T e^t$ and $[1 \quad t]^T e^t$, so the general solution is

$$\begin{bmatrix} x \\ y \end{bmatrix} = C \underbrace{\begin{bmatrix} 0 \\ 1 \end{bmatrix} e^t}_{\substack{\text{solution} \\ \mathbf{v}e^{\lambda t}}} + D \underbrace{\begin{bmatrix} 1 \\ t \end{bmatrix} e^t}_{\substack{\text{solution} \\ (\mathbf{v}t+\mathbf{b})e^{\lambda t}}},$$

as we found before.

Procedure 2.2   Repeated real eigenvalues

To solve a system of linear constant-coefficient first-order differential equations $\dot{\mathbf{x}} = \mathbf{A}\mathbf{x}$, where $\mathbf{A}$ is an $n \times n$ matrix with some repeated real eigenvalues (where any eigenvalue is repeated at most once), do the following.

(a) For the non-repeated eigenvalues $\lambda_1, \lambda_2, \ldots, \lambda_k$ and corresponding eigenvectors $\mathbf{v}_1, \mathbf{v}_2, \ldots, \mathbf{v}_k$, write down the set S of solutions of the form $\mathbf{v}_i e^{\lambda_i t}$.

(b) Examine the eigenvector equations corresponding to each repeated eigenvalue, and attempt to construct two linearly independent eigenvectors to add two solutions to S.

   If this fails, then for each repeated eigenvalue λ_i that gives rise to only one eigenvector $\mathbf{v}_i$, construct a solution $(\mathbf{v}_i t + \mathbf{b}_i)e^{\lambda_i t}$ for which $(\mathbf{A} - \lambda_i \mathbf{I})\mathbf{b}_i = \mathbf{v}_i$, and add it and the solution $\mathbf{v}_i e^{\lambda_i t}$ to the set S.

(c) If S contains n linearly independent solutions, then the general solution of the system of differential equations is an arbitrary linear combination of the solutions in S.

This procedure covers only the case where an eigenvalue is repeated once. It could be extended to cover the case where an eigenvalue is repeated several times, but we choose not to generalize.

This arbitrary linear combination will contain n arbitrary constants.

---

*Exercise 2.5

A particle moves in the plane in such a way that its position (x, y) at any time t satisfies the simultaneous differential equations
$$\begin{cases} \dot{x} = 2x + 3y, \\ \dot{y} = \phantom{2x + {}} 2y. \end{cases}$$
Find the position (x, y) of the particle at time t if its position is $(4, 3)$ at time $t = 0$.

So far, all our examples and exercises have involved *real* eigenvalues. We now investigate what happens when the characteristic equation has at least one complex root (giving a **complex eigenvalue**). In fact, since the arguments leading to Procedure 2.1 did not rely on the eigenvalues being real, Procedure 2.1 also applies whenever the eigenvalues are distinct — it does not matter whether they are real or complex. However, using Procedure 2.1 for complex eigenvalues leads to a complex-valued solution involving complex arbitrary constants. For a system of differential equations with real coefficients, we would generally want real-valued solutions. So here we see how to adapt Procedure 2.1 to obtain a real-valued solution when some of the eigenvalues are complex.

For matrices $\mathbf{A}$ which are real (ours always are), complex roots occur as complex conjugate pairs $a \pm bi$.

We begin with an example which is simple enough for us to be able to apply a direct method in order to find the general solution. We then solve the system again by applying a matrix method based on Procedure 2.1, which has the advantage that it can be extended to larger systems of equations.

Example 2.5

Solve the system of differential equations

$$\begin{cases} \dot{x} = y, \\ \dot{y} = -x. \end{cases} \tag{2.8}$$

Solution

If we differentiate the first equation, giving $\ddot{x} = \dot{y}$, and substitute for $\dot{y}$ in the second equation, we obtain $\ddot{x} = -x$, so $\ddot{x} + x = 0$. This second-order differential equation has auxiliary equation $\lambda^2 + 1 = 0$, so the general solution is $x = C\cos t + D\sin t$. Therefore $y = \dot{x} = -C\sin t + D\cos t$. Thus the general solution of Equations (2.8) is

See Unit 3.

$$\begin{bmatrix} x \\ y \end{bmatrix} = C \begin{bmatrix} \cos t \\ -\sin t \end{bmatrix} + D \begin{bmatrix} \sin t \\ \cos t \end{bmatrix}.$$

Note that if we want *real* solutions, then C and D must be real.

Now we shall obtain the same general solution using a matrix method based on Procedure 2.1.

The matrix of coefficients is

$$\mathbf{A} = \begin{bmatrix} 0 & 1 \\ -1 & 0 \end{bmatrix}.$$

The characteristic equation is $\lambda^2 + 1 = 0$, giving the complex eigenvalues $\lambda = i$ and $\lambda = -i$. The eigenvector equations are

$$-\lambda x + y = 0 \quad \text{and} \quad -x - \lambda y = 0.$$

$\boxed{\lambda = i}$ The eigenvector equations become

$$-ix + y = 0 \quad \text{and} \quad -x - iy = 0,$$

Note that the first equation is i times the second equation.

which reduce to the single equation $y = ix$. It follows that $\begin{bmatrix} 1 & i \end{bmatrix}^T$ is an eigenvector corresponding to $\lambda = i$.

$\boxed{\lambda = -i}$ The eigenvector equations become

$$ix + y = 0 \quad \text{and} \quad -x + iy = 0,$$

Here, the second equation is i times the first equation.

which reduce to the single equation $y = -ix$. It follows that $\begin{bmatrix} 1 & -i \end{bmatrix}^T$ is an eigenvector corresponding to $\lambda = -i$.

Now since Procedure 2.1 works for complex as well as real eigenvalues, the general solution of the given system of differential equations can be written as

Note that the λ and $\mathbf{v}$ occur in complex conjugate pairs. (The complex conjugate of a vector $\mathbf{v}$ is the vector $\overline{\mathbf{v}}$ whose elements are the complex conjugates of the respective elements of $\mathbf{v}$.)

$$\begin{bmatrix} x \\ y \end{bmatrix} = C \begin{bmatrix} 1 \\ i \end{bmatrix} e^{it} + D \begin{bmatrix} 1 \\ -i \end{bmatrix} e^{-it},$$

where C and D are arbitrary *complex* constants.

If we are interested only in *real-valued* solutions, then we need to rewrite the above solution in such a way as to eliminate the terms involving i. We do this by using Euler's formula, which gives

$$e^{it} = \cos t + i\sin t \quad \text{and} \quad e^{-it} = \cos t - i\sin t$$

You saw Euler's formula in *Unit 1*. It was used in a similar way in *Unit 3*.

(replacing t by $-t$ and using $\cos(-t) = \cos t$ and $\sin(-t) = -\sin t$).

Then

$$x = C(\cos t + i \sin t) + D(\cos t - i \sin t)$$
$$= (C + D) \cos t + (Ci - Di) \sin t,$$

$$y = Ci(\cos t + i \sin t) - Di(\cos t - i \sin t)$$
$$= (Ci - Di) \cos t - (C + D) \sin t.$$

Writing $\alpha = C + D$ and $\beta = Ci - Di$, we have

$$x = \alpha \cos t + \beta \sin t \quad \text{and} \quad y = \beta \cos t - \alpha \sin t.$$

Since C and D are arbitrary
complex constants, so are α
and β.

Thus we can write the general solution of Equations (2.8) as

$$\begin{bmatrix} x \\ y \end{bmatrix} = \alpha \begin{bmatrix} \cos t \\ -\sin t \end{bmatrix} + \beta \begin{bmatrix} \sin t \\ \cos t \end{bmatrix},$$

where α and β are arbitrary complex constants. For real-valued solutions we must use only real values for α and β. ∎

In Example 2.5, notice that

$$\begin{bmatrix} 1 \\ i \end{bmatrix} e^{it} = \begin{bmatrix} \cos t + i \sin t \\ -\sin t + i \cos t \end{bmatrix} = \begin{bmatrix} \cos t \\ -\sin t \end{bmatrix} + i \begin{bmatrix} \sin t \\ \cos t \end{bmatrix},$$

so

$$\text{Re} \left(\begin{bmatrix} 1 \\ i \end{bmatrix} e^{it} \right) = \begin{bmatrix} \cos t \\ -\sin t \end{bmatrix} \quad \text{and} \quad \text{Im} \left(\begin{bmatrix} 1 \\ i \end{bmatrix} e^{it} \right) = \begin{bmatrix} \sin t \\ \cos t \end{bmatrix},$$

and these are the expressions that appear in our final solution.

In general, complex eigenvalues of a real matrix $\mathbf{A}$ occur in complex conjugate pairs λ and $\overline{\lambda}$, with corresponding complex conjugate eigenvectors $\mathbf{v}$ and $\overline{\mathbf{v}}$. These give rise to two complex solutions, $\mathbf{v}e^{\lambda t}$ and $\overline{\mathbf{v}}e^{\overline{\lambda} t}$, which contribute the terms

$$C\mathbf{v}e^{\lambda t} + D\overline{\mathbf{v}}e^{\overline{\lambda} t}$$

to the general solution (where C and D are arbitrary complex constants). To obtain a real-valued solution, this expression can be rewritten in the form

$$\alpha \, \text{Re}(\mathbf{v}e^{\lambda t}) + \beta \, \text{Im}(\mathbf{v}e^{\lambda t}),$$

The components of $\text{Re}(\mathbf{v}e^{\lambda t})$
and $\text{Im}(\mathbf{v}e^{\lambda t})$ are sinusoidal
functions.

where α and β are arbitrary real constants.

Procedure 2.3   Complex eigenvalues

To obtain a real-valued solution of a system of linear constant-coefficient first-order differential equations $\dot{\mathbf{x}} = \mathbf{A}\mathbf{x}$, where $\mathbf{A}$ is an $n \times n$ matrix with distinct eigenvalues, some of which are complex (occurring in complex conjugate pairs λ and $\overline{\lambda}$, with corresponding complex conjugate eigenvectors $\mathbf{v}$ and $\overline{\mathbf{v}}$), do the following.

If any of the real eigenvalues
are repeated, this procedure
will need to be adapted as in
Procedure 2.2.

(a) Find the eigenvalues $\lambda_1, \lambda_2, \ldots, \lambda_n$ and a corresponding set of eigenvectors $\mathbf{v}_1, \mathbf{v}_2, \ldots, \mathbf{v}_n$.

(b) Write down the general solution in the form

$$\mathbf{x} = C_1 \mathbf{v}_1 e^{\lambda_1 t} + C_2 \mathbf{v}_2 e^{\lambda_2 t} + \cdots + C_n \mathbf{v}_n e^{\lambda_n t},$$

where $C_1, C_2, \ldots, C_n$ are arbitrary complex constants.

(c) Replace the terms $\mathbf{v}e^{\lambda t}$ and $\overline{\mathbf{v}}e^{\overline{\lambda} t}$ appearing in the general solution with $\text{Re}(\mathbf{v}e^{\lambda t})$ and $\text{Im}(\mathbf{v}e^{\lambda t})$.

The general solution will then be real-valued for real $C_1, C_2, \ldots, C_n$.

Example 2.6

Solve the system of differential equations

$$\begin{cases} \dot{x} = 3x - y, \\ \dot{y} = 2x + y, \end{cases}$$

given that $x = 3$ and $y = 1$ when $t = 0$.

Solution

The matrix of coefficients is

$$\mathbf{A} = \begin{bmatrix} 3 & -1 \\ 2 & 1 \end{bmatrix}.$$

The eigenvalues of $\mathbf{A}$ are $\lambda = 2 + i$ and $\overline{\lambda} = 2 - i$, corresponding to eigenvectors $\mathbf{v} = [1 \quad 1 - i]^T$ and $\overline{\mathbf{v}} = [1 \quad 1 + i]^T$, respectively. So the general solution can be written as

$$\mathbf{x} = C\mathbf{v}e^{\lambda t} + D\overline{\mathbf{v}}e^{\overline{\lambda} t} = C \begin{bmatrix} 1 \\ 1 - i \end{bmatrix} e^{(2+i)t} + D \begin{bmatrix} 1 \\ 1 + i \end{bmatrix} e^{(2-i)t},$$

where C and D are arbitrary complex constants.

To obtain a real-valued solution, we follow Procedure 2.3 and write

$$\begin{aligned} \mathbf{v}e^{\lambda t} &= \begin{bmatrix} 1 \\ 1 - i \end{bmatrix} e^{(2+i)t} \\ &= e^{2t} \begin{bmatrix} 1 \\ 1 - i \end{bmatrix} e^{it} \\ &= e^{2t} \begin{bmatrix} 1 \\ 1 - i \end{bmatrix} (\cos t + i \sin t) \\ &= e^{2t} \begin{bmatrix} \cos t + i \sin t \\ (1 - i)(\cos t + i \sin t) \end{bmatrix} \\ &= e^{2t} \begin{bmatrix} \cos t + i \sin t \\ (\cos t + \sin t) + i(\sin t - \cos t) \end{bmatrix} \\ &= \underbrace{e^{2t} \begin{bmatrix} \cos t \\ \cos t + \sin t \end{bmatrix}}_{\text{real part}} + \underbrace{i\, e^{2t} \begin{bmatrix} \sin t \\ \sin t - \cos t \end{bmatrix}}_{\text{imaginary part}}. \end{aligned}$$

The real-valued general solution of the given system of equations is therefore

$$\begin{bmatrix} x \\ y \end{bmatrix} = \alpha\, e^{2t} \begin{bmatrix} \cos t \\ \cos t + \sin t \end{bmatrix} + \beta e^{2t} \begin{bmatrix} \sin t \\ \sin t - \cos t \end{bmatrix}, \tag{2.9}$$

where α and β are arbitrary real constants.

In order to find the required particular solution, we substitute $x = 3$, $y = 1$ and $t = 0$ into Equation (2.9), to obtain

$$\begin{bmatrix} 3 \\ 1 \end{bmatrix} = \alpha \begin{bmatrix} 1 \\ 1 \end{bmatrix} + \beta \begin{bmatrix} 0 \\ -1 \end{bmatrix},$$

so $3 = \alpha$ and $1 = \alpha - \beta$, giving $\beta = 2$, and the solution is therefore

$$\begin{bmatrix} x \\ y \end{bmatrix} = \begin{bmatrix} e^{2t}(3 \cos t + 2 \sin t) \\ e^{2t}(\cos t + 5 \sin t) \end{bmatrix}. \quad \blacksquare$$

We shall ask you to solve systems of linear constant-coefficient first-order differential equations by hand only for 2×2 and 3×3 coefficient matrices, but you may well encounter larger systems when you use the computer algebra package for the course.

End-of-section Exercises

Exercise 2.6

Using the eigenvalues and eigenvectors given, find the real-valued solution of each of the following systems of differential equations, given that $x = y = 1$ when $t = 0$.

(a) $\begin{cases} \dot{x} = 2x + 3y \\ \dot{y} = 2x + y \end{cases}$

(The matrix $\begin{bmatrix} 2 & 3 \\ 2 & 1 \end{bmatrix}$ has eigenvalues 4 and -1, corresponding to eigenvectors $[3 \quad 2]^T$ and $[1 \quad -1]^T$, respectively.)

(b) $\begin{cases} \dot{x} = -3x - 2y \\ \dot{y} = 4x + y \end{cases}$

(The matrix $\begin{bmatrix} -3 & -2 \\ 4 & 1 \end{bmatrix}$ has eigenvalues $-1 + 2i$ and $-1 - 2i$, corresponding to eigenvectors $[1 \quad -1 - i]^T$ and $[1 \quad -1 + i]^T$, respectively.)

Exercise 2.7

Write down the general solution of each of the following systems of equations.

(a) $\begin{cases} \dot{x} = x - z \\ \dot{y} = x + 2y + z \\ \dot{z} = 2x + 2y + 3z \end{cases}$

(The matrix $\begin{bmatrix} 1 & 0 & -1 \\ 1 & 2 & 1 \\ 2 & 2 & 3 \end{bmatrix}$ has eigenvalues 1, 2 and 3, corresponding to eigenvectors $[1 \quad -1 \quad 0]^T$, $[-2 \quad 1 \quad 2]^T$ and $[1 \quad -1 \quad -2]^T$, respectively.)

(b) $\begin{cases} \dot{x} = 5x - 6y - 6z \\ \dot{y} = -x + 4y + 2z \\ \dot{z} = 3x - 6y - 4z \end{cases}$

(The matrix $\begin{bmatrix} 5 & -6 & -6 \\ -1 & 4 & 2 \\ 3 & -6 & -4 \end{bmatrix}$ has eigenvalues 1 and 2 (repeated), with corresponding eigenvectors $[3 \quad -1 \quad 3]^T$ and $[2l + 2k \quad l \quad k]^T$, respectively, where k and l are arbitrary real numbers, not both zero.)

Exercise 2.8

Find the general real-valued solution of the following system of equations.

$\begin{cases} \dot{x} = x + z \\ \dot{y} = y \\ \dot{z} = -x + y \end{cases}$

Find the solution for which $x = y = 1$ and $z = 2$ when $t = 0$.

(The matrix $\begin{bmatrix} 1 & 0 & 1 \\ 0 & 1 & 0 \\ -1 & 1 & 0 \end{bmatrix}$ has eigenvalues 1, $\lambda = \frac{1}{2} + \frac{\sqrt{3}}{2}i$ and $\bar{\lambda} = \frac{1}{2} - \frac{\sqrt{3}}{2}i$, corresponding to the eigenvectors $[1 \quad 1 \quad 0]^T$, $\mathbf{v} = [1 \quad 0 \quad -\frac{1}{2} + \frac{\sqrt{3}}{2}i]^T$ and $\bar{\mathbf{v}} = [1 \quad 0 \quad -\frac{1}{2} - \frac{\sqrt{3}}{2}i]^T$, respectively.)

3 First-order inhomogeneous systems

In the previous section you saw how to solve a system of differential equations of the form $\dot{\mathbf{x}} = \mathbf{A}\mathbf{x}$, where $\mathbf{A}$ is a given constant-coefficient matrix. We now extend our discussion to systems of the form

$$\dot{\mathbf{x}} = \mathbf{A}\mathbf{x} + \mathbf{h}(t),$$

where $\mathbf{h}(t)$ is a given function of t. Our method involves finding a 'particular integral' for the system, and mirrors the approach we took for inhomogeneous second-order differential equations in *Unit 3*.

Here we write $\mathbf{h}(t)$ to emphasize that $\mathbf{h}$ is a function of t. Henceforth we shall abbreviate this to $\mathbf{h}$.

3.1 A basic result

In *Unit 3* we discussed inhomogeneous differential equations such as

$$\frac{d^2y}{dx^2} + 9y = 2e^{3x} + 18x + 18. \tag{3.1}$$

See *Unit 3*, Example 2.8.

To solve such an equation, we proceed as follows.

(a) We first find the *complementary function* of the corresponding homogeneous equation

$$\frac{d^2y}{dx^2} + 9y = 0,$$

which is

$$y_{\mathrm{c}} = C_1 \cos 3x + C_2 \sin 3x,$$

where C_1 and C_2 are arbitrary constants.

(b) We then find a *particular integral* of the inhomogeneous equation (3.1),

$$y_{\mathrm{p}} = \tfrac{1}{9}e^{3x} + 2x + 2.$$

The general solution y of the original equation is then obtained by adding these two functions (using the principle of superposition) to give

$$y = y_{\mathrm{c}} + y_{\mathrm{p}} = (C_1 \cos 3x + C_2 \sin 3x) + \left(\tfrac{1}{9}e^{3x} + 2x + 2\right). \tag{3.2}$$

A similar situation holds for systems of linear first-order differential equations. For example, in order to find the general solution of the inhomogeneous system

$$\begin{cases} \dot{x} = 3x + 2y + 4e^{3t}, \\ \dot{y} = x + 4y - e^{3t}, \end{cases} \tag{3.3}$$

which in matrix form becomes

$$\begin{bmatrix} \dot{x} \\ \dot{y} \end{bmatrix} = \begin{bmatrix} 3 & 2 \\ 1 & 4 \end{bmatrix} \begin{bmatrix} x \\ y \end{bmatrix} + \begin{bmatrix} 4e^{3t} \\ -e^{3t} \end{bmatrix},$$

This is $\dot{\mathbf{x}} = \mathbf{A}\mathbf{x} + \mathbf{h}$, where $\mathbf{h} = [4e^{3t} \quad -e^{3t}]^T$.

we first find the general solution of the corresponding homogeneous system

$$\begin{cases} \dot{x} = 3x + 2y, \\ \dot{y} = x + 4y, \end{cases}$$

which is the **complementary function**

$$\begin{bmatrix} x_{\mathrm{c}} \\ y_{\mathrm{c}} \end{bmatrix} = \alpha \begin{bmatrix} 1 \\ 1 \end{bmatrix} e^{5t} + \beta \begin{bmatrix} -2 \\ 1 \end{bmatrix} e^{2t},$$

where α and β are arbitrary constants (see Example 2.1(a)).

We next find a particular solution, or **particular integral**, of the original system (3.3), namely

$$\begin{bmatrix} x_{\mathrm{p}} \\ y_{\mathrm{p}} \end{bmatrix} = \begin{bmatrix} 3 \\ -2 \end{bmatrix} e^{3t},$$

as we shall show in Subsection 3.2. The general solution of the original system (3.3) is then obtained by adding these two:

$$\begin{bmatrix} x \\ y \end{bmatrix} = \begin{bmatrix} x_{\mathrm{c}} \\ y_{\mathrm{c}} \end{bmatrix} + \begin{bmatrix} x_{\mathrm{p}} \\ y_{\mathrm{p}} \end{bmatrix} = \alpha \begin{bmatrix} 1 \\ 1 \end{bmatrix} e^{5t} + \beta \begin{bmatrix} -2 \\ 1 \end{bmatrix} e^{2t} + \begin{bmatrix} 3 \\ -2 \end{bmatrix} e^{3t}.$$

To describe the above expression as 'the general solution' is perhaps premature, because it is not immediately obvious that it is even a solution. In order to establish that this is the case, we may use the following general result.

> ### Theorem 3.1   Principle of superposition
>
> If $\mathbf{x}_1$ is a solution of the system $\dot{\mathbf{x}} = \mathbf{A}\mathbf{x} + \mathbf{h}_1$ and $\mathbf{x}_2$ is a solution of the system $\dot{\mathbf{x}} = \mathbf{A}\mathbf{x} + \mathbf{h}_2$, then $p\mathbf{x}_1 + q\mathbf{x}_2$ is a solution of the system $\dot{\mathbf{x}} = \mathbf{A}\mathbf{x} + p\mathbf{h}_1 + q\mathbf{h}_2$, where p and q are constants.

This result is easy to prove, for we have

$$\frac{d}{dt}(p\mathbf{x}_1 + q\mathbf{x}_2) = p\dot{\mathbf{x}}_1 + q\dot{\mathbf{x}}_2$$
$$= p(\mathbf{A}\mathbf{x}_1 + \mathbf{h}_1) + q(\mathbf{A}\mathbf{x}_2 + \mathbf{h}_2)$$
$$= \mathbf{A}(p\mathbf{x}_1 + q\mathbf{x}_2) + p\mathbf{h}_1 + q\mathbf{h}_2.$$

The particular case that is relevant here corresponds to choosing $\mathbf{h}_1 = \mathbf{0}$ and $\mathbf{h}_2 = \mathbf{h}$, say, and putting $p = q = 1$, $\mathbf{x}_1 = \mathbf{x}_{\mathrm{c}}$, the complementary function, and $\mathbf{x}_2 = \mathbf{x}_{\mathrm{p}}$, a particular integral. Then the above result gives rise to the following theorem.

> ### Theorem 3.2
>
> If $\mathbf{x}_{\mathrm{c}}$ is the complementary function of the homogeneous system $\dot{\mathbf{x}} = \mathbf{A}\mathbf{x}$, and $\mathbf{x}_{\mathrm{p}}$ is a particular integral of the system $\dot{\mathbf{x}} = \mathbf{A}\mathbf{x} + \mathbf{h}$, then $\mathbf{x}_{\mathrm{c}} + \mathbf{x}_{\mathrm{p}}$ is the general solution of the system $\dot{\mathbf{x}} = \mathbf{A}\mathbf{x} + \mathbf{h}$.

*Exercise 3.1 _____

Write down the general solution of the system

$$\begin{cases} \dot{x} = 3x + 2y + \ t, \\ \dot{y} = \ x + 4y + 7t, \end{cases}$$

given that a particular integral is

$$x_{\mathrm{p}} = t + \tfrac{4}{5}, \quad y_{\mathrm{p}} = -2t - \tfrac{7}{10}.$$

The matrix $\begin{bmatrix} 3 & 2 \\ 1 & 4 \end{bmatrix}$ has eigenvalues 5 and 2, corresponding to eigenvectors $[1 \ \ 1]^T$ and $[-2 \ \ 1]^T$, respectively.

_____

At this stage it is natural to ask how we were able to find the above particular integral (although it is easy to verify that it *is* a solution to the given system, by direct substitution). Before we address that question in detail, we should emphasize the importance of the principle of superposition. Consider the following example, paying particular attention to the form of $\mathbf{h}$, which is made up of both exponential and linear terms.

We use the term *particular integral* rather than particular solution. The latter is more appropriately used for the solution to system (3.3) that satisfies given initial or boundary conditions.

Example 3.1

Find the general solution of the system

$$\begin{cases} \dot{x} = 3x + 2y + 4e^{3t} + 2t, \\ \dot{y} = x + 4y - e^{3t} + 14t. \end{cases}$$

Here $\mathbf{h} = \begin{bmatrix} 4e^{3t} + 2t \\ -e^{3t} + 14t \end{bmatrix}$.

Solution

Choosing $\mathbf{h}_1 = [4e^{3t} \quad -e^{3t}]^T$, we see from the above discussion that $\mathbf{x}_1 = [3 \quad -2]^T e^{3t}$ is a solution of $\dot{\mathbf{x}} = \mathbf{Ax} + \mathbf{h}_1$. Also, choosing $\mathbf{h}_2 = [t \quad 7t]^T$ gives $\mathbf{x}_2 = [t + \frac{4}{5} \quad -2t - \frac{7}{10}]^T$ as a solution of $\dot{\mathbf{x}} = \mathbf{Ax} + \mathbf{h}_2$. Thus, from the principle of superposition, $\mathbf{x}_1 + 2\mathbf{x}_2$ is a particular integral of the given system written as $\dot{\mathbf{x}} = \mathbf{Ax} + \mathbf{h}_1 + 2\mathbf{h}_2$. Hence, by Theorem 3.2, using the complementary function found above, the general solution is

See Equations (3.3) and Exercise 3.1.

$$\begin{bmatrix} x \\ y \end{bmatrix} = \left(\alpha \begin{bmatrix} 1 \\ 1 \end{bmatrix} e^{5t} + \beta \begin{bmatrix} -2 \\ 1 \end{bmatrix} e^{2t} \right) + \left(\begin{bmatrix} 3 \\ -2 \end{bmatrix} e^{3t} + \begin{bmatrix} 2t + \frac{8}{5} \\ -4t - \frac{7}{5} \end{bmatrix} \right). \quad \blacksquare$$

Example 3.1 illustrates a general technique, the principle of which is to break down the term $\mathbf{h}$ into a sum of manageable components.

3.2   Finding particular integrals

We now show you how to find a particular integral $\mathbf{x}_p$ in some special cases. We consider the system $\dot{\mathbf{x}} = \mathbf{Ax} + \mathbf{h}$ in the situations where $\mathbf{h}$ is a vector whose components are:

(a) polynomial functions;
(b) exponential functions;
(c) sinusoidal functions.

Our treatment will be similar to that of *Unit 3*, where we found particular integrals for linear second-order differential equations using the method of undetermined coefficients. As in that unit, a number of exceptional cases arise, where our methods need to be slightly modified.

To illustrate the ideas involved, we consider the system

$$\dot{\mathbf{x}} = \mathbf{Ax} + \mathbf{h}, \quad \text{where } \mathbf{A} = \begin{bmatrix} 3 & 2 \\ 1 & 4 \end{bmatrix}. \tag{3.4}$$

The first stage in solving any inhomogeneous system is to find the complementary function, that is, the solution of the system $\dot{\mathbf{x}} = \mathbf{Ax}$, which as you saw in Subsection 3.1 is

$$\begin{bmatrix} x_c \\ y_c \end{bmatrix} = \alpha \begin{bmatrix} 1 \\ 1 \end{bmatrix} e^{5t} + \beta \begin{bmatrix} -2 \\ 1 \end{bmatrix} e^{2t}. \tag{3.5}$$

To this complementary function we add a particular integral that depends on the form of $\mathbf{h}$. We now look at examples of the above three forms for $\mathbf{h}$, and derive a particular integral in each case.

Example 3.2

Find the general solution of the system

$$\begin{cases} \dot{x} = 3x + 2y + t, \\ \dot{y} = x + 4y + 7t. \end{cases}$$

Here $\mathbf{h} = [t \quad 7t]^T$, so $\mathbf{h}$ is linear.

Solution

The complementary function is given in Equation (3.5).

We note that $\mathbf{h}$ consists entirely of linear functions, so it seems natural to seek a particular integral of the form

$$\begin{bmatrix} x \\ y \end{bmatrix} = \begin{bmatrix} at + b \\ ct + d \end{bmatrix},$$

where a, b, c and d are constants that we need to determine. We find them by substituting $x = at + b$, $y = ct + d$ into the above system. This gives the simultaneous equations

$$\begin{cases} a = 3(at + b) + 2(ct + d) + t, \\ c = (at + b) + 4(ct + d) + 7t, \end{cases}$$

which give, on rearranging,

$$\begin{cases} (3a + 2c + 1)t + (3b + 2d - a) = 0, \\ (a + 4c + 7)t + (b + 4d - c) = 0. \end{cases} \tag{3.6}$$

Equating the coefficients of t to zero in Equations (3.6) gives

$$\begin{cases} 3a + 2c + 1 = 0, \\ a + 4c + 7 = 0, \end{cases}$$

which have the solution

$$a = 1, \quad c = -2.$$

Equating the constant terms to zero in Equations (3.6), and putting $a = 1$, $c = -2$, gives the equations

$$\begin{cases} 3b + 2d - 1 = 0, \\ b + 4d + 2 = 0, \end{cases}$$

which have the solution

$$b = \tfrac{4}{5}, \quad d = -\tfrac{7}{10}.$$

Thus the required particular integral is

$$\begin{bmatrix} x_{\mathrm{p}} \\ y_{\mathrm{p}} \end{bmatrix} = \begin{bmatrix} t + \tfrac{4}{5} \\ -2t - \tfrac{7}{10} \end{bmatrix},$$

and the general solution is

$$\begin{bmatrix} x \\ y \end{bmatrix} = \begin{bmatrix} x_{\mathrm{c}} \\ y_{\mathrm{c}} \end{bmatrix} + \begin{bmatrix} x_{\mathrm{p}} \\ y_{\mathrm{p}} \end{bmatrix}$$

$$= \alpha \begin{bmatrix} 1 \\ 1 \end{bmatrix} e^{5t} + \beta \begin{bmatrix} -2 \\ 1 \end{bmatrix} e^{2t} + \begin{bmatrix} t + \tfrac{4}{5} \\ -2t - \tfrac{7}{10} \end{bmatrix}. \quad \blacksquare$$

You may have been tempted to use a simpler trial solution, of the form

$$\begin{bmatrix} x \\ y \end{bmatrix} = \begin{bmatrix} at \\ ct \end{bmatrix}.$$

Unfortunately, this does not work — try it and see! You may recall something similar in *Unit 3*.

These equations hold for *all* values of t, which means that each of the bracketed terms must be zero.

Exercise 3.2

Find the general solution of the system

$$\begin{cases} \dot{x} = x + 4y - t + 2, \\ \dot{y} = x - 2y + 5t. \end{cases}$$

For the complementary function, see Example 2.2.

Example 3.3

Find the general solution of the system

$$\begin{cases} \dot{x} = 3x + 2y + 4e^{3t}, \\ \dot{y} = x + 4y - e^{3t}. \end{cases}$$

Here $\mathbf{h} = [4e^{3t} \quad -e^{3t}]^T$, so $\mathbf{h}$ is exponential.

Solution

The complementary function is given in Equation (3.5). We note that $\mathbf{h}$ consists entirely of exponentials, so it seems natural to seek a particular integral of the form

$$\begin{bmatrix} x \\ y \end{bmatrix} = \begin{bmatrix} ae^{3t} \\ be^{3t} \end{bmatrix} = \begin{bmatrix} a \\ b \end{bmatrix} e^{3t},$$

where a and b are constants that we need to determine. We find them by substituting $x = ae^{3t}$, $y = be^{3t}$ into the above system. This gives the simultaneous equations

$$\begin{cases} 3ae^{3t} = 3ae^{3t} + 2be^{3t} + 4e^{3t}, \\ 3be^{3t} = ae^{3t} + 4be^{3t} - e^{3t}, \end{cases}$$

or, on dividing by e^{3t},

$$\begin{cases} 3a = 3a + 2b + 4, \\ 3b = a + 4b - 1. \end{cases}$$

This method fails when $\mathbf{h}$ involves e^{5t} or e^{2t}, which occur in the complementary function. We deal with such examples in the 'Exceptional cases' subsection below. You may recall similar failures in *Unit 3*.

Rearranging these equations gives

$$\begin{cases} 2b = -4, \\ a + b = 1, \end{cases}$$

which have the solution

$$a = 3, \quad b = -2.$$

Thus the required particular integral is

$$\begin{bmatrix} x_{\mathrm{p}} \\ y_{\mathrm{p}} \end{bmatrix} = \begin{bmatrix} 3e^{3t} \\ -2e^{3t} \end{bmatrix}$$

$$= \begin{bmatrix} 3 \\ -2 \end{bmatrix} e^{3t},$$

and the general solution is

$$\begin{bmatrix} x \\ y \end{bmatrix} = \begin{bmatrix} x_{\mathrm{c}} \\ y_{\mathrm{c}} \end{bmatrix} + \begin{bmatrix} x_{\mathrm{p}} \\ y_{\mathrm{p}} \end{bmatrix}$$

$$= \alpha \begin{bmatrix} 1 \\ 1 \end{bmatrix} e^{5t} + \beta \begin{bmatrix} -2 \\ 1 \end{bmatrix} e^{2t} + \begin{bmatrix} 3 \\ -2 \end{bmatrix} e^{3t}. \quad \blacksquare$$

Exercise 3.3

Find the general solution of the system

$$\begin{cases} \dot{x} = x + 4y + 4e^{-t}, \\ \dot{y} = x - 2y + 5e^{-t}. \end{cases}$$

The complementary function is the same as that of Exercise 3.2.

Example 3.4

Find the general solution of the system

$$\begin{cases} \dot{x} = 3x + 2y - 2\sin 3t, \\ \dot{y} = x + 4y - 3\sin 3t - 7\cos 3t. \end{cases}$$

Here

$$\mathbf{h} = \begin{bmatrix} -2\sin 3t \\ -3\sin 3t - 7\cos 3t \end{bmatrix},$$

so $\mathbf{h}$ is sinusoidal.

Solution

The complementary function is given in Equation (3.5). We note that **h** consists entirely of sine and cosine terms, so it seems natural to seek a particular integral of the form

$$\begin{bmatrix} x \\ y \end{bmatrix} = \begin{bmatrix} a\sin 3t + b\cos 3t \\ c\sin 3t + d\cos 3t \end{bmatrix},$$

Note that we need both $\sin 3t$ and $\cos 3t$ in each component of the particular integral.

where a, b, c and d are constants that we need to determine. We find them by substituting $x = a\sin 3t + b\cos 3t$, $y = c\sin 3t + d\cos 3t$ into the above system. This gives the simultaneous equations

$$\begin{cases} (2 - 3a - 3b - 2c)\sin 3t + (3a - 3b - 2d)\cos 3t = 0, \\ (3 - a - 4c - 3d)\sin 3t + (7 - b + 3c - 4d)\cos 3t = 0. \end{cases}$$

These equations hold for *all* values of t, so each of the bracketed terms must be zero, which gives the four simultaneous equations

$$\begin{cases} 3a + 3b + 2c \quad\;\; = 2, \\ 3a - 3b \quad\quad - 2d = 0, \\ a \quad\quad + 4c + 3d = 3, \\ \quad\; b - 3c + 4d = 7. \end{cases} \tag{3.7}$$

Using the Gaussian elimination method, as in *Unit 9*, we can solve these equations to give $a = \frac{211}{221}$, $b = \frac{11}{221}$, $c = -\frac{112}{221}$, $d = \frac{300}{221}$.

We omit the details, but you can easily verify that this is correct by substituting these values for a, b, c and d into Equations (3.7).

Thus the required particular integral is

$$\begin{bmatrix} x_p \\ y_p \end{bmatrix} = \frac{1}{221} \begin{bmatrix} 211\sin 3t + 11\cos 3t \\ -112\sin 3t + 300\cos 3t \end{bmatrix},$$

and the general solution is

$$\begin{bmatrix} x \\ y \end{bmatrix} = \begin{bmatrix} x_c \\ y_c \end{bmatrix} + \begin{bmatrix} x_p \\ y_p \end{bmatrix}$$

$$= \alpha \begin{bmatrix} 1 \\ 1 \end{bmatrix} e^{5t} + \beta \begin{bmatrix} -2 \\ 1 \end{bmatrix} e^{2t} + \frac{1}{221} \begin{bmatrix} 211\sin 3t + 11\cos 3t \\ -112\sin 3t + 300\cos 3t \end{bmatrix}. \quad \blacksquare$$

Exercise 3.4

Find the general solution of the system

$$\begin{cases} \dot{x} = x + 4y - \cos 2t - 4\sin 2t, \\ \dot{y} = x - 2y + \sin 2t. \end{cases}$$

The complementary function is the same as that of Exercises 3.2 and 3.3.

Procedure 3.1   Particular integral

To find a particular integral $\mathbf{x}_p = [x_p \quad y_p]^T$ for the system $\dot{\mathbf{x}} = \mathbf{A}\mathbf{x} + \mathbf{h}$, do the following.

(a) When the elements of **h** are polynomials of degree less than or equal to k, choose x_p and y_p to be polynomials of degree k.

(b) When the elements of **h** are multiples of the same exponential function, choose x_p and y_p to be multiples of this exponential function.

(c) When the elements of **h** are linear combinations of the sinusoidal functions $\sin \omega t$ and $\cos \omega t$, choose x_p and y_p to be linear combinations of these functions.

Note that we need both $\sin \omega t$ and $\cos \omega t$ in each component of the particular integral.

To determine the coefficients in x_p and y_p, substitute into the system of differential equations and equate coefficients.

Exceptional cases

In *Unit 3* we discussed the differential equation

$$\frac{d^2y}{dx^2} - 4y = 2e^{2x}.$$

See *Unit 3*, Example 2.6.

The complementary function is $y_c = \alpha e^{-2x} + \beta e^{2x}$, where α and β are arbitrary constants. For the particular integral, it would be natural to try $y = ke^{2x}$, where k is a constant to be determined. However, as you saw in *Unit 3*, this fails since e^{2x} is already included in the complementary function. Instead, we insert an extra factor x, and try a particular integral of the form $y = kxe^{2x}$.

A similar situation holds for systems of linear differential equations in cases where the usual trial solution is part of the complementary function, as we show in the following example.

Example 3.5

Find the general solution of the system

$$\begin{cases} \dot{x} = 3x + 2y + 6e^{2t}, \\ \dot{y} = x + 4y + 3e^{2t}. \end{cases} \quad (3.8)$$

Here $\mathbf{h} = [6e^{2t} \quad 3e^{2t}]^T$.

Solution

The complementary function is

$$\begin{bmatrix} x_c \\ y_c \end{bmatrix} = \alpha \begin{bmatrix} 1 \\ 1 \end{bmatrix} e^{5t} + \beta \begin{bmatrix} -2 \\ 1 \end{bmatrix} e^{2t},$$

See Equation (3.5).

where α and β are arbitrary constants. Since the complementary function includes an e^{2t} term, a particular integral of the form

$$\begin{bmatrix} x \\ y \end{bmatrix} = \begin{bmatrix} a_1 e^{2t} \\ a_2 e^{2t} \end{bmatrix} = \begin{bmatrix} a_1 \\ a_2 \end{bmatrix} e^{2t}$$

will not work. For, if we substitute this into the system of equations, we obtain

$$\begin{cases} 2a_1 e^{2t} = 3a_1 e^{2t} + 2a_2 e^{2t} + 6e^{2t}, \\ 2a_2 e^{2t} = a_1 e^{2t} + 4a_2 e^{2t} + 3e^{2t}, \end{cases}$$

or, on dividing by e^{2t} and rearranging,

$$\begin{cases} a_1 + 2a_2 = -6, \\ a_1 + 2a_2 = -3. \end{cases}$$

These equations clearly have no solution, so the method fails.

However, there is a method that will succeed. First write $\mathbf{v}_1 = [1 \quad 1]^T$, $\mathbf{v}_2 = [-2 \quad 1]^T$, $\lambda_1 = 5$, $\lambda_2 = 2$, so that $\mathbf{v}_1$, $\mathbf{v}_2$ are eigenvectors corresponding respectively to the eigenvalues λ_1, λ_2, and write $\mathbf{h} = \mathbf{k}e^{\lambda_2 t}$, where $\mathbf{k} = [6 \quad 3]^T$. Now $\mathbf{k}$ can be written as a linear combination of the linearly independent eigenvectors $\mathbf{v}_1$ and $\mathbf{v}_2$:

$$\mathbf{k} = p\mathbf{v}_1 + q\mathbf{v}_2. \quad (3.9)$$

Any n-dimensional vector $\mathbf{v}$ can be written as a linear combination of n linearly independent n-dimensional vectors.

In this case, $[6 \quad 3]^T = p[1 \quad 1]^T + q[-2 \quad 1]^T$, so $p = 4$ and $q = -1$. Next we look for a trial solution of the form

$$\mathbf{x} = (a\mathbf{v}_1 + b\mathbf{v}_2 t)e^{\lambda_2 t}. \quad (3.10)$$

Substituting this and $\mathbf{h} = \mathbf{k}e^{\lambda_2 t} = p\mathbf{v}_1 e^{\lambda_2 t} + q\mathbf{v}_2 e^{\lambda_2 t}$ into $\dot{\mathbf{x}} = \mathbf{A}\mathbf{x} + \mathbf{h}$ gives

$$b\mathbf{v}_2 e^{\lambda_2 t} + \lambda_2(a\mathbf{v}_1 + b\mathbf{v}_2 t)e^{\lambda_2 t} = \mathbf{A}(a\mathbf{v}_1 + b\mathbf{v}_2 t)e^{\lambda_2 t} + p\mathbf{v}_1 e^{\lambda_2 t} + q\mathbf{v}_2 e^{\lambda_2 t}.$$

Dividing by $e^{\lambda_2 t}$ and using the fact that $\mathbf{A}\mathbf{v}_1 = \lambda_1\mathbf{v}_1$ and $\mathbf{A}\mathbf{v}_2 = \lambda_2\mathbf{v}_2$, we obtain

$$a(\lambda_2 - \lambda_1)\mathbf{v}_1 + b\mathbf{v}_2 = p\mathbf{v}_1 + q\mathbf{v}_2.$$

Equating the coefficients of $\mathbf{v}_1$ and $\mathbf{v}_2$ gives

$$a = p/(\lambda_2 - \lambda_1) \quad \text{and} \quad b = q.$$

We know $\lambda_1 = 5$, $\lambda_2 = 2$, $p = 4$ and $q = -1$, so $a = -\tfrac{4}{3}$ and $b = -1$, and a particular integral is

$$\mathbf{x}_{\mathrm{p}} = \left(-\tfrac{4}{3}\begin{bmatrix}1\\1\end{bmatrix} - 1\begin{bmatrix}-2\\1\end{bmatrix}t\right)e^{2t} = \begin{bmatrix}2t - \tfrac{4}{3}\\-t - \tfrac{4}{3}\end{bmatrix}e^{2t}.$$

So the general solution of Equations (3.8) is

$$\mathbf{x} = \alpha\begin{bmatrix}1\\1\end{bmatrix}e^{5t} + \beta\begin{bmatrix}-2\\1\end{bmatrix}e^{2t} + \begin{bmatrix}2t - \tfrac{4}{3}\\-t - \tfrac{4}{3}\end{bmatrix}e^{2t}. \quad \blacksquare$$

> **Procedure 3.2   Particular integral — special case**
>
> To find a particular integral $\mathbf{x}_{\mathrm{p}} = [x_{\mathrm{p}} \ \ y_{\mathrm{p}}]^T$ for the system $\dot{\mathbf{x}} = \mathbf{A}\mathbf{x} + \mathbf{h}$, where $\mathbf{A}$ has distinct real eigenvalues λ_1 and λ_2, with corresponding eigenvectors $\mathbf{v}_1$ and $\mathbf{v}_2$, respectively, and $\mathbf{h} = \mathbf{k}e^{\lambda_2 t}$, first determine p and q such that
>
> $$\mathbf{k} = p\mathbf{v}_1 + q\mathbf{v}_2.$$
>
> Then a particular integral has the form
>
> $$\mathbf{x}_{\mathrm{p}} = (a\mathbf{v}_1 + b\mathbf{v}_2 t)e^{\lambda_2 t},$$
>
> where $a = p/(\lambda_2 - \lambda_1)$ and $b = q$.

A similar procedure can be followed if $\mathbf{h}$ contains polynomial or sinusoidal components, but we do not go into the details here.

End-of-section Exercises

Exercise 3.5

Solve the system of differential equations

$$\begin{cases} \dot{x} = 2x + 3y + \ e^{2t}, \\ \dot{y} = 2x + \ y + 4e^{2t}, \end{cases}$$

subject to the initial conditions $x(0) = \tfrac{5}{6}$, $y(0) = \tfrac{2}{3}$.

The matrix $\begin{bmatrix}2 & 3\\2 & 1\end{bmatrix}$ has eigenvectors $[1 \ \ -1]^T$ and $[3 \ \ 2]^T$, corresponding to eigenvalues -1 and 4, respectively.

Exercise 3.6

Find the general solution of the system of differential equations

$$\begin{cases} \dot{x} = 2x + 3y + \ e^{4t}, \\ \dot{y} = 2x + \ y + 2e^{4t}. \end{cases}$$

See the margin note for Exercise 3.5.

*Exercise 3.7

Find the general solution of the system of differential equations

$$\begin{cases} \dot{x} = 2x + 3y + t, \\ \dot{y} = 2x + \ y + \sin t. \end{cases}$$

(*Hint*: Use the principle of superposition.)

See the margin note for Exercise 3.5.

4   Second-order systems

In this section we show how the methods introduced earlier in this unit can be adapted to finding the solutions of certain systems of homogeneous second-order differential equations. We then consider a particular case in which the solutions are all sinusoidal. Such cases arise often in connection with oscillating mechanical systems or electrical circuits.

4.1   Homogeneous second-order systems

We now turn our attention to systems of linear constant-coefficient second-order differential equations of the form $\ddot{\mathbf{x}} = \mathbf{A}\mathbf{x}$. You have seen that the general solution of a first-order system $\dot{\mathbf{x}} = \mathbf{A}\mathbf{x}$ of n equations can be written as a linear combination of n linearly independent solutions involving n arbitrary constants. In a similar way, it can be shown that the general solution of a second-order system $\ddot{\mathbf{x}} = \mathbf{A}\mathbf{x}$ of n equations can be written as a linear combination of $2n$ linearly independent solutions involving $2n$ arbitrary constants. The following example will show you what is involved in the solution of such systems; the treatment is similar to that of Example 2.1.

We shall not prove this.

Example 4.1

Find the general solution of the system of differential equations

$$\begin{cases} \ddot{x} = x + 4y, \\ \ddot{y} = x - 2y. \end{cases} \tag{4.1}$$

Solution

In order to find the general solution of this pair of equations, it is sufficient to find four linearly independent solutions and write down an arbitrary linear combination of them.

So we begin by attempting to find solutions of the form

$$x = Ce^{\mu t}, \quad y = De^{\mu t},$$

where C and D are constants.

The reason for using μ instead of λ will become apparent as we proceed.

Since $\ddot{x} = C\mu^2 e^{\mu t}$ and $\ddot{y} = D\mu^2 e^{\mu t}$, we have, on substituting the expressions for x and y into Equations (4.1),

$$\begin{cases} C\mu^2 e^{\mu t} = Ce^{\mu t} + 4De^{\mu t}, \\ D\mu^2 e^{\mu t} = Ce^{\mu t} - 2De^{\mu t}. \end{cases}$$

Cancelling the $e^{\mu t}$ terms, we obtain

$$\begin{bmatrix} 1 & 4 \\ 1 & -2 \end{bmatrix} \begin{bmatrix} C \\ D \end{bmatrix} = \mu^2 \begin{bmatrix} C \\ D \end{bmatrix},$$

so μ^2 is an eigenvalue of $\mathbf{A} = \begin{bmatrix} 1 & 4 \\ 1 & -2 \end{bmatrix}$. However, from Example 2.2 we know that the eigenvalues of $\mathbf{A}$ are 2 and -3, so $\mu = \pm\sqrt{2}$ and $\mu = \pm\sqrt{3}i$.

The eigenvalue 2 corresponds to an eigenvector $[4 \ \ 1]^T$, and it is easy to verify that the values $\mu = \pm\sqrt{2}$ provide us with two linearly independent solutions of Equations (4.1), namely

The verification can be done by direct substitution.

$$\mathbf{x}_1 = \begin{bmatrix} 4 \\ 1 \end{bmatrix} e^{\sqrt{2}t} \quad \text{and} \quad \mathbf{x}_2 = \begin{bmatrix} 4 \\ 1 \end{bmatrix} e^{-\sqrt{2}t}.$$

The eigenvalue -3 corresponds to an eigenvector $[1 \quad -1]^T$, and choosing $\mu = \sqrt{3}i$ gives a further solution

$$\begin{bmatrix} 1 \\ -1 \end{bmatrix} e^{\sqrt{3}it} = \begin{bmatrix} 1 \\ -1 \end{bmatrix} (\cos \sqrt{3}t + i \sin \sqrt{3}t);$$

Here we use Euler's formula to write down the exponential in terms of sinusoids.

we can verify that the real and imaginary parts of the expression on the right-hand side are both solutions of Equations (4.1). Thus we have found two more linearly independent solutions of Equations (4.1), namely

Choosing $\mu = -\sqrt{3}i$ leads to the same two linearly independent solutions.

$$\mathbf{x}_3 = \begin{bmatrix} 1 \\ -1 \end{bmatrix} \cos \sqrt{3}t \quad \text{and} \quad \mathbf{x}_4 = \begin{bmatrix} 1 \\ -1 \end{bmatrix} \sin \sqrt{3}t.$$

Using a version of the principle of superposition applicable to second-order systems, we can now take linear combinations of $\mathbf{x}_1$, $\mathbf{x}_2$, $\mathbf{x}_3$ and $\mathbf{x}_4$ to find further solutions. The expression

We do not prove this.

$$\mathbf{x} = C_1\mathbf{x}_1 + C_2\mathbf{x}_2 + C_3\mathbf{x}_3 + C_4\mathbf{x}_4,$$

where C_1, C_2, C_3, C_4 are arbitrary constants, is the general solution of Equations (4.1). ∎

Note that there are four arbitrary constants, as expected.

Comparing the above solution with that of Example 2.2, we notice many similarities. The main difference is that λ is replaced by μ^2, giving rise to four values for μ, instead of two for λ. Consequently, we obtain a general solution with four arbitrary constants.

In general, consider a system of differential equations of the form $\ddot{\mathbf{x}} = \mathbf{A}\mathbf{x}$. If we try an exponential solution of the form $\mathbf{x} = \mathbf{v}e^{\mu t}$, where $\mathbf{v}$ is a constant column vector, then $\ddot{\mathbf{x}} = \mathbf{v}\mu^2 e^{\mu t}$, and the system of differential equations becomes $\mathbf{v}\mu^2 e^{\mu t} = \mathbf{A}\mathbf{v}e^{\mu t}$. Dividing this equation by $e^{\mu t}$ and rearranging, we have

This discussion mirrors the corresponding discussion in Section 2 (page 110).

$$\mathbf{A}\mathbf{v} = \mu^2\mathbf{v}.$$

Thus $\mathbf{v}$ is an eigenvector of $\mathbf{A}$, and μ^2 is the corresponding eigenvalue.

Theorem 4.1

If μ^2 is an eigenvalue of the matrix $\mathbf{A}$ corresponding to an eigenvector $\mathbf{v}$, then $\mathbf{x} = \mathbf{v}e^{\mu t}$ is a solution of the system of differential equations $\ddot{\mathbf{x}} = \mathbf{A}\mathbf{x}$.

If $\mathbf{x} = \mathbf{v}e^{\mu t}$, then $\dot{\mathbf{x}} = \mu\mathbf{v}e^{\mu t}$ and $\ddot{\mathbf{x}} = \mu^2\mathbf{v}e^{\mu t} = \mathbf{A}\mathbf{v}e^{\mu t} = \mathbf{A}\mathbf{x}$.

Example 4.2

Find the general solution of the system of differential equations

$$\begin{cases} \ddot{x} = 3x + 2y, \\ \ddot{y} = x + 4y. \end{cases}$$

Solution

The matrix of coefficients is $\mathbf{A} = \begin{bmatrix} 3 & 2 \\ 1 & 4 \end{bmatrix}$. The eigenvectors of $\mathbf{A}$ are $[1 \quad 1]^T$ and $[-2 \quad 1]^T$, corresponding to the eigenvalues $\lambda = 5$ and $\lambda = 2$, respectively.

Using the notation of Example 4.1, it follows that μ has the values $\sqrt{5}, -\sqrt{5}, \sqrt{2}$ and $-\sqrt{2}$, and that the general solution is

$$\begin{bmatrix} x \\ y \end{bmatrix} = C_1 \begin{bmatrix} 1 \\ 1 \end{bmatrix} e^{\sqrt{5}t} + C_2 \begin{bmatrix} 1 \\ 1 \end{bmatrix} e^{-\sqrt{5}t} + C_3 \begin{bmatrix} -2 \\ 1 \end{bmatrix} e^{\sqrt{2}t} + C_4 \begin{bmatrix} -2 \\ 1 \end{bmatrix} e^{-\sqrt{2}t}. \quad ∎$$

*Exercise 4.1

Find the general solution of the system of differential equations

$$\begin{cases} \ddot{x} = 5x + 2y, \\ \ddot{y} = 2x + 5y. \end{cases}$$

The matrix $\begin{bmatrix} 5 & 2 \\ 2 & 5 \end{bmatrix}$ has eigenvectors $[1 \quad 1]^T$ and $[1 \quad -1]^T$, corresponding to eigenvalues 7 and 3, respectively.

The above ideas can be formalized in the following procedure.

Procedure 4.1   Second-order homogeneous linear systems

To solve a system $\ddot{\mathbf{x}} = \mathbf{A}\mathbf{x}$, where $\mathbf{A}$ is an $n \times n$ matrix with n distinct real eigenvalues, do the following.

(a) Find the eigenvalues $\lambda_1, \lambda_2, \ldots, \lambda_n$ of $\mathbf{A}$, and a corresponding set of eigenvectors $\mathbf{v}_1, \mathbf{v}_2, \ldots, \mathbf{v}_n$.

(b) Each *positive* eigenvalue, μ^2 say, corresponding to an eigenvector $\mathbf{v}$, gives rise to two linearly independent solutions

$$\mathbf{v}e^{\mu t} \quad \text{and} \quad \mathbf{v}e^{-\mu t}.$$

Each *negative* eigenvalue, $-\omega^2$ say, corresponding to an eigenvector $\mathbf{v}$, gives rise to two linearly independent solutions

$$\mathbf{v}\cos \omega t \quad \text{and} \quad \mathbf{v}\sin \omega t.$$

A *zero* eigenvalue corresponding to an eigenvector $\mathbf{v}$ gives rise to two linearly independent solutions

$$\mathbf{v} \quad \text{and} \quad \mathbf{v}t.$$

(c) The general solution is then an arbitrary linear combination of the $2n$ linearly independent solutions found in step (b), involving $2n$ arbitrary constants.

Complex eigenvalues and repeated real eigenvalues are not discussed here, but they can be dealt with in a fashion similar to that for the first-order case.

We do not show this here, but you can verify it in any particular case (see Example 4.3 below). It is analogous to the case of a single second-order differential equation with both roots of the auxiliary equation equal to zero.

We illustrate this procedure in the following example.

Example 4.3

Find the general solution of the following system of differential equations.

$$\begin{cases} \ddot{x} = 3x + 2y + 2z \\ \ddot{y} = 2x + 2y \\ \ddot{z} = 2x \qquad + 4z \end{cases}$$

Solution

The matrix of coefficients is $\mathbf{A} = \begin{bmatrix} 3 & 2 & 2 \\ 2 & 2 & 0 \\ 2 & 0 & 4 \end{bmatrix}$. The eigenvectors of $\mathbf{A}$ are $[2 \quad 1 \quad 2]^T$, corresponding to the eigenvalue $\lambda = 6$, $[1 \quad 2 \quad -2]^T$, corresponding to the eigenvalue $\lambda = 3$, and $[-2 \quad 2 \quad 1]^T$, corresponding to the eigenvalue $\lambda = 0$. It follows from Procedure 4.1 that the general solution of the above system is

$$\begin{bmatrix} x \\ y \\ z \end{bmatrix} = \begin{bmatrix} 2 \\ 1 \\ 2 \end{bmatrix} (C_1 e^{\sqrt{6}t} + C_2 e^{-\sqrt{6}t}) + \begin{bmatrix} 1 \\ 2 \\ -2 \end{bmatrix} (C_3 e^{\sqrt{3}t} + C_4 e^{-\sqrt{3}t})$$

$$+ \begin{bmatrix} -2 \\ 2 \\ 1 \end{bmatrix} (C_5 + C_6 t). \quad \blacksquare$$

You may like to verify that $[-2 \quad 2 \quad 1]^T$ and $[-2 \quad 2 \quad 1]^T t$ are both solutions of the system.

Exercise 4.2

Find the general solution of the system of differential equations

$$\begin{cases} \ddot{x} = 2x + y - z, \\ \ddot{y} = \quad\;\; -3y + 2z, \\ \ddot{z} = \qquad\qquad 4z. \end{cases}$$

The matrix $\begin{bmatrix} 2 & 1 & -1 \\ 0 & -3 & 2 \\ 0 & 0 & 4 \end{bmatrix}$
has eigenvalues 2, -3 and 4, corresponding to eigenvectors $[1 \;\; 0 \;\; 0]^T$, $[1 \;\; -5 \;\; 0]^T$ and $[-5 \;\; 4 \;\; 14]^T$, respectively.

4.2 Simple harmonic motion

Simple harmonic motion is an often observed phenomenon. It arises, for example, if a quantity satisfies a second-order differential equation of the form

$$\ddot{x} = -\omega^2 x,$$

where ω is a constant. In this case solutions are of the form

$$x = \alpha \cos \omega t + \beta \sin \omega t,$$

where α and β are arbitrary constants.

In Subsection 1.3 we developed a model for the horizontal motion of a ball-bearing within a bowl of specified shape. The resulting equations were

$$\begin{cases} \ddot{x} = -5x + 4y, \\ \ddot{y} = \quad 4x - 5y, \end{cases}$$

where $x(t)$ and $y(t)$ are the horizontal coordinates of the ball-bearing at time t. These second-order differential equations may be expressed in matrix form as

$$\begin{bmatrix} \ddot{x} \\ \ddot{y} \end{bmatrix} = \begin{bmatrix} -5 & 4 \\ 4 & -5 \end{bmatrix} \begin{bmatrix} x \\ y \end{bmatrix}.$$

The matrix $\begin{bmatrix} -5 & 4 \\ 4 & -5 \end{bmatrix}$ has eigenvectors $\begin{bmatrix} 1 \\ 1 \end{bmatrix}$ and $\begin{bmatrix} 1 \\ -1 \end{bmatrix}$, corresponding to eigenvalues -1 and -9, respectively.

It follows from Procedure 4.1 that the general solution is

$$\begin{bmatrix} x \\ y \end{bmatrix} = \begin{bmatrix} 1 \\ 1 \end{bmatrix} (C_1 \cos t + C_2 \sin t) + \begin{bmatrix} 1 \\ -1 \end{bmatrix} (C_3 \cos 3t + C_4 \sin 3t),$$

where C_1, C_2, C_3 and C_4 are arbitrary constants.

Let us now consider the paths that a ball-bearing takes for given initial conditions. The following illustrates just four of the many possibilities.

(a) $x(0) = 1$, $y(0) = \quad 1$, $\dot{x}(0) = \quad 0$, $\dot{y}(0) = 0$.
(b) $x(0) = 1$, $y(0) = -1$, $\dot{x}(0) = \quad 0$, $\dot{y}(0) = 0$.
(c) $x(0) = 1$, $y(0) = \quad 0$, $\dot{x}(0) = \quad 0$, $\dot{y}(0) = 0$.
(d) $x(0) = 1$, $y(0) = \quad 2$, $\dot{x}(0) = -1$, $\dot{y}(0) = 1$.

In case (a) we find $C_1 = 1$ and $C_2 = C_3 = C_4 = 0$, so the solution is $[x \;\; y]^T = [1 \;\; 1]^T \cos t$, and the ball-bearing performs simple harmonic motion in the direction of the vector $[1 \;\; 1]^T$, that is, along the line $y = x$, with angular frequency 1 (as shown in Figure 4.1).

In case (b) we find $C_3 = 1$ and $C_1 = C_2 = C_4 = 0$, so the solution is $[x \quad y]^T = [1 \quad -1]^T \cos 3t$, and the ball-bearing performs simple harmonic motion in the direction of the vector $[1 \quad -1]^T$, that is, along the line $y = -x$, with angular frequency 3 (as shown in Figure 4.2).

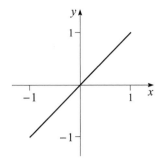

Figure 4.1   Figure 4.2

In case (c) we find $C_1 = C_3 = \frac{1}{2}$ and $C_2 = C_4 = 0$, so the solution is $[x \quad y]^T = \frac{1}{2}[1 \quad 1]^T \cos t + \frac{1}{2}[1 \quad -1]^T \cos 3t$, which is a combination of the previous motions (as shown in Figure 4.3).

In case (d) we find $C_1 = \frac{3}{2}$, $C_3 = -\frac{1}{2}$, $C_2 = 0$ and $C_4 = -\frac{1}{3}$, so the solution is $[x \quad y]^T = [1 \quad 1]^T(\frac{3}{2}\cos t) + [1 \quad -1]^T(-\frac{1}{2}\cos 3t - \frac{1}{3}\sin 3t)$ (as shown in Figure 4.4).

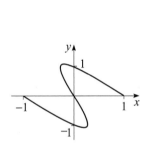 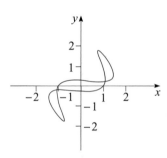

Figure 4.3   Figure 4.4

*Exercise 4.3

An object moves in a plane so that its coordinates at time t satisfy the equations

$$\begin{cases} \ddot{x} = -\frac{25}{7}x + \frac{6}{7}y, \\ \ddot{y} = \frac{9}{7}x - \frac{10}{7}y. \end{cases}$$

Find two directions in which the object can describe simple harmonic motion along a straight line. Give the angular frequencies of such motions.

End-of-section Exercise

*Exercise 4.4

Find the general solution of the system of equations

$$\begin{cases} \ddot{x} = x + 4y, \\ \ddot{y} = x + y. \end{cases}$$

5 Solving systems on the computer

In this section you will see how systems of linear constant-coefficient differential equations can be solved using the computer algebra package for the course. Note that these activities simply verify solutions found in the text, so you should not spend too much time on them.

Use your computer to complete the following activities.

PC

Activity 5.1

(a) Solve the initial-value problem
$$\begin{bmatrix} \dot{x} \\ \dot{y} \end{bmatrix} = \begin{bmatrix} 3 & 2 \\ 1 & 4 \end{bmatrix} \begin{bmatrix} x \\ y \end{bmatrix}, \qquad \begin{bmatrix} x(0) \\ y(0) \end{bmatrix} = \begin{bmatrix} 1 \\ 4 \end{bmatrix}.$$
Compare your answer with that obtained in Example 2.1.

(b) Find the general solution of the system
$$\begin{bmatrix} \dot{x} \\ \dot{y} \end{bmatrix} = \begin{bmatrix} 3 & 2 \\ 1 & 4 \end{bmatrix} \begin{bmatrix} x \\ y \end{bmatrix} + \begin{bmatrix} 4e^{3t} + 2t \\ -e^{3t} + 14t \end{bmatrix}.$$
Compare your answer with that obtained in Example 3.1.

Activity 5.2

(a) Find the general solution of the system
$$\begin{bmatrix} \dot{x} \\ \dot{y} \\ \dot{z} \end{bmatrix} = \begin{bmatrix} 3 & 2 & 2 \\ 2 & 2 & 0 \\ 2 & 0 & 4 \end{bmatrix} \begin{bmatrix} x \\ y \\ z \end{bmatrix}.$$
Compare your answer with that obtained in Example 2.3.

(b) Solve the initial-value problem
$$\begin{bmatrix} \dot{x} \\ \dot{y} \\ \dot{z} \end{bmatrix} = \begin{bmatrix} 3 & 2 & 2 \\ 2 & 2 & 0 \\ 2 & 0 & 4 \end{bmatrix} \begin{bmatrix} x \\ y \\ z \end{bmatrix} + \begin{bmatrix} e^t \\ 2e^t \\ 0 \end{bmatrix}, \qquad \begin{bmatrix} x(0) \\ y(0) \\ z(0) \end{bmatrix} = \begin{bmatrix} 0 \\ 0 \\ 0 \end{bmatrix}.$$

This system of differential equations appeared in Equations (2.2), but no solution was obtained in the text.

Activity 5.3

Find the general solution of the system
$$\begin{bmatrix} \dot{x} \\ \dot{y} \\ \dot{z} \end{bmatrix} = \begin{bmatrix} 5 & 0 & 3 \\ 3 & 2 & 3 \\ -6 & 0 & -4 \end{bmatrix} \begin{bmatrix} x \\ y \\ z \end{bmatrix}.$$
Compare your answer with that obtained in Example 2.4.

As you saw in Example 2.4, this coefficient matrix has a repeated eigenvalue but it is possible to find three linearly independent eigenvectors.

Activity 5.4

Solve the initial-value problem
$$\begin{bmatrix} \dot{x} \\ \dot{y} \end{bmatrix} = \begin{bmatrix} 2 & 3 \\ 0 & 2 \end{bmatrix} \begin{bmatrix} x \\ y \end{bmatrix}, \qquad \begin{bmatrix} x(0) \\ y(0) \end{bmatrix} = \begin{bmatrix} 4 \\ 3 \end{bmatrix}.$$
Compare your answer with that obtained in Exercise 2.5.

As you saw in Exercise 2.5, this coefficient matrix has a repeated eigenvalue and only one linearly independent eigenvector can be found.

Activity 5.5

Solve the initial-value problem
$$\begin{bmatrix} \dot{x} \\ \dot{y} \end{bmatrix} = \begin{bmatrix} 3 & -1 \\ 2 & 1 \end{bmatrix} \begin{bmatrix} x \\ y \end{bmatrix}, \qquad \begin{bmatrix} x(0) \\ y(0) \end{bmatrix} = \begin{bmatrix} 3 \\ 1 \end{bmatrix}.$$
Compare your answer with that obtained in Example 2.6.

As you saw in Example 2.6, this coefficient matrix has complex eigenvalues and eigenvectors.

Outcomes

After studying this unit you should be able to:

- understand and use the terminology associated with systems of linear constant-coefficient differential equations;
- obtain the general solution of a homogeneous system of two or three first-order differential equations, by applying knowledge of the eigenvalues and eigenvectors of the coefficient matrix;
- obtain a particular solution of an inhomogeneous system of two first-order differential equations in certain simple cases, by using a trial solution;
- understand the role of the principle of superposition in determining a particular integral of an inhomogeneous linear system of differential equations;
- obtain the general solution of an inhomogeneous system of two or three first-order differential equations, by combining its complementary function and a particular integral;
- apply given initial conditions to obtain the solution of an initial-value problem which features a system of two first-order differential equations;
- obtain the general solution of a homogeneous system of two or three second-order equations, by applying knowledge of the eigenvalues and eigenvectors of the coefficient matrix;
- understand how systems of linear constant-coefficient differential equations arise in mathematical models of the real world.

Solutions to the exercises

Section 2

2.1

(a) $\begin{bmatrix} \dot{x} \\ \dot{y} \end{bmatrix} = \begin{bmatrix} 2 & 1 \\ 1 & 0 \end{bmatrix} \begin{bmatrix} x \\ y \end{bmatrix} + \begin{bmatrix} 1 \\ -2 \end{bmatrix}$; inhomogeneous.

(b) $\begin{bmatrix} \dot{x} \\ \dot{y} \end{bmatrix} = \begin{bmatrix} 0 & 1 \\ 0 & 0 \end{bmatrix} \begin{bmatrix} x \\ y \end{bmatrix} + \begin{bmatrix} 0 \\ t \end{bmatrix}$; inhomogeneous.

(c) $\begin{bmatrix} \dot{x} \\ \dot{y} \\ \dot{z} \end{bmatrix} = \begin{bmatrix} 5 & 0 & 0 \\ 1 & 2 & 1 \\ 1 & 1 & 2 \end{bmatrix} \begin{bmatrix} x \\ y \\ z \end{bmatrix}$; homogeneous.

2.2 The matrix of coefficients is $\mathbf{A} = \begin{bmatrix} 5 & 2 \\ 2 & 5 \end{bmatrix}$.

We are given that the eigenvectors of $\mathbf{A}$ are $[1 \ \ 1]^T$ with corresponding eigenvalue $\lambda = 7$, and $[1 \ \ -1]^T$ with corresponding eigenvalue $\lambda = 3$. The general solution is therefore

$$\begin{bmatrix} x \\ y \end{bmatrix} = \alpha \begin{bmatrix} 1 \\ 1 \end{bmatrix} e^{7t} + \beta \begin{bmatrix} 1 \\ -1 \end{bmatrix} e^{3t}.$$

Since $x = 4$ and $y = 0$ when $t = 0$, we have

$$\begin{cases} 4 = \alpha + \beta, \\ 0 = \alpha - \beta. \end{cases}$$

Thus $\alpha = 2$ and $\beta = 2$, so

$$\begin{bmatrix} x \\ y \end{bmatrix} = 2 \begin{bmatrix} 1 \\ 1 \end{bmatrix} e^{7t} + 2 \begin{bmatrix} 1 \\ -1 \end{bmatrix} e^{3t}$$

$$= \begin{bmatrix} 2 \\ 2 \end{bmatrix} e^{7t} + \begin{bmatrix} 2 \\ -2 \end{bmatrix} e^{3t}.$$

2.3 The matrix of coefficients is $\mathbf{A} = \begin{bmatrix} 5 & 0 & 0 \\ 1 & 2 & 1 \\ 1 & 1 & 2 \end{bmatrix}$.

We are given that the eigenvectors of $\mathbf{A}$ are $[2 \ \ 1 \ \ 1]^T$, $[0 \ \ 1 \ \ 1]^T$ and $[0 \ \ 1 \ \ -1]^T$, corresponding to the eigenvalues 5, 3 and 1, respectively.

The general solution is therefore

$$\begin{bmatrix} x \\ y \\ z \end{bmatrix} = \alpha \begin{bmatrix} 2 \\ 1 \\ 1 \end{bmatrix} e^{5t} + \beta \begin{bmatrix} 0 \\ 1 \\ 1 \end{bmatrix} e^{3t} + \gamma \begin{bmatrix} 0 \\ 1 \\ -1 \end{bmatrix} e^{t}.$$

Since $x = 4$, $y = 6$ and $z = 0$ when $t = 0$, we have

$$\begin{cases} 4 = 2\alpha, \\ 6 = \alpha + \beta + \gamma, \\ 0 = \alpha + \beta - \gamma. \end{cases}$$

Thus $\alpha = 2$, $\beta = 1$ and $\gamma = 3$, so

$$\begin{bmatrix} x \\ y \\ z \end{bmatrix} = 2 \begin{bmatrix} 2 \\ 1 \\ 1 \end{bmatrix} e^{5t} + \begin{bmatrix} 0 \\ 1 \\ 1 \end{bmatrix} e^{3t} + 3 \begin{bmatrix} 0 \\ 1 \\ -1 \end{bmatrix} e^{t}$$

$$= \begin{bmatrix} 4 \\ 2 \\ 2 \end{bmatrix} e^{5t} + \begin{bmatrix} 0 \\ 1 \\ 1 \end{bmatrix} e^{3t} + \begin{bmatrix} 0 \\ 3 \\ -3 \end{bmatrix} e^{t}.$$

2.4 The matrix of coefficients is $\mathbf{A} = \begin{bmatrix} 0 & 0 & 1 \\ 0 & 1 & 0 \\ 1 & 0 & 0 \end{bmatrix}$.

We are given that the eigenvectors are $[1 \ \ 0 \ \ -1]^T$ and $[k \ \ l \ \ k]^T$, corresponding to the eigenvalues -1 and 1 (repeated), respectively. But

$$[k \ \ l \ \ k]^T = k[1 \ \ 0 \ \ 1]^T + l[0 \ \ 1 \ \ 0]^T,$$

so the general solution is

$$\begin{bmatrix} x \\ y \\ z \end{bmatrix} = \alpha \begin{bmatrix} 1 \\ 0 \\ -1 \end{bmatrix} e^{-t} + \beta \begin{bmatrix} 1 \\ 0 \\ 1 \end{bmatrix} e^{t} + \gamma \begin{bmatrix} 0 \\ 1 \\ 0 \end{bmatrix} e^{t}.$$

Since $x = 7$, $y = 5$ and $z = 1$ when $t = 0$, we have

$$7 = \alpha + \beta, \quad 5 = \gamma \quad \text{and} \quad 1 = -\alpha + \beta.$$

Thus $\alpha = 3$, $\beta = 4$ and $\gamma = 5$, so

$$\begin{bmatrix} x \\ y \\ z \end{bmatrix} = 3 \begin{bmatrix} 1 \\ 0 \\ -1 \end{bmatrix} e^{-t} + 4 \begin{bmatrix} 1 \\ 0 \\ 1 \end{bmatrix} e^{t} + 5 \begin{bmatrix} 0 \\ 1 \\ 0 \end{bmatrix} e^{t}$$

$$= \begin{bmatrix} 3 \\ 0 \\ -3 \end{bmatrix} e^{-t} + \begin{bmatrix} 4 \\ 5 \\ 4 \end{bmatrix} e^{t}.$$

2.5 The matrix of coefficients is $\mathbf{A} = \begin{bmatrix} 2 & 3 \\ 0 & 2 \end{bmatrix}$, and the eigenvalues are $\lambda = 2$ (repeated).

The eigenvector equations are

$$(2 - \lambda)x + 3y = 0 \quad \text{and} \quad (2 - \lambda)y = 0,$$

which reduce, when $\lambda = 2$, to

$$3y = 0 \quad \text{and} \quad 0 = 0,$$

so $y = 0$. It follows that an eigenvector corresponding to $\lambda = 2$ is $[1 \ \ 0]^T$, and that one solution is $[1 \ \ 0]^T e^{2t}$.

To find the general solution, we solve the equation $(\mathbf{A} - \lambda\mathbf{I})\mathbf{b} = \mathbf{v}$, where $\mathbf{A} - \lambda\mathbf{I} = \mathbf{A} - 2\mathbf{I} = \begin{bmatrix} 0 & 3 \\ 0 & 0 \end{bmatrix}$, $\mathbf{v} = [1 \ \ 0]^T$ and $\mathbf{b} = [b_1 \ \ b_2]^T$. This gives

$$\begin{bmatrix} 0 & 3 \\ 0 & 0 \end{bmatrix} \begin{bmatrix} b_1 \\ b_2 \end{bmatrix} = \begin{bmatrix} 1 \\ 0 \end{bmatrix},$$

which reduces to $3b_2 = 1$ with no condition on b_1, so $b_2 = \frac{1}{3}$ and we can take $b_1 = 0$, giving a solution

$$\left(\begin{bmatrix} 1 \\ 0 \end{bmatrix} t + \begin{bmatrix} 0 \\ \frac{1}{3} \end{bmatrix} \right) e^{2t} = \begin{bmatrix} t \\ \frac{1}{3} \end{bmatrix} e^{2t}.$$

Thus the general solution is

$$\begin{bmatrix} x \\ y \end{bmatrix} = \alpha \begin{bmatrix} 1 \\ 0 \end{bmatrix} e^{2t} + \beta \begin{bmatrix} t \\ \frac{1}{3} \end{bmatrix} e^{2t}.$$

Since $x = 4$ and $y = 3$ when $t = 0$, we have

$$4 = \alpha \quad \text{and} \quad 3 = \frac{1}{3}\beta,$$

giving $\alpha = 4$ and $\beta = 9$. Thus the required solution is

$$\begin{bmatrix} x \\ y \end{bmatrix} = 4 \begin{bmatrix} 1 \\ 0 \end{bmatrix} e^{2t} + 9 \begin{bmatrix} t \\ \frac{1}{3} \end{bmatrix} e^{2t} = \begin{bmatrix} 9t + 4 \\ 3 \end{bmatrix} e^{2t}.$$

2.6 (a) The matrix of coefficients is $\mathbf{A} = \begin{bmatrix} 2 & 3 \\ 2 & 1 \end{bmatrix}$.

Using the given eigenvalues and eigenvectors, we obtain the general solution

$$\begin{bmatrix} x \\ y \end{bmatrix} = \alpha \begin{bmatrix} 3 \\ 2 \end{bmatrix} e^{4t} + \beta \begin{bmatrix} 1 \\ -1 \end{bmatrix} e^{-t}.$$

Since $x = y = 1$ when $t = 0$, we have

$$1 = 3\alpha + \beta \quad \text{and} \quad 1 = 2\alpha - \beta,$$

giving $\alpha = \frac{2}{5}$ and $\beta = -\frac{1}{5}$. The required solution is therefore

$$\begin{bmatrix} x \\ y \end{bmatrix} = \frac{2}{5} \begin{bmatrix} 3 \\ 2 \end{bmatrix} e^{4t} - \frac{1}{5} \begin{bmatrix} 1 \\ -1 \end{bmatrix} e^{-t}$$

$$= \begin{bmatrix} \frac{6}{5} \\ \frac{4}{5} \end{bmatrix} e^{4t} + \begin{bmatrix} -\frac{1}{5} \\ \frac{1}{5} \end{bmatrix} e^{-t}.$$

(b) The matrix of coefficients is $\mathbf{A} = \begin{bmatrix} -3 & -2 \\ 4 & 1 \end{bmatrix}$.

Using the given eigenvalues and eigenvectors, we obtain the general solution

$$\begin{bmatrix} x \\ y \end{bmatrix} = C \begin{bmatrix} 1 \\ -1-i \end{bmatrix} e^{(-1+2i)t} + D \begin{bmatrix} 1 \\ -1+i \end{bmatrix} e^{(-1-2i)t}.$$

Now

$$\begin{bmatrix} 1 \\ -1-i \end{bmatrix} e^{(-1+2i)t} = \begin{bmatrix} e^{-t}(\cos 2t + i \sin 2t) \\ (-1-i)e^{-t}(\cos 2t + i \sin 2t) \end{bmatrix}$$

$$= \begin{bmatrix} e^{-t}\cos 2t + ie^{-t}\sin 2t \\ e^{-t}(\sin 2t - \cos 2t) - ie^{-t}(\sin 2t + \cos 2t) \end{bmatrix}.$$

So we have

$$\mathrm{Re}\left(\begin{bmatrix} 1 \\ -1-i \end{bmatrix} e^{(-1+2i)t} \right) = \begin{bmatrix} \cos 2t \\ \sin 2t - \cos 2t \end{bmatrix} e^{-t},$$

$$\mathrm{Im}\left(\begin{bmatrix} 1 \\ -1-i \end{bmatrix} e^{(-1+2i)t} \right) = \begin{bmatrix} \sin 2t \\ -\sin 2t - \cos 2t \end{bmatrix} e^{-t},$$

and the general real-valued solution can be written as

$$\begin{bmatrix} x \\ y \end{bmatrix} = C \begin{bmatrix} \cos 2t \\ \sin 2t - \cos 2t \end{bmatrix} e^{-t}$$

$$+ D \begin{bmatrix} \sin 2t \\ -\sin 2t - \cos 2t \end{bmatrix} e^{-t}.$$

Since $x = y = 1$ when $t = 0$, we have

$$1 = C \quad \text{and} \quad 1 = -C - D,$$

so $C = 1$, $D = -2$, and the required particular solution is

$$\begin{bmatrix} x \\ y \end{bmatrix} = \begin{bmatrix} \cos 2t - 2\sin 2t \\ 3\sin 2t + \cos 2t \end{bmatrix} e^{-t}.$$

2.7

(a) $\begin{bmatrix} x \\ y \\ z \end{bmatrix} = \alpha \begin{bmatrix} 1 \\ -1 \\ 0 \end{bmatrix} e^{t} + \beta \begin{bmatrix} -2 \\ 1 \\ 2 \end{bmatrix} e^{2t} + \gamma \begin{bmatrix} 1 \\ -1 \\ -2 \end{bmatrix} e^{3t}$

(b) $\begin{bmatrix} x \\ y \\ z \end{bmatrix} = \alpha \begin{bmatrix} 3 \\ -1 \\ 3 \end{bmatrix} e^{t} + \beta \begin{bmatrix} 2 \\ 1 \\ 0 \end{bmatrix} e^{2t} + \gamma \begin{bmatrix} 2 \\ 0 \\ 1 \end{bmatrix} e^{2t}$

2.8 Using the given eigenvalues and eigenvectors in Procedure 2.3, we have

$$\mathbf{v}e^{\lambda t} = \begin{bmatrix} 1 \\ 0 \\ -\frac{1}{2} + \frac{\sqrt{3}}{2}i \end{bmatrix} e^{(\frac{1}{2} + \frac{\sqrt{3}}{2}i)t}$$

$$= e^{\frac{1}{2}t} \begin{bmatrix} 1 \\ 0 \\ -\frac{1}{2} + \frac{\sqrt{3}}{2}i \end{bmatrix} \left(\cos\left(\tfrac{\sqrt{3}}{2}t\right) + i \sin\left(\tfrac{\sqrt{3}}{2}t\right) \right)$$

$$= e^{\frac{1}{2}t} \begin{bmatrix} \cos\left(\tfrac{\sqrt{3}}{2}t\right) + i \sin\left(\tfrac{\sqrt{3}}{2}t\right) \\ 0 \\ \left(-\tfrac{1}{2} + \tfrac{\sqrt{3}}{2}i\right)\left(\cos\left(\tfrac{\sqrt{3}}{2}t\right) + i \sin\left(\tfrac{\sqrt{3}}{2}t\right)\right) \end{bmatrix}$$

$$= e^{\frac{1}{2}t} \underbrace{\begin{bmatrix} \cos\left(\tfrac{\sqrt{3}}{2}t\right) \\ 0 \\ -\tfrac{1}{2}\cos\left(\tfrac{\sqrt{3}}{2}t\right) - \tfrac{\sqrt{3}}{2}\sin\left(\tfrac{\sqrt{3}}{2}t\right) \end{bmatrix}}_{\text{real part}}$$

$$+ i\, e^{\frac{1}{2}t} \underbrace{\begin{bmatrix} \sin\left(\tfrac{\sqrt{3}}{2}t\right) \\ 0 \\ \tfrac{\sqrt{3}}{2}\cos\left(\tfrac{\sqrt{3}}{2}t\right) - \tfrac{1}{2}\sin\left(\tfrac{\sqrt{3}}{2}t\right) \end{bmatrix}}_{\text{imaginary part}}.$$

Thus the general real-valued solution is

$$\begin{bmatrix} x \\ y \\ z \end{bmatrix} = C_1 \begin{bmatrix} 1 \\ 1 \\ 0 \end{bmatrix} e^{t}$$

$$+ C_2 e^{\frac{1}{2}t} \begin{bmatrix} \cos\left(\tfrac{\sqrt{3}}{2}t\right) \\ 0 \\ -\tfrac{1}{2}\cos\left(\tfrac{\sqrt{3}}{2}t\right) - \tfrac{\sqrt{3}}{2}\sin\left(\tfrac{\sqrt{3}}{2}t\right) \end{bmatrix}$$

$$+ C_3 e^{\frac{1}{2}t} \begin{bmatrix} \sin\left(\tfrac{\sqrt{3}}{2}t\right) \\ 0 \\ \tfrac{\sqrt{3}}{2}\cos\left(\tfrac{\sqrt{3}}{2}t\right) - \tfrac{1}{2}\sin\left(\tfrac{\sqrt{3}}{2}t\right) \end{bmatrix},$$

where C_1, C_2 and C_3 are real constants.

Putting $x = y = 1$ and $z = 2$ when $t = 0$, we have

$$\begin{bmatrix} 1 \\ 1 \\ 2 \end{bmatrix} = C_1 \begin{bmatrix} 1 \\ 1 \\ 0 \end{bmatrix} + C_2 \begin{bmatrix} 1 \\ 0 \\ -\frac{1}{2} \end{bmatrix} + C_3 \begin{bmatrix} 0 \\ 0 \\ \frac{\sqrt{3}}{2} \end{bmatrix},$$

so $C_1 + C_2 = 1$, $C_1 = 1$ and $-\frac{1}{2}C_2 + \frac{\sqrt{3}}{2}C_3 = 2$, which give $C_2 = 0$ and $C_3 = \frac{4}{\sqrt{3}}$. Thus the required solution is

$$\begin{bmatrix} x \\ y \\ z \end{bmatrix} = \begin{bmatrix} 1 \\ 1 \\ 0 \end{bmatrix} e^{t} + \frac{4}{\sqrt{3}} e^{\frac{1}{2}t} \begin{bmatrix} \sin\left(\tfrac{\sqrt{3}}{2}t\right) \\ 0 \\ \tfrac{\sqrt{3}}{2}\cos\left(\tfrac{\sqrt{3}}{2}t\right) - \tfrac{1}{2}\sin\left(\tfrac{\sqrt{3}}{2}t\right) \end{bmatrix}.$$

Section 3

3.1 $\begin{bmatrix} x \\ y \end{bmatrix} = \alpha \begin{bmatrix} 1 \\ 1 \end{bmatrix} e^{5t} + \beta \begin{bmatrix} -2 \\ 1 \end{bmatrix} e^{2t} + \begin{bmatrix} t + \frac{4}{5} \\ -2t - \frac{7}{10} \end{bmatrix}$

3.2 From Example 2.2, the complementary function is
$$\begin{bmatrix} x_c \\ y_c \end{bmatrix} = \alpha \begin{bmatrix} 4 \\ 1 \end{bmatrix} e^{2t} + \beta \begin{bmatrix} 1 \\ -1 \end{bmatrix} e^{-3t}.$$
For a particular integral, we try
$$\begin{bmatrix} x \\ y \end{bmatrix} = \begin{bmatrix} at + b \\ ct + d \end{bmatrix},$$
where a, b, c, d are constants to be determined.
Substituting $x = at + b$, $y = ct + d$ into the differential equations gives
$$\begin{cases} a = (at + b) + 4(ct + d) - t + 2, \\ c = (at + b) - 2(ct + d) + 5t, \end{cases}$$
which become
$$\begin{cases} (a + 4c - 1)t + (b + 4d + 2 - a) = 0, \\ (a - 2c + 5)t + (b - 2d - c) = 0. \end{cases}$$
Equating the coefficients of t to zero gives
$$\begin{cases} a + 4c - 1 = 0, \\ a - 2c + 5 = 0, \end{cases}$$
which have the solution $a = -3$, $c = 1$.
Equating the constant terms to zero, and putting $a = -3$, $c = 1$, gives
$$\begin{cases} b + 4d + 5 = 0, \\ b - 2d - 1 = 0, \end{cases}$$
which have the solution $b = -1$, $d = -1$.
Thus the required particular integral is
$$\begin{bmatrix} x_p \\ y_p \end{bmatrix} = \begin{bmatrix} -3t - 1 \\ t - 1 \end{bmatrix},$$
and the general solution is
$$\begin{bmatrix} x \\ y \end{bmatrix} = \begin{bmatrix} x_c \\ y_c \end{bmatrix} + \begin{bmatrix} x_p \\ y_p \end{bmatrix}$$
$$= \alpha \begin{bmatrix} 4 \\ 1 \end{bmatrix} e^{2t} + \beta \begin{bmatrix} 1 \\ -1 \end{bmatrix} e^{-3t} + \begin{bmatrix} -3t - 1 \\ t - 1 \end{bmatrix}.$$

3.3 The complementary function is
$$\begin{bmatrix} x_c \\ y_c \end{bmatrix} = \alpha \begin{bmatrix} 4 \\ 1 \end{bmatrix} e^{2t} + \beta \begin{bmatrix} 1 \\ -1 \end{bmatrix} e^{-3t}.$$
For a particular integral, we try
$$\begin{bmatrix} x \\ y \end{bmatrix} = \begin{bmatrix} a \\ b \end{bmatrix} e^{-t},$$
where a and b are constants to be determined.
Substituting $x = ae^{-t}$, $y = be^{-t}$ into the differential equations gives
$$\begin{cases} -ae^{-t} = ae^{-t} + 4be^{-t} + 4e^{-t}, \\ -be^{-t} = ae^{-t} - 2be^{-t} + 5e^{-t}, \end{cases}$$
which, on dividing by e^{-t} and rearranging, become
$$\begin{cases} 2a + 4b = -4, \\ a - b = -5. \end{cases}$$
These equations have the solution $a = -4$, $b = 1$.
Thus the required particular integral is
$$\begin{bmatrix} x_p \\ y_p \end{bmatrix} = \begin{bmatrix} -4 \\ 1 \end{bmatrix} e^{-t},$$

and the general solution is
$$\begin{bmatrix} x \\ y \end{bmatrix} = \begin{bmatrix} x_c \\ y_c \end{bmatrix} + \begin{bmatrix} x_p \\ y_p \end{bmatrix}$$
$$= \alpha \begin{bmatrix} 4 \\ 1 \end{bmatrix} e^{2t} + \beta \begin{bmatrix} 1 \\ -1 \end{bmatrix} e^{-3t} + \begin{bmatrix} -4 \\ 1 \end{bmatrix} e^{-t}.$$

3.4 The complementary function is
$$\begin{bmatrix} x_c \\ y_c \end{bmatrix} = \alpha \begin{bmatrix} 4 \\ 1 \end{bmatrix} e^{2t} + \beta \begin{bmatrix} 1 \\ -1 \end{bmatrix} e^{-3t}.$$
For a particular integral, we try
$$\begin{bmatrix} x \\ y \end{bmatrix} = \begin{bmatrix} a \sin 2t + b \cos 2t \\ c \sin 2t + d \cos 2t \end{bmatrix},$$
where a, b, c, d are constants to be determined.
Substituting
$$x = a \sin 2t + b \cos 2t, \quad y = c \sin 2t + d \cos 2t$$
into the differential equations gives, on rearranging,
$$\begin{cases} (a + 4c + 2b - 4) \sin 2t + (b + 4d - 2a - 1) \cos 2t = 0, \\ (a - 2c + 2d + 1) \sin 2t + (b - 2d - 2c) \cos 2t = 0. \end{cases}$$
Equating the coefficients of $\sin 2t$ and $\cos 2t$ to zero gives the equations
$$\begin{cases} a + 2b + 4c = 4, \\ -2a + b + 4d = 1, \\ a - 2c + 2d = -1, \\ b - 2c - 2d = 0, \end{cases}$$
which have the solution $a = 0$, $b = 1$, $c = \frac{1}{2}$, $d = 0$.
Thus the required particular integral is
$$\begin{bmatrix} x_p \\ y_p \end{bmatrix} = \begin{bmatrix} \cos 2t \\ \frac{1}{2} \sin 2t \end{bmatrix},$$
and the general solution is
$$\begin{bmatrix} x \\ y \end{bmatrix} = \begin{bmatrix} x_c \\ y_c \end{bmatrix} + \begin{bmatrix} x_p \\ y_p \end{bmatrix}$$
$$= \alpha \begin{bmatrix} 4 \\ 1 \end{bmatrix} e^{2t} + \beta \begin{bmatrix} 1 \\ -1 \end{bmatrix} e^{-3t} + \begin{bmatrix} \cos 2t \\ \frac{1}{2} \sin 2t \end{bmatrix}.$$

3.5 The complementary function is
$$\begin{bmatrix} x_c \\ y_c \end{bmatrix} = \alpha \begin{bmatrix} 1 \\ -1 \end{bmatrix} e^{-t} + \beta \begin{bmatrix} 3 \\ 2 \end{bmatrix} e^{4t}.$$
We try a particular integral $\begin{bmatrix} x \\ y \end{bmatrix} = \begin{bmatrix} a \\ b \end{bmatrix} e^{2t}$. Then
$$\begin{cases} 2ae^{2t} = 2ae^{2t} + 3be^{2t} + e^{2t}, \\ 2be^{2t} = 2ae^{2t} + be^{2t} + 4e^{2t}, \end{cases}$$
which give $3b + 1 = 0$ and $b - 2a = 4$, so $b = -\frac{1}{3}$ and $a = -\frac{13}{6}$. The general solution is therefore
$$\begin{bmatrix} x \\ y \end{bmatrix} = \alpha \begin{bmatrix} 1 \\ -1 \end{bmatrix} e^{-t} + \beta \begin{bmatrix} 3 \\ 2 \end{bmatrix} e^{4t} - \frac{1}{6} \begin{bmatrix} 13 \\ 2 \end{bmatrix} e^{2t}.$$
Putting $t = 0$, we obtain
$$\tfrac{5}{6} = \alpha + 3\beta - \tfrac{13}{6}, \quad \tfrac{2}{3} = -\alpha + 2\beta - \tfrac{1}{3},$$
so $\alpha + 3\beta = 3$ and $-\alpha + 2\beta = 1$, which give $\alpha = \frac{3}{5}$ and $\beta = \frac{4}{5}$.
The required solution is therefore
$$\begin{bmatrix} x \\ y \end{bmatrix} = \tfrac{3}{5} \begin{bmatrix} 1 \\ -1 \end{bmatrix} e^{-t} + \tfrac{4}{5} \begin{bmatrix} 3 \\ 2 \end{bmatrix} e^{4t} - \tfrac{1}{6} \begin{bmatrix} 13 \\ 2 \end{bmatrix} e^{2t}.$$

3.6 These equations are of the form $\dot{\mathbf{x}} = \mathbf{A}\mathbf{x} + \mathbf{k}e^{4t}$, where $\mathbf{x} = \begin{bmatrix} x \\ y \end{bmatrix}$, $\mathbf{A} = \begin{bmatrix} 2 & 3 \\ 2 & 1 \end{bmatrix}$, $\mathbf{k} = \begin{bmatrix} 1 \\ 2 \end{bmatrix}$, and $\lambda_1 = -1$, $\lambda_2 = 4$ are the eigenvalues corresponding to eigenvectors $\mathbf{v}_1 = \begin{bmatrix} 1 & -1 \end{bmatrix}^T$ and $\mathbf{v}_2 = \begin{bmatrix} 3 & 2 \end{bmatrix}^T$, respectively.

Using Procedure 3.2, $\mathbf{k} = p\mathbf{v}_1 + q\mathbf{v}_2$ for some numbers p and q, i.e. $\begin{bmatrix} 1 & 2 \end{bmatrix}^T = p\begin{bmatrix} 1 & -1 \end{bmatrix}^T + q\begin{bmatrix} 3 & 2 \end{bmatrix}^T$, which gives $p = -\frac{4}{5}$ and $q = \frac{3}{5}$. A particular integral is of the form $\mathbf{x}_p = (a\mathbf{v}_1 + b\mathbf{v}_2 t)e^{4t}$, where $a = p/(\lambda_2 - \lambda_1)$ and $b = q$. Substituting our values for p and q into these expressions gives $a = -\frac{4}{5}/5 = -\frac{4}{25}$ and $b = \frac{3}{5}$, hence a particular integral is

$$\mathbf{x}_p = \left(-\frac{4}{25} \begin{bmatrix} 1 \\ -1 \end{bmatrix} + \frac{3}{5} \begin{bmatrix} 3 \\ 2 \end{bmatrix} t \right) e^{4t}.$$

The required general solution is therefore

$$\mathbf{x} = \alpha \begin{bmatrix} 1 \\ -1 \end{bmatrix} e^{-t} + \beta \begin{bmatrix} 3 \\ 2 \end{bmatrix} e^{4t} + \frac{1}{25} \begin{bmatrix} 45t - 4 \\ 30t + 4 \end{bmatrix} e^{4t}.$$

3.7 We can choose $\mathbf{h}_1 = \begin{bmatrix} t & 0 \end{bmatrix}^T$ and $\mathbf{h}_2 = \begin{bmatrix} 0 & \sin t \end{bmatrix}^T$, then use the principle of superposition.

Choosing a particular integral
$$\begin{bmatrix} x & y \end{bmatrix}^T = \begin{bmatrix} at + b & ct + d \end{bmatrix}^T$$
with $\mathbf{h}_1 = \begin{bmatrix} t & 0 \end{bmatrix}^T$, and substituting into the original system, we obtain
$$\begin{cases} a = 2(at + b) + 3(ct + d) + t, \\ c = 2(at + b) + (ct + d), \end{cases}$$
so
$$\begin{cases} 2a & + 3c & = -1, \\ 2a & + c & = 0, \\ -a + 2b & + 3d = & 0, \\ 2b - & c + d = & 0, \end{cases}$$
which have the solution $a = \frac{1}{4}$, $b = -\frac{7}{16}$, $c = -\frac{1}{2}$, $d = \frac{3}{8}$. Hence $\frac{1}{16}\begin{bmatrix} 4t - 7 & -8t + 6 \end{bmatrix}^T$ is a particular integral of the system $\dot{\mathbf{x}} = \mathbf{A}\mathbf{x} + \mathbf{h}_1$.

Choosing a particular integral
$$\begin{bmatrix} x & y \end{bmatrix}^T = \begin{bmatrix} a\sin t + b\cos t & c\sin t + d\cos t \end{bmatrix}^T$$
with $\mathbf{h}_2 = \begin{bmatrix} 0 & \sin t \end{bmatrix}^T$, and substituting into the original system, we obtain
$$\begin{cases} a\cos t - b\sin t = 2(a\sin t + b\cos t) \\ \qquad\qquad + 3(c\sin t + d\cos t), \\ c\cos t - d\sin t = 2(a\sin t + b\cos t) \\ \qquad\qquad + (c\sin t + d\cos t) + \sin t, \end{cases}$$
which simplify to
$$\begin{cases} (2a + b + 3c)\sin t + (-a + 2b + 3d)\cos t = 0, \\ (2a + c + d + 1)\sin t + (2b - c + d)\cos t = 0. \end{cases}$$
So
$$\begin{cases} 2a + b + 3c & = 0, \\ -a + 2b & + 3d = 0, \\ 2a & + c + d = -1, \\ 2b - & c + d = 0, \end{cases}$$
which have the solution $a = -\frac{15}{34}$, $b = \frac{9}{34}$, $c = \frac{7}{34}$, $d = -\frac{11}{34}$. Hence $\frac{1}{34}\begin{bmatrix} -15\sin t + 9\cos t & 7\sin t - 11\cos t \end{bmatrix}^T$ is a particular integral of the system $\dot{\mathbf{x}} = \mathbf{A}\mathbf{x} + \mathbf{h}_2$.

Using the principle of superposition, the required general solution is

$$\begin{bmatrix} x \\ y \end{bmatrix} = \alpha \begin{bmatrix} 3 \\ 2 \end{bmatrix} e^{4t} + \beta \begin{bmatrix} 1 \\ -1 \end{bmatrix} e^{-t}$$
$$+ \frac{1}{16} \begin{bmatrix} 4t - 7 \\ -8t + 6 \end{bmatrix} + \frac{1}{34} \begin{bmatrix} -15\sin t + 9\cos t \\ 7\sin t - 11\cos t \end{bmatrix}.$$

Section 4

4.1 The matrix of coefficients is $\mathbf{A} = \begin{bmatrix} 5 & 2 \\ 2 & 5 \end{bmatrix}$, and we are given that the eigenvectors are $\begin{bmatrix} 1 & 1 \end{bmatrix}^T$ corresponding to the eigenvalue $\lambda = 7$, and $\begin{bmatrix} 1 & -1 \end{bmatrix}^T$ corresponding to the eigenvalue $\lambda = 3$.

It follows that the general solution is
$$\begin{bmatrix} x \\ y \end{bmatrix} = C_1 \begin{bmatrix} 1 \\ 1 \end{bmatrix} e^{\sqrt{7}t} + C_2 \begin{bmatrix} 1 \\ 1 \end{bmatrix} e^{-\sqrt{7}t}$$
$$+ C_3 \begin{bmatrix} 1 \\ -1 \end{bmatrix} e^{\sqrt{3}t} + C_4 \begin{bmatrix} 1 \\ -1 \end{bmatrix} e^{-\sqrt{3}t}.$$

4.2 Using the given eigenvalues and eigenvectors, we obtain the general solution
$$\begin{bmatrix} x \\ y \\ z \end{bmatrix} = C_1 \begin{bmatrix} 1 \\ 0 \\ 0 \end{bmatrix} e^{\sqrt{2}t} + C_2 \begin{bmatrix} 1 \\ 0 \\ 0 \end{bmatrix} e^{-\sqrt{2}t}$$
$$+ C_3 \begin{bmatrix} 1 \\ -5 \\ 0 \end{bmatrix} \cos(\sqrt{3}t) + C_4 \begin{bmatrix} 1 \\ -5 \\ 0 \end{bmatrix} \sin(\sqrt{3}t)$$
$$+ C_5 \begin{bmatrix} -5 \\ 4 \\ 14 \end{bmatrix} e^{2t} + C_6 \begin{bmatrix} -5 \\ 4 \\ 14 \end{bmatrix} e^{-2t}.$$

4.3 The matrix of coefficients is $\mathbf{A} = \begin{bmatrix} -\frac{25}{7} & \frac{6}{7} \\ \frac{9}{7} & -\frac{10}{7} \end{bmatrix}$.

The characteristic equation of $\mathbf{A}$ is $\lambda^2 + 5\lambda + 4 = 0$, so the eigenvalues are $\lambda = -4$ and $\lambda = -1$.

The eigenvector equations are
$$\begin{cases} (-\frac{25}{7} - \lambda)x + \frac{6}{7}y = 0, \\ \frac{9}{7}x + (-\frac{10}{7} - \lambda)y = 0. \end{cases}$$

$\boxed{\lambda = -4}$ The eigenvector equations become
$$\begin{cases} \frac{3}{7}x + \frac{6}{7}y = 0, \\ \frac{9}{7}x + \frac{18}{7}y = 0, \end{cases}$$
which reduce to the equation $-2y = x$, so a corresponding eigenvector is $\begin{bmatrix} -2 & 1 \end{bmatrix}^T$.

$\boxed{\lambda = -1}$ The eigenvector equations become
$$\begin{cases} -\frac{18}{7}x + \frac{6}{7}y = 0, \\ \frac{9}{7}x - \frac{3}{7}y = 0, \end{cases}$$
which reduce to the equation $y = 3x$, so a corresponding eigenvector is $\begin{bmatrix} 1 & 3 \end{bmatrix}^T$.

The general solution is therefore

$$\begin{bmatrix} x \\ y \end{bmatrix} = \begin{bmatrix} -2 \\ 1 \end{bmatrix} (C_1 \cos 2t + C_2 \sin 2t)$$

$$+ \begin{bmatrix} 1 \\ 3 \end{bmatrix} (C_3 \cos t + C_4 \sin t).$$

The object describes simple harmonic motion along the eigenvectors, so there are two possibilities for simple harmonic motion along a straight line:

- motion in the direction of the vector $[-2 \ \ 1]^T$ (that is, the line $x + 2y = 0$) with angular frequency 2 (corresponding to $C_3 = C_4 = 0$);

- motion in the direction of the vector $[1 \ \ 3]^T$ (that is, the line $y = 3x$) with angular frequency 1 (corresponding to $C_1 = C_2 = 0$).

4.4 The matrix of coefficients is $\mathbf{A} = \begin{bmatrix} 1 & 4 \\ 1 & 1 \end{bmatrix}$.

The characteristic equation is $\lambda^2 - 2\lambda - 3 = 0$, so the eigenvalues are $\lambda = 3$ and $\lambda = -1$. Solving the eigenvector equations, we obtain eigenvectors $[2 \ \ 1]^T$ and $[-2 \ \ 1]^T$, respectively. Using Procedure 4.1, we then have

$$\begin{bmatrix} x \\ y \end{bmatrix} = \begin{bmatrix} 2 \\ 1 \end{bmatrix} \left(C_1 e^{\sqrt{3}t} + C_2 e^{-\sqrt{3}t} \right)$$

$$+ \begin{bmatrix} -2 \\ 1 \end{bmatrix} (C_3 \cos t + C_4 \sin t).$$

UNIT 12   *Functions of several variables*

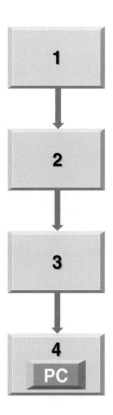

Study guide for Unit 12

This unit extends the calculus of functions of one variable to functions of several variables. It would be helpful if you can recall the Second Derivative Test (the use of the second derivative to classify maxima and minima) and Taylor polynomials for functions of one variable (although these topics are introduced from scratch).

We shall also discuss the application of functions of several variables to mechanics, and you should make sure that you can recall the concept of potential energy from *Unit 8* (in particular, the potential energy of a stretched or compressed spring).

Sections 1 and 2 contain material that will be needed in later units of the course.

One of the methods that we introduce is based on finding the eigenvalues of a matrix, so you may need to refer back to *Unit 10* as you work through Section 3.

You will use the computer algebra package for the course in Section 4.

We recommend that you study the Introduction and Section 1 over two study sessions (perhaps breaking at the end of Subsection 1.2), and that you allocate a study session to each of Sections 2, 3 and 4.

Introduction

So far in this course, most of the mathematical models have concerned physical quantities that vary with respect to a single variable. This variable has usually been time. In this unit we look at models that depend on more than one variable.

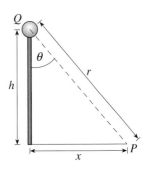

Figure 0.1

As a simple example, let us consider the illumination from a street lamp, as shown in Figure 0.1. (That is, we are considering the illumination falling on, say, a flat paving slab at the point P, due to a street lamp placed at the point Q.) There are a number of variable quantities here. To simplify things a little, let us assume that the power rating of the light bulb is fixed at 1000 watts. Nevertheless, the height h of the bulb above the street, the distance x of P from the base of the lamp, the distance r from P to Q, and the angle θ (as shown) are all features that could be taken into consideration.

It is possible to express h and x in terms of r and θ, or to express r and θ in terms of h and x. The quantities h and x are easy to measure, but the physics of the situation gives the illumination at P more readily in terms of the two variables r and θ, via the equation

$$I(r,\theta) = \frac{1000\cos\theta}{r^2}, \tag{0.1}$$

where I is the 'brightness' of the illumination per square metre falling on the slab at P.

The technical term for 'brightness' in this sense is *luminance*. The form of its dependence on r is due to the fact that the surface area of a sphere of radius r is proportional to r^2. The reason for its dependence on θ is that the light is falling obliquely on the slab.

In order to express I in terms of h and x rather than r and θ, we use the formulas $\cos\theta = \dfrac{h}{\sqrt{h^2 + x^2}}$ and $r^2 = h^2 + x^2$, giving

$$I(h,x) = \frac{1000h}{(h^2 + x^2)^{3/2}}. \tag{0.2}$$

In Equation (0.1) the two independent variables are r and θ, while in Equation (0.2) the independent variables are h and x. Thus the initial choice of variables in a problem can affect the form of the function that we need to consider, and may well affect the difficulty of our calculations. In this case, it is quite reasonable to represent I as a function of the two variables h and x, so let us suppose that we have made that choice.

Often we wish to gain some physical insight into a problem, but, as with Equation (0.2), the practical implications of a particular formula are not obvious. However, we can gain some understanding of this situation if we keep the height h fixed, at say 3 metres, and vary the distance x. The function $I = I(h,x)$ now becomes a function of the single variable x, so we can sketch its graph, as shown in Figure 0.2. We can now see that the point of brightest illumination is when P is immediately below the lamp (as intuition might lead us to expect).

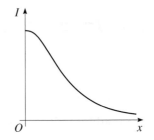

Figure 0.2

Suppose now that we keep the point P fixed at, say, $x = 10$ metres, but vary the height of the lamp. Once again, I becomes a function of a single variable, in this case h, and again we can sketch a graph, as shown in Figure 0.3. This time the result is perhaps a little more unexpected, for our graph tells us that there is an optimum height for the lamp at which the illumination on the horizontal slab at P is greatest. (This is because, as h increases, there is a trade-off between the increasing distance of the lamp from P, which tends to decrease the illumination, and the decreasing obliqueness of the angle, which tends to increase the illumination.)

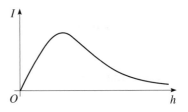

Figure 0.3

You may well wonder if it is possible to sketch a graph that represents the variation of I when both variables h and x are allowed to change. Indeed it is, but we need more than two dimensions, and the resulting surface can be hard to interpret. (We shall look at such surfaces in Section 1.)

A *surface* here is a set of points in space where coordinates satisfy a particular equation.

In order to deal sensibly with functions of two or more variables, we need mathematical tools similar to those that we have at our disposal for functions of a single variable. We should like to be able to differentiate these functions, to locate the points at which they take their greatest (or least) values, and to approximate them by polynomials. This may enable us to understand the behaviour of such functions and so give us an insight into the physical situations from which they arise. In fact, we need to develop a form of calculus that applies to such functions, and that is the purpose of this unit.

Section 1 concentrates on functions of two variables. We show how such functions may be used to define a surface, and we then extend the notion of derivative in order to investigate the slope of such a surface. Section 2 provides a brief discussion of Taylor polynomials for functions of one variable and then extends the discussion to Taylor polynomials for functions of several variables. Section 3 discusses the main topic of the unit: the classification of stationary points (points where the first derivatives are zero) for functions of two or more variables. Section 4 broadens the approach to include applications to mechanics.

1 Functions of two variables

Our main objective in this section is to extend some of the ideas of the calculus of functions of one variable: most importantly, the concepts of *derivative*, *stationary point*, *local maximum* and *local minimum*. However, before we discuss the *calculus* of functions of two variables, we need to discuss the *concept* of a function of two variables. We introduce the concept with a physical situation.

1.1 Introducing functions of two variables

Imagine an experiment in which a thin flat metal disc of radius 2 metres is heated (see Figure 1.1(a)). At a particular moment, we record the temperatures at various points on its upper surface.

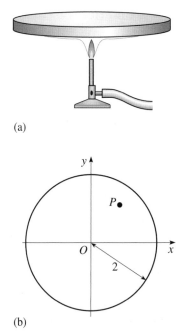

(a)

We could specify the points on the surface of the disc by means of a Cartesian coordinate system, using the centre of the disc as the origin, as shown in Figure 1.1(b). The temperature may well vary over the surface of the disc, so that the temperature at O is higher than at P, for example. Nevertheless, at any given moment, each point (x, y) of the disc has a well-defined temperature (Θ, say, in degrees Celsius). We could denote this temperature by $\Theta(x, y)$ to remind ourselves that the value of Θ depends on our particular choice of x and y. We say that Θ is a function of the two variables x and y, and that the *dependent variable* Θ is a function of the two *independent variables* x and y.

(b)

There is a natural restriction on the independent variables x and y arising from the physical situation: $\Theta(x, y)$ has been defined only for points (x, y) lying on the disc. That is, the domain of the function Θ is the set of points (x, y) in the plane such that $x^2 + y^2 \leq 4$.

Figure 1.1

Suppose that a mathematical model of this situation predicts that

$$\Theta(x, y) = 10(10e^{-(x^2+y^2)} + 1) \quad (x^2 + y^2 \leq 4). \tag{1.1}$$

Then it is a simple matter to calculate the predicted temperature at any point on the disc. For example, at the point $(1, 1.5)$ the predicted temperature (in degrees Celsius) is

$$\Theta(1, 1.5) = 10(10e^{-(1^2+1.5^2)} + 1) = 10(10e^{-3.25} + 1) \simeq 13.9.$$

Exercise 1.1

Given $f(x, y) = 3x^2 - 2y^3$, evaluate the following.

*(a) $f(2, 3)$ *(b) $f(3, 2)$ *(c) $f(a, b)$ *(d) $f(b, a)$

(e) $f(2a, b)$ (f) $f(a - b, 0)$ (g) $f(x, 2)$ (h) $f(y, x)$

Exercise 1.2

Figure 1.2 shows a double pendulum consisting of two light model rods OA and AB with a smooth joint at A. The rods move in a vertical plane, with O attached to a fixed point by means of a frictionless hinge. A particle of mass m is attached to B, and the angles θ and ϕ are as shown.

Express the potential energy U of the system (taking a horizontal line through O as the datum) in terms of the independent variables θ and ϕ. What is the least possible value of U?

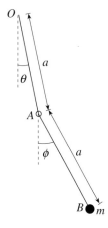

Figure 1.2

1.2   Geometric interpretation

A function of two variables expresses a dependent variable in terms of two independent variables, so there are three varying quantities altogether. Thus a graph of such a function will require three dimensions.

Definition

A **function of two variables** is a function f whose domain is $\mathbb{R}^2$ (or a subset of $\mathbb{R}^2$) and whose codomain is $\mathbb{R}$. Thus, for each point (x, y) in the domain of f, there is a unique value z defined by

$$z = f(x, y).$$

The set of all points with coordinates $(x, y, z) = (x, y, f(x, y))$, plotted in a three-dimensional Cartesian coordinate system, is the **surface with equation** $z = f(x, y)$.

Each variable is in $\mathbb{R}$, hence the domain of a function of two variables is denoted by $\mathbb{R}^2$.

The definition of a function of two variables generalizes in a straightforward way: a **function of n variables** is a function whose domain is $\mathbb{R}^n$ (or a subset of $\mathbb{R}^n$) and whose codomain is $\mathbb{R}$.

The simplest of all surfaces $z = f(x, y)$ for a function of two variables arises from choosing f to be the zero function. We then have the equation $z = 0$, and the surface is the plane that contains the x- and y-axes, known as the (x, y)-plane.

More generally, the surface corresponding to any *linear* function of two variables $z = f(x, y) = Ax + By + C$ (where A, B and C are constants) is a **plane**.

For example, the equation $z = f(x, y) = -\frac{2}{3}x - 2y + 2$ represents a plane passing through the three points $(3, 0, 0)$, $(0, 1, 0)$ and $(0, 0, 2)$, and extending indefinitely. Part of this plane is illustrated in Figure 1.3.

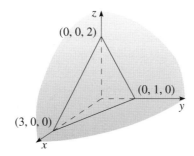

Figure 1.3

The surfaces corresponding to the functions $p(x, y) = x^2 + y^2$ (see Figure 1.4(a)) and $h(x, y) = y^2 - x^2$ (see Figure 1.4(b)) are not planes, but you will see later that their behaviour near the origin is of particular interest. The function $p(x, y)$ is a **paraboloid** (which can be obtained by plotting the parabola $z = x^2$ in the (x, z)-plane and then rotating it about the z-axis). The function $h(x, y)$ is a **hyperboloid** (which cannot be obtained by rotating a curve about the z-axis or any other axis).

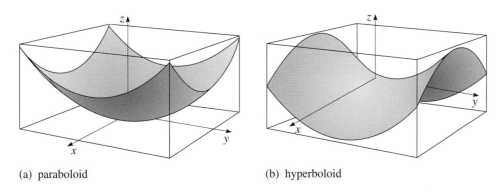

(a) paraboloid   (b) hyperboloid

Figure 1.4

Section functions

In general, the surface representing a function may be complicated and difficult to visualize. The computer algebra package for the course can be put to good use here, in that you can use it to plot a function and view it from various perspectives. But this may not be enough, and it is often helpful to consider the function obtained by fixing all the independent variables except one at specific values. In the case of the function $p(x, y) = x^2 + y^2$, for example, we might choose to fix the value of y at 2, in which case we are left with the function of a *single variable*

$$p(x, 2) = x^2 + 4.$$

This function is known as a **section function** of $p(x, y) = x^2 + y^2$ with y fixed at 2.

In the case of the surfaces shown in Figure 1.4, it is worth looking at their behaviour near the origin. The section functions $p(x, 0)$ and $p(0, y)$, and $h(x, 0)$ and $h(0, y)$, are quite illuminating. They show, very clearly, properties of the surfaces that you may have already observed.

The section functions $p(x,0)$ and $p(0,y)$ are shown in Figures 1.5 and 1.6, respectively.

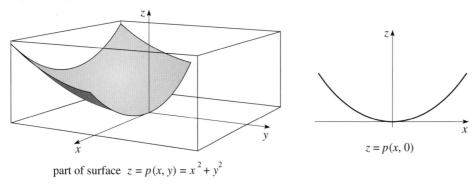

part of surface $z = p(x, y) = x^2 + y^2$

$z = p(x, 0)$

Figure 1.5

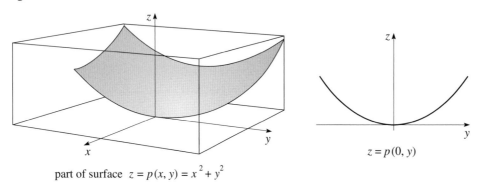

part of surface $z = p(x, y) = x^2 + y^2$

$z = p(0, y)$

Figure 1.6

The surface $z = p(x,y) = x^2 + y^2$ has a local minimum at the origin; correspondingly, each of the section functions $p(x,0)$ and $p(0,y)$ has a local minimum there.

The section functions $h(x,0)$ and $h(0,y)$ are shown in Figures 1.7 and 1.8, respectively.

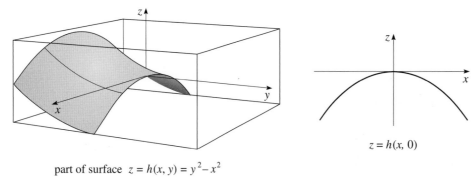

part of surface $z = h(x, y) = y^2 - x^2$

$z = h(x, 0)$

Figure 1.7

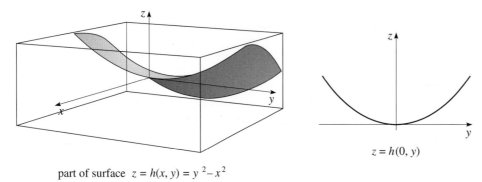

part of surface $z = h(x, y) = y^2 - x^2$

$z = h(0, y)$

Figure 1.8

The surface $z = h(x, y) = y^2 - x^2$ has neither a local maximum nor a local minimum at the origin, corresponding to the fact that the section function $h(x, 0)$ has a local maximum at the origin, while the section function $h(0, y)$ has a local minimum there.

Of course, we have not yet defined what we mean by a (local) maximum or minimum of a function of two variables (that comes in Section 3), but it is already clear that a surface can behave in a more complicated fashion than the graph of a function of one variable.

It is worth spending a little time at this point to recall how to use calculus to justify that the section functions $h(x, 0)$ and $h(0, y)$ have a local maximum and a local minimum, respectively, at the origin.

A standard method in this context is the Second Derivative Test, which applies to 'sufficiently smooth' functions of one variable. (In this context, 'sufficiently smooth' means that the first and second derivatives exist.) If $f(x)$ is a function whose first and second derivatives exist, and at some point $x = a$ we have $f'(a) = 0$, then a is a *stationary point* of $f(x)$. Often (but not always) it will be a local maximum or a local minimum. The **Second Derivative Test** is based on the evaluation of $f''(x)$ at a. There are three possibilities.

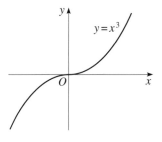

(a) If $f''(a)$ is *negative*, then f has a *local maximum* at a.

(b) If $f''(a)$ is *positive*, then f has a *local minimum* at a.

(c) If $f''(a) = 0$, then the test is inconclusive. There may still be a local maximum or a local minimum at a, but another possibility is that there is a *point of inflection*, such as occurs at $x = 0$ for the function $f(x) = x^3$ (see Figure 1.9).

Figure 1.9

Example 1.1

Use the Second Derivative Test to verify that $h(x, 0)$ has a local maximum at $x = 0$ and that $h(0, y)$ has a local minimum at $y = 0$, where $h(x, y) = y^2 - x^2$.

Solution

We have $h(x, 0) = -x^2$. So $\dfrac{d}{dx}(-x^2) = -2x$, and this is zero when $x = 0$. Thus $h(x, 0)$ has a stationary point at $x = 0$. Now $\dfrac{d^2}{dx^2}(-x^2) = -2$, which is negative for all values of x, so this stationary point is a local maximum.

We have $h(0, y) = y^2$. So $\dfrac{d}{dy}(y^2) = 2y$, and this is zero when $y = 0$. Thus $h(0, y)$ has a stationary point at $y = 0$. Now $\dfrac{d^2}{dy^2}(y^2) = 2$, which is positive for all values of y, so this stationary point is a local minimum. ∎

Exercise 1.3 _____

Show that the section function of $F(x, y) = 100e^{-(x^2 + y^2)}$ with y fixed at 0 has a local maximum at $x = 0$.

The concept of a *section function* can be extended easily to functions of more than two variables. For example, the section function of $w(x, y, t) = \dfrac{x}{y + 2t}$ with x fixed at 3 and t fixed at 1 is $w(3, y, 1) = \dfrac{3}{y + 2}$, which is a function of y only.

The domain of w should be restricted so that $y + 2t$ can never be zero.

(Section functions are always functions of *one* variable, so we have to fix the values of all the variables except one to obtain a section function.) One obvious advantage of considering section functions (rather than the original function of two or more variables) is that we can apply the familiar calculus techniques for functions of one variable.

1.3 First-order partial derivatives

As a first step towards our goal of extending the ideas of calculus to functions of two (or more) variables, we begin by recalling the role played by the tangent to a graph in the calculus of functions of one variable. If we imagine a tangent line sliding along a graph, then each time the line is horizontal, we have a stationary point. We apply the same idea to functions of two variables, only this time we slide a *tangent plane* over the surface. Let us be a little more precise about this.

In most cases, the tangent line to a curve C at a point P on C is the straight line that *touches* C at P, but does not *cross* the curve at that point.

Sometimes, however, even if C is a smooth curve as it goes through P, it is not possible to find a line with the 'non-crossing' property. Suppose, for example, that C is the graph of $y = x^3$ (see Figure 1.9) and P is the origin. Then every straight line through the origin 'crosses' C, as you may verify by placing a ruler at various angles through P on Figure 1.9. Nevertheless, the line that is the x-axis seems to be a good candidate for the 'tangent line' to C at $(0,0)$; intuitively, it seems to pass through the curve at a 'zero angle'. Let us try to make this idea more mathematically robust.

Consider again a general curve C and a point P on C at which we wish to find a tangent line (see Figure 1.10). If Q is a point on the curve close to P, then the *chord* through P and Q is the straight line through these points. If C is smooth enough to have a derivative at P then, as Q approaches P, the chord through P and Q approaches a well-defined line through P, which is defined to be the **tangent line** to C at P.

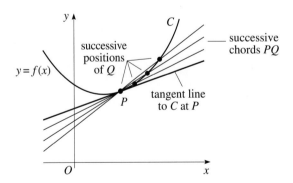

Figure 1.10

The tangent line at P is the line that has the same *slope* as C at that point. To return to the case of the curve $y = f(x) = x^3$ (see Figure 1.9), since $f'(0) = 0$, the slope of C at $(0,0)$ is 0, so the tangent line to C at $(0,0)$ is the x-axis, that is, the line $y = 0$.

More generally, if the curve C is defined by the function $y = f(x)$, then at the point $P = (a, f(a)) = (a, b)$, the slope of C is $f'(a)$ and the equation of the tangent line is $y - b = f'(a)(x - a)$, this being the equation of a line through (a, b) with slope $f'(a)$.

In a similar way, a smooth surface without breaks or folds has a *tangent plane*. In the cases of the paraboloid and the hyperboloid in Figure 1.4, the surface is horizontal at the point $(0,0,0)$, so, for each of these surfaces, the tangent plane at $(0,0,0)$ is the (x,y)-plane. In the case of the paraboloid, the (x,y)-plane touches the surface at that point, but does not cut through it. The hyperboloid, however, lies partly above and partly below the (x,y)-plane, so (as with the tangent line at $(0,0)$ to $y = x^3$) the (x,y)-plane cuts the hyperboloid — despite having the same 'slope in any direction' as the hyperboloid at $(0,0,0)$.

The tangent plane can be defined by a 'limiting' construction similar to that for the tangent line. We need three points to define a plane, so if P is a point on a smooth surface S, we must take two further points Q and R on the surface, and we must ensure that P, Q and R never lie on a straight line (when projected onto the (x,y)-plane). Then, as Q and R separately approach P (from distinct directions), the plane through P, Q and R will approach a well-defined plane, the **tangent plane** at P (see Figure 1.11).

There are some technicalities concerning the choice of Q and R, but they are not important in this context.

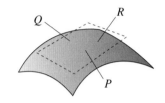

Just as the slope of a curve C at a point P on C is equal to the slope of the tangent line at P, so the 'slope' of the surface S at the point P on S is equal to the 'slope' of the tangent plane at P. But what *is* this slope?

Figure 1.11

Imagine that the surface is a hillside and that you are walking across it (see Figure 1.12). Let us suppose that you want to measure the 'slope' of the hill at some particular point. You immediately encounter a problem: in which direction should you measure the slope? If you choose a direction pointing 'straight up the hill' you will get one value, and if you choose to move 'round the hill' you will get another. We shall choose two specific directions in which to measure the slope: the x-direction and the y-direction. On a smooth hill, this will be sufficient to determine the slope in every direction (as you will see in Subsection 1.4). So we start by examining the rate at which a function of two variables changes when we keep one of the variables fixed.

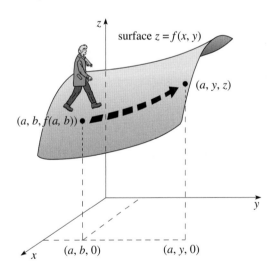

Figure 1.12

Suppose that you are walking over the surface defined by the equation $z = f(x,y)$ and that you are at the point $(a,b,f(a,b)) = (a,b,c)$. If $c > 0$, then directly below you is the point $(a,b,0)$ lying in the (x,y)-plane (see Figure 1.12). Now you begin to move across the surface, taking care to ensure that the value of x stays fixed at a. As you move, the value of y changes, and your height z above the (x,y)-plane varies. We are going to investigate the rate of change of the height z with y, which you would recognize as the slope (at some particular point) of the path along which you are walking. We refer to this slope as the *slope of the surface in the y-direction* (at the point in question).

As a specific example, consider the function

$$f(x, y) = x^2 - y^3 + 2xy^2.$$

Suppose that we are trying to find the slope of this surface in the y-direction at the point $(2, 1, 7)$ on the surface. First we construct the section function of $f(x, y)$ with x fixed at 2:

$$f(2, y) = 4 - y^3 + 4y^2.$$

Then we differentiate this function with respect to y, to obtain

$$\frac{df}{dy}(2, y) = -3y^2 + 8y.$$

Finally, we put $y = 1$ into this expression and obtain the value 5 for the slope of the surface in the y-direction at $(2, 1, 7)$.

This process would be the same for any fixed value of x and so can be generalized: fix x at some constant value, then differentiate $f(x, y)$ with respect to y, using all the standard rules of differentiation and *treating x as a constant*. The result is the expression $-3y^2 + 4xy$. This is the *partial derivative* of the function $f(x, y) = x^2 - y^3 + 2xy^2$ with respect to y, denoted by $\partial f / \partial y$. So we have

$$\frac{\partial f}{\partial y}(x, y) = -3y^2 + 4xy.$$

If we put $x = 2$ and $y = 1$ in this expression, then we obtain

$$\frac{\partial f}{\partial y}(2, 1) = 5,$$

which is the same value as we found above.

The same method can be used to find the slope in the x-direction, but this time we keep y fixed and differentiate with respect to x. We obtain

$$\frac{\partial f}{\partial x}(x, y) = 2x + 2y^2.$$

Putting $x = 2$ and $y = 1$ into this expression, we obtain the value 6 for the slope of the surface in the x-direction at $(2, 1, 7)$.

More formally, the partial derivatives of a function $f(x, y)$ with respect to x and y are given by

$$\frac{\partial f}{\partial x} = \lim_{\delta x \to 0} \frac{f(x + \delta x, y) - f(x, y)}{\delta x} \tag{1.2}$$

and

$$\frac{\partial f}{\partial y} = \lim_{\delta y \to 0} \frac{f(x, y + \delta y) - f(x, y)}{\delta y}, \tag{1.3}$$

where δx and δy denote (small) increments in the values of x and y, respectively.

Note the important difference between the symbols:

'delta' symbol δ represents an increment;

'partial dee' symbol ∂ represents partial differentiation.

We shall need the more formal definitions later, but for now the following definitions will suffice.

The use of the 'partial dee' symbol ∂ (rather than d) for partial derivatives distinguishes them from ordinary derivatives.

The ordinary derivative of $f(t)$ with respect to t is formally defined as

$$\frac{df}{dt} = \lim_{h \to 0} \frac{f(t + h) - f(t)}{h}.$$

Definitions

Given a function f of two variables (say x and y), the **partial derivative** $\partial f/\partial x$ is obtained by differentiating $f(x,y)$ with respect to x while treating y as a constant. Similarly, the **partial derivative** $\partial f/\partial y$ is obtained by differentiating $f(x,y)$ with respect to y while treating x as a constant.

The partial derivatives $\partial f/\partial x$ and $\partial f/\partial y$ represent the slopes of the surface $z = f(x,y)$ at the point $(x, y, f(x,y))$ in the x- and y-directions, respectively. These partial derivatives are the **first-order partial derivatives** or the **first partial derivatives** of the function f.

The expression $\partial f/\partial x$ is read as 'partial dee f by dee x'.

We shall define second-order and higher-order partial derivatives in Section 2.

We shall also use the alternative notation f_x for $\partial f/\partial x$ and f_y for $\partial f/\partial y$.

Example 1.2

Calculate $\partial f/\partial x$ and $\partial f/\partial y$ for

$$f(x,y) = \sqrt{xy} + xy^2 \quad (x > 0,\ y > 0).$$

Find the slopes of the corresponding surface $z = \sqrt{xy} + xy^2$ in the x- and y-directions at the point $(4, 1, 6)$ on the surface.

Solution

First we treat y as a constant and differentiate with respect to x (remembering that $\sqrt{xy} = \sqrt{x}\sqrt{y}$), to obtain

$$\frac{\partial f}{\partial x} = \frac{\sqrt{y}}{2\sqrt{x}} + y^2.$$

So the slope in the x-direction at $(4, 1, 6)$ is

$$\left(\sqrt{1}/(2\sqrt{4})\right) + 1 = \tfrac{5}{4}.$$

Now we treat x as a constant and differentiate f with respect to y, to obtain

$$\frac{\partial f}{\partial y} = \frac{\sqrt{x}}{2\sqrt{y}} + 2xy.$$

So the slope in the y-direction at $(4, 1, 6)$ is

$$\left(\sqrt{4}/(2\sqrt{1})\right) + (2 \times 4 \times 1) = 9. \quad \blacksquare$$

In general, $\partial f/\partial x$ and $\partial f/\partial y$ are functions of the two variables x and y, so in Example 1.2 we could write

$$\frac{\partial f}{\partial x}(x,y) = \frac{\sqrt{y}}{2\sqrt{x}} + y^2, \quad \frac{\partial f}{\partial y}(x,y) = \frac{\sqrt{x}}{2\sqrt{y}} + 2xy,$$

or, alternatively,

$$f_x(x,y) = \frac{\sqrt{y}}{2\sqrt{x}} + y^2, \quad f_y(x,y) = \frac{\sqrt{x}}{2\sqrt{y}} + 2xy,$$

if we wish to emphasize the fact that the partial derivatives are themselves functions. Thus we could write

$$f_x(4, 1) = \tfrac{5}{4}, \quad f_y(4, 1) = 9,$$

for the slopes in the x- and y-directions, respectively, at the point in question.

*Exercise 1.4

Given $f(x,y) = (x^2 + y^3)\sin(xy)$, calculate $\partial f/\partial x$ and $\partial f/\partial y$.

Of course, the two independent variables need not be denoted by x and y; any variable names will do, as the next example shows.

Example 1.3

Given $f(\alpha, t) = \alpha \sin(\alpha t)$, calculate $f_\alpha(\frac{\pi}{2}, 1)$ and $f_t(\frac{\pi}{2}, 1)$.

Solution

Differentiating partially with respect to α gives $f_\alpha = \sin(\alpha t) + \alpha t \cos(\alpha t)$, so

$$f_\alpha(\tfrac{\pi}{2}, 1) = \sin\tfrac{\pi}{2} + \tfrac{\pi}{2}\cos\tfrac{\pi}{2} = 1.$$

Differentiating partially with respect to t gives $f_t = \alpha^2 \cos(\alpha t)$, so

$$f_t(\tfrac{\pi}{2}, 1) = (\tfrac{\pi}{2})^2 \cos\tfrac{\pi}{2} = 0. \quad \blacksquare$$

*Exercise 1.5

Given $u(\theta, \phi) = \sin\theta + \phi\tan\theta$, calculate u_θ and u_ϕ.

Often, a mathematical model will generate a relationship between variables. For example, we have the formula $V = \frac{1}{3}\pi r^2 h$ for the volume V of a cone in terms of the radius r of its circular base and its height h. We could introduce a function $f(r,h) = \frac{1}{3}\pi r^2 h$ and write the partial derivatives as $\partial f/\partial r$ and $\partial f/\partial h$. But it is often more convenient to let V denote both the variable and the function that defines it, enabling us to write $\partial V/\partial r$ in place of $\partial f/\partial r$, and $\partial V/\partial h$ in place of $\partial f/\partial h$, thus keeping the number of symbols to a minimum.

The notion of partial derivative can be extended to functions of more than two variables. For example, for a function $f(x,y,t)$ of three variables, to calculate $\partial f/\partial x$, we keep y and t fixed, and differentiate with respect to x (and similarly for the other partial derivatives).

*Exercise 1.6

(a) Find the first partial derivatives of the function

$$f(x,y,t) = x^2 y^3 t^4 + 2xy + 4t^2 x^2 + y.$$

(b) Given $z = (1+x)^2 + (1+y)^3$, calculate $\partial z/\partial x$ and $\partial z/\partial y$. Sketch the section functions $z(x,0)$ and $z(0,y)$. What is the relevance of the value of $(\partial z/\partial x)(0,0)$ to the graph of $z(x,0)$, and what is the relevance of the value of $(\partial z/\partial y)(0,0)$ to the graph of $z(0,y)$?

1.4   Slope in an arbitrary direction

Suppose that the walker in Figure 1.12 is not walking in either the x-direction or the y-direction, but in some other direction. Can we use the partial derivatives $(\partial f/\partial x)(a,b)$ and $(\partial f/\partial y)(a,b)$ to find the slope at the point (a,b,c) in this other direction?

To answer this question, we start by looking at the formal definitions of partial derivatives in Equations (1.2) and (1.3), and use them to investigate what happens when we move a small amount in a particular direction.

For a function $z = f(x, y)$, the equations are

$$\frac{\partial f}{\partial x} = \lim_{\delta x \to 0} \frac{f(x + \delta x, y) - f(x, y)}{\delta x}, \tag{1.2}$$

$$\frac{\partial f}{\partial y} = \lim_{\delta y \to 0} \frac{f(x, y + \delta y) - f(x, y)}{\delta y}. \tag{1.3}$$

Small increments

If we write $\delta z_1 = f(x + \delta x, y) - f(x, y)$ and $\delta z_2 = f(x, y + \delta y) - f(x, y)$, then δz_1 is the change, or *increment*, in the value of z corresponding to a (small) increment δx in the value of x. Similarly, δz_2 is the increment in the value of z corresponding to a (small) increment δy in the value of y. So we have

$$\frac{\partial f}{\partial x} = \lim_{\delta x \to 0} \frac{\delta z_1}{\delta x}, \quad \frac{\partial f}{\partial y} = \lim_{\delta y \to 0} \frac{\delta z_2}{\delta y}. \tag{1.4}$$

The expressions of the form $\dfrac{\delta *}{\delta t}$ here are quotients, *not* derivatives.

We know from Subsection 1.3 that $\partial f / \partial x$ and $\partial f / \partial y$ are the slopes of $z = f(x, y)$ in the x- and y-directions, respectively. To find the slope of $z = f(x, y)$ in an arbitrary direction, we need to find the increment δz in the value of f when we move a short distance in that direction. Such a movement can be achieved by small increments δx and δy, and Equations (1.4) relate these approximately to the corresponding increments δz_1 and δz_2, as shown below.

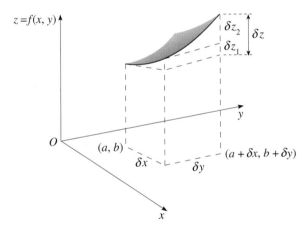

Figure 1.13

Figure 1.13 shows a small part of the surface $z = f(x, y)$ and the point (a, b) in the (x, y)-plane. We are interested in the effect on z when x and y are increased by the small amounts δx and δy, respectively. The increment δz is produced by moving first from (a, b) to $(a + \delta x, b)$, and then from $(a + \delta x, b)$ to $(a + \delta x, b + \delta y)$. We shall specify δz_1 to be the increment in z on moving from (a, b) to $(a + \delta x, b)$, and δz_2 to be the increment in z on moving from $(a + \delta x, b)$ to $(a + \delta x, b + \delta y)$.

We consider δz_1 first. This is $f(a + \delta x, b) - f(a, b)$, the difference between the function values at (a, b) and $(a + \delta x, b)$. Since x has moved from a to $a + \delta x$ while y has remained constant, the increment in z is approximately equal to the increment in x multiplied by the partial derivative with respect to x, i.e.

$$\delta z_1 \simeq \frac{\partial f}{\partial x}(a, b)\, \delta x. \tag{1.5}$$

This follows from the first of Equations (1.4).

The approximation used here holds because for small δx, we can take the slope $\partial f / \partial x$ in the x-direction to be almost constant on the interval between $x = a$ and $x = a + \delta x$. Similarly, for small δy, the slope $\partial f / \partial y$ in the y-direction can be taken to be almost constant on the interval between $y = b$ and $y = b + \delta y$.

153

The increment δz_2 is obtained by holding x constant at the value $a + \delta x$ while incrementing y from b to $b + \delta y$. It is thus approximately equal to the increment in y multiplied by the partial derivative with respect to y, i.e.

$$\delta z_2 \simeq \frac{\partial f}{\partial y}(a + \delta x, b)\,\delta y. \tag{1.6}$$

At this point in the argument, it is necessary to assume that f is a sufficiently smooth function so that the methods of calculus that we require can be applied. We assume, in particular, that the partial derivatives are continuous. So, for small δx, we have

$$\frac{\partial f}{\partial y}(a + \delta x, b) \simeq \frac{\partial f}{\partial y}(a, b). \tag{1.7}$$

Putting Equations (1.5), (1.6) and (1.7) together, we now have our expression linking small increments in z with small increments in x and y:

$$\delta z = \delta z_1 + \delta z_2 \simeq \frac{\partial f}{\partial x}(a, b)\,\delta x + \frac{\partial f}{\partial y}(a, b)\,\delta y, \tag{1.8}$$

which may be easier to remember when written in the form

$$\delta z \simeq \frac{\partial z}{\partial x}\,\delta x + \frac{\partial z}{\partial y}\,\delta y. \tag{1.9}$$

The approximation (1.9) has an important application to error analysis, as the next example shows.

Example 1.4

The volume V of a cone of height h with base radius r is given by

$$V = \tfrac{1}{3}\pi r^2 h.$$

Determine the approximate change in the volume if the radius increases from 2 to $2 + \delta r$ and the height increases from 5 to $5 + \delta h$.

If the radius and height measurements are each subject to an error of magnitude up to 0.01, how accurate is the estimate

$$V \simeq \tfrac{1}{3} \times \pi \times 2^2 \times 5 = \tfrac{20}{3}\pi \; (= 20.94, \text{ to four significant figures})$$

of the volume?

Solution

Calculating the partial derivatives of $V = V(r, h)$ with respect to r and h, we have

$$\frac{\partial V}{\partial r} = \tfrac{2}{3}\pi r h, \quad \frac{\partial V}{\partial h} = \tfrac{1}{3}\pi r^2.$$

Setting $r = 2$ and $h = 5$, we calculate

$$\frac{\partial V}{\partial r}(2, 5) = \tfrac{2}{3}\pi \times 2 \times 5 = \tfrac{20}{3}\pi, \quad \frac{\partial V}{\partial h}(2, 5) = \tfrac{1}{3}\pi \times 2^2 = \tfrac{4}{3}\pi,$$

and thus, from approximation (1.8),

$$\delta V \simeq \tfrac{20}{3}\pi\,\delta r + \tfrac{4}{3}\pi\,\delta h,$$

which answers the first part of the question.

If the maximum possible magnitudes of δr and δh are 0.01, the maximum possible magnitude of δV is approximately

$$\left(\tfrac{20}{3} + \tfrac{4}{3}\right)\pi \times 0.01 = 8\pi \times 0.01 \simeq 0.25.$$

Thus the volume estimate of 20.94 may compare with an actual value as high as 21.19 or as low as 20.69. The estimate is accurate to only two significant figures (and should be given as $V = 21$, correct to two significant figures). ■

Exercise 1.7

Given $z = (1+x)^2 + (1+y)^3$, find the approximate increment δz in z when x is incremented from 0 to δx and y is incremented from 2 to $2 + \delta y$.

(*Hint*: You may wish to use your solution to Exercise 1.6(b).)

Rate of change along a curve

Now we focus on the rate of change of $z = f(x,y)$ if (x,y) is constrained to move along a curve in the (x,y)-plane. Let us suppose that x and y are themselves functions of a parameter t, so that as t varies, the point $(x(t), y(t))$ moves along a curve in the (x,y)-plane, passing through (a,b) when $t = t_0$ and through $(a + \delta x, b + \delta y)$ when $t = t_0 + \delta t$. From Equation (1.9) we have

You may recall from previous studies that a curve described in terms of a parameter, say t, in this way is called a *parametrized curve*.

$$\frac{\delta z}{\delta t} \simeq \frac{\partial z}{\partial x}\frac{\delta x}{\delta t} + \frac{\partial z}{\partial y}\frac{\delta y}{\delta t}. \tag{1.10}$$

Having introduced the parameter t, we can think of x, y and z as functions of the single variable t. Thinking of them in this way, we have $\delta x = x(t_0 + \delta t) - x(t_0)$, $\delta y = y(t_0 + \delta t) - y(t_0)$ and $\delta z = z(t_0 + \delta t) - z(t_0)$. Thus

$$\frac{\delta x}{\delta t} = \frac{x(t_0 + \delta t) - x(t_0)}{\delta t}, \quad \frac{\delta y}{\delta t} = \frac{y(t_0 + \delta t) - y(t_0)}{\delta t}, \quad \frac{\delta z}{\delta t} = \frac{z(t_0 + \delta t) - z(t_0)}{\delta t}.$$

So, from the definition of an ordinary derivative, as $\delta t \to 0$, these become dx/dt, dy/dt and dz/dt, respectively. Hence, as $\delta t \to 0$, approximation (1.10) becomes

$$\frac{dz}{dt}(t_0) = \frac{\partial z}{\partial x}(a,b)\frac{dx}{dt}(t_0) + \frac{\partial z}{\partial y}(a,b)\frac{dy}{dt}(t_0).$$

The $\dfrac{d*}{dt}$ are derivatives, not quotients.

This may remind you of the Chain Rule for the derivative of z with respect to t if z is a function of the single variable x, and x is a function of t; i.e. if $z = z(x(t))$, then

On the curve, z, x and y are functions of t only, so it is consistent to write, for example, $\dfrac{dz}{dt}$ rather than $\dfrac{\partial z}{\partial t}$.

$$\frac{dz}{dt} = \frac{dz}{dx}\frac{dx}{dt}.$$

Indeed, the formula for the rate of change along a parametrized curve is the two-dimensional analogue of the Chain Rule of ordinary differentiation.

Chain Rule

Let $z = f(x,y)$ be a function whose first partial derivatives exist and are continuous. Then the rate of change of z with respect to t along a curve parametrized by $(x(t), y(t))$ is given by

$$\frac{dz}{dt} = \frac{\partial z}{\partial x}\frac{dx}{dt} + \frac{\partial z}{\partial y}\frac{dy}{dt}. \tag{1.11}$$

Exercise 1.8

Given $z = \sin x - 3\cos y$, find the rate of change of z along the curve $(x(t), y(t))$, where $x(t) = t^2$, $y(t) = 2t$.

The above form of the Chain Rule is easy to remember, but if there is a reason to emphasize that the partial derivatives are evaluated at a particular point, then it may be convenient to write it as

$$\frac{dz}{dt}(t_0) = \frac{\partial f}{\partial x}(a, b) \times \frac{dx}{dt}(t_0) + \frac{\partial f}{\partial y}(a, b) \times \frac{dy}{dt}(t_0),$$

where $x(t_0) = a$ and $y(t_0) = b$.

The Chain Rule is of fundamental importance and we shall refer back to it both in this unit and in the remainder of the course. For the moment, we use it to continue our discussion of the slope of a surface.

Slope in an arbitrary direction

We want to find the slope of $z = f(x, y)$ at a point $(a, b, c) = (a, b, f(a, b))$ on the surface in an arbitrary given direction. This given direction is specified by a straight line through (a, b) in the (x, y)-plane. Suppose that on this line x and y are functions of the parameter t, so that $x = x(t)$ and $y = y(t)$. Let us also take $x(0) = a$ and $y(0) = b$. Then our straight line can be parametrized as

$$x(t) = a + t \cos \alpha, \quad y(t) = b + t \sin \alpha,$$

where α is the anticlockwise angle the line makes with the positive x-axis and t measures the distance along this line, as illustrated in Figure 1.14. As (x, y) moves along this line, the point $(x, y, f(x, y))$ moves along a curve in the surface $z = f(x, y)$ (see Figure 1.15).

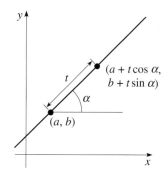

Figure 1.14

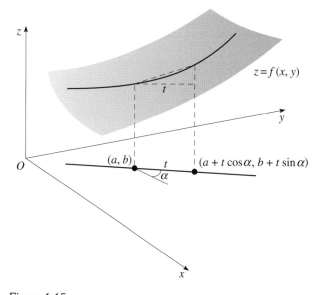

Figure 1.15

The advantage of defining the line in terms of the parameter t is that the derivative of z with respect to t is the quantity we are looking for — the slope of the surface $z = f(x, y)$ at the point (a, b, c), in the direction that makes an angle α with the direction of the x-axis (see Figure 1.15).

Moreover, we can now use the Chain Rule given in Equation (1.11). Since $dx/dt = \cos \alpha$ and $dy/dt = \sin \alpha$, we obtain

$$\frac{dz}{dt} = \frac{\partial z}{\partial x} \cos \alpha + \frac{\partial z}{\partial y} \sin \alpha. \tag{1.12}$$

That is, we have shown that the slope of the surface $z = f(x, y)$ at the point $(a, b, f(a, b))$ in the direction making an anticlockwise angle α with the positive x-axis is

$$\frac{\partial f}{\partial x}(a,b)\cos\alpha + \frac{\partial f}{\partial y}(a,b)\sin\alpha$$

or

$$f_x(a,b)\cos\alpha + f_y(a,b)\sin\alpha.$$

This defines the slope of a surface *in a particular direction*. But what is *the* slope of the surface at $(a,b,f(a,b))$? The answer is that it can be thought of as a vector, with a component $f_x(a,b)$ in the x-direction and a component $f_y(a,b)$ in the y-direction, i.e. as the vector $f_x(a,b)\mathbf{i} + f_y(a,b)\mathbf{j}$. The advantage of this formulation is that the slope in the direction of an arbitrary unit vector $\widehat{\mathbf{d}} = (\cos\alpha)\mathbf{i} + (\sin\alpha)\mathbf{j}$ in the (x,y)-plane is the dot product of the vectors $f_x(a,b)\mathbf{i} + f_y(a,b)\mathbf{j}$ and $\widehat{\mathbf{d}}$. This idea is important enough to deserve some terminology of its own.

$|\widehat{\mathbf{d}}| = \cos^2\alpha + \sin^2\alpha = 1$

Definition

The vector **grad** $f(a,b) = f_x(a,b)\mathbf{i} + f_y(a,b)\mathbf{j}$ is called the **gradient** of the function $f(x,y)$ at the point (a,b), and is alternatively denoted by $\boldsymbol{\nabla} f(a,b)$. Thus $\boldsymbol{\nabla} f(x,y)$ is a (vector) function of two variables, called the **gradient function**.

The symbol $\boldsymbol{\nabla}$ is called 'del', or sometimes 'nabla'.

The result concerning the slope of a surface can now be written as follows.

Slope of a surface

Let $z = f(x,y)$ be a surface described by a function whose first partial derivatives exist and are continuous. Then the slope of the surface at the point $(a,b,f(a,b))$ in the direction of the unit vector $\widehat{\mathbf{d}} = (\cos\alpha)\mathbf{i} + (\sin\alpha)\mathbf{j}$ in the (x,y)-plane is the dot product

$$(\boldsymbol{\nabla} f(a,b)) \cdot \widehat{\mathbf{d}} = f_x(a,b)\cos\alpha + f_y(a,b)\sin\alpha. \qquad (1.13)$$

---

*Exercise 1.9 _____

Given the surface S defined by $z = f(x,y) = 2x^2y + 3xy^3$, find the following.

(a) The gradient function $\boldsymbol{\nabla} f(x,y) = f_x\mathbf{i} + f_y\mathbf{j}$.

(b) The slope of the surface at the point $(2,1,14)$ in the direction of the vector $\widehat{\mathbf{d}} = \frac{3}{5}\mathbf{i} + \frac{4}{5}\mathbf{j}$.

*Exercise 1.10 _____

By varying the angle α (measured anticlockwise from the positive x-axis), we can examine the slope of the surface at the fixed point (a,b,c) in any direction we wish.

Calculate the greatest slope of the surface $z = f(x,y) = \frac{1}{2}x^2 + \sqrt{3}y^2$ at the point $(2,1,2+\sqrt{3})$ on the surface. Show that this greatest slope is in the direction of $\boldsymbol{\nabla} f(2,1)$.

_____

In general, as the result from Exercise 1.10 illustrates, the direction of the gradient function $\boldsymbol{\nabla} f(x,y)$ at a point (a,b) corresponds to the direction of greatest slope of the surface $z = f(x,y)$ at the point $(a,b,f(a,b))$. To see this, we observe that $\boldsymbol{\nabla} f \cdot \widehat{\mathbf{d}} = |\boldsymbol{\nabla} f||\widehat{\mathbf{d}}|\cos\theta = |\boldsymbol{\nabla} f|\cos\theta$, where θ is the angle between $\boldsymbol{\nabla} f$ and $\widehat{\mathbf{d}}$, and $\theta = 0$ gives the maximum value.

End-of-section Exercises

Exercise 1.11

Given $z = y \sin x$, find the rate of change of z along the curve $(x(t), y(t))$, where $x = e^t$ and $y = t^2$. Evaluate this rate of change at $t = 0$.

Exercise 1.12

Given the surface defined by $z = f(x, y) = (x + 2y)^3 - (2x - y)^2$, find each of the following:

(a) the gradient function $\nabla f(x, y) = f_x \mathbf{i} + f_y \mathbf{j}$;

(b) the slope of the surface at the point $(1, 0, -3)$ in the direction of the vector $\mathbf{i} + \mathbf{j}$.

2 Taylor polynomials

The aim of this unit is to extend the techniques of calculus to functions of two (or more) variables, in order to be able to tackle a wider range of problems in applied mathematics. However, before continuing, it is necessary to review Taylor polynomials and Taylor approximations as they apply to functions of one variable. These are revised in Subsection 2.1. Subsection 2.2 introduces higher-order partial derivatives of functions of two variables (which are conceptually very like their counterparts for functions of one variable). In Subsection 2.3 we generalize Taylor polynomials and Taylor approximations to functions of two variables.

2.1 Functions of one variable

Many useful functions (e.g. trigonometric and exponential functions) cannot generally be evaluated exactly, so the best we can do is approximate them. Polynomial functions are often used as approximations because they are easy to evaluate and manipulate. In many cases, a good approximation to a function f can be obtained near some point a in the domain of f by finding the polynomial of a chosen degree that agrees with f at a, and also agrees with the first few derivatives of f evaluated at a. For example, the function $f(x) = \sin x$ can be approximated reasonably well near $x = 0$ by the first-order polynomial $p_1(x) = x$ (see Figure 2.1).

p_1 has the subscript 1 because it is a *first*-order polynomial.

So $\sin x \simeq x$ is a good approximation for small x (say $|x| \leq 0.1$). This is because the functions $y = x$ and $y = \sin x$ at $x = 0$ agree in value (they are both 0), in their first derivatives (they are both 1), and in their second derivatives (they are both 0).

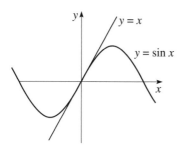

Figure 2.1

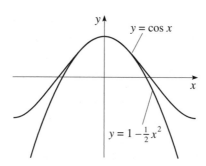

Figure 2.2

Similarly, the function $f(x) = \cos x$ can be approximated quite well near $x = 0$ by the quadratic (second-order) polynomial $p_2(x) = 1 - \frac{1}{2}x^2$ (see Figure 2.2). The reason is that $p_2(x)$ and $\cos x$ agree at $x = 0$ in their values, and also in the values of their first, second and third derivatives.

Exercise 2.1

Verify the above statements concerning $p_1(x)$ and $p_2(x)$. That is, check that $p_1(0) = \sin 0$, $p_1'(0) = \cos 0$, $p_1''(0) = -\sin 0$, $p_2(0) = \cos 0$, $p_2'(0) = -\sin 0$, $p_2''(0) = -\cos 0$ and $p_2'''(0) = \sin 0$.

We call $p_1(x) = x$ the *tangent approximation* to the function $f(x) = \sin x$ near $x = 0$, or the *Taylor polynomial of degree 1* for $f(x) = \sin x$ about $x = 0$. Similarly, $p_2(x) = 1 - \frac{1}{2}x^2$ is the *quadratic approximation* to the function $f(x) = \cos x$ near $x = 0$, or the *Taylor polynomial of degree 2* for $f(x) = \cos x$ about $x = 0$.

In fact, $p_1(x)$ is also the quadratic approximation to $\sin x$, and $p_2(x)$ is also the cubic approximation to $\cos x$.

Definition

For a function $f(x)$ that has n continuous derivatives near $x = a$, the **Taylor polynomial of degree n about $x = a$**, or the **nth-order Taylor polynomial about $x = a$**, is

$$p_n(x) = f(a) + f'(a)(x - a) + \tfrac{1}{2!}f''(a)(x - a)^2 + \tfrac{1}{3!}f'''(a)(x - a)^3$$
$$+ \cdots + \tfrac{1}{n!}f^{(n)}(a)(x - a)^n. \tag{2.1}$$

We use the phrases 'Taylor polynomial of degree n' and 'nth-order Taylor polynomial' synonymously.

If $a = 0$, expression (2.1) becomes the simpler expression

$$p_n(x) = f(0) + f'(0)x + \tfrac{1}{2!}f''(0)x^2 + \tfrac{1}{3!}f'''(0)x^3$$
$$+ \cdots + \tfrac{1}{n!}f^{(n)}(0)x^n. \tag{2.2}$$

This is known as a Maclaurin series.

Example 2.1

For the function $f(x) = e^{2x}$, calculate $f(0)$, $f'(0)$, $f''(0)$ and $f'''(0)$. Write down the third-order Taylor polynomial $p_3(x)$ for $f(x)$ about $x = 0$.

Solution

Since $f(x) = e^{2x}$, it follows that

$$f'(x) = 2e^{2x}, \quad f''(x) = 4e^{2x}, \quad f'''(x) = 8e^{2x}.$$

Therefore

$$f(0) = 1, \quad f'(0) = 2, \quad f''(0) = 4, \quad f'''(0) = 8.$$

The third-order Taylor polynomial for e^{2x} about $x = 0$ is therefore

$$p_3(x) = 1 + 2x + \tfrac{4}{2!}x^2 + \tfrac{8}{3!}x^3 = 1 + 2x + 2x^2 + \tfrac{4}{3}x^3. \quad \blacksquare$$

For the functions that you will meet in the remainder of this course, successive higher-order Taylor polynomials will give successively better approximations, at least for values of x that are reasonably close to a. This claim will be enhanced in *Unit 26*, where you will see a theorem (Taylor's Theorem) that makes a statement about the possible size of the error involved in approximating a function by a Taylor polynomial.

Exercise 2.2

For $f(x) = e^{2x}$ (as in Example 2.1), write down the Taylor polynomials $p_0(x)$, $p_1(x)$ and $p_2(x)$ about $x = 0$. Evaluate $p_0(0.1)$, $p_1(0.1)$ and $p_2(0.1)$, and compare these values with the value of $f(0.1)$ obtained on a calculator.

One important application of Taylor polynomials is in examining the local behaviour of a function. Suppose that the function $f(t)$ has a stationary point at $t = a$ (so $f'(a) = 0$). One consequence of Taylor's Theorem is that close to $t = a$, the behaviour of $f(t)$ will be the same as the behaviour of the second-order Taylor polynomial for $f(t)$ about $t = a$. So we can use the second-order Taylor polynomial about $t = a$ to determine the nature of this stationary point. Close to $t = a$, we have

$$f(t) \simeq p_2(t) = f(a) + \tfrac{1}{2!}f''(a)(t - a)^2.$$

The change in independent variable from x to t has no particular significance.

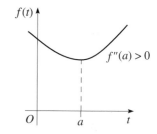

The behaviour of the function $f(t)$ near $t = a$ is determined by the sign of $f''(a)$, assuming $f''(a) \neq 0$ (see Figure 2.3). In fact,

$$f(t) - f(a) \simeq \tfrac{1}{2!}f''(a)(t - a)^2;$$

thus if $f''(a) \neq 0$, the right-hand side of this equation does not change sign near $t = a$. So either $f(t) \geq f(a)$ near $t = a$ (if $f''(a) > 0$), or $f(t) \leq f(a)$ near $t = a$ (if $f''(a) < 0$).

So if $f''(a) > 0$, $f(t)$ has a local minimum at $t = a$, and if $f''(a) < 0$, $f(t)$ has a local maximum at $t = a$. However, if $f''(a) = 0$, the polynomial $p_2(t)$ can tell us nothing about the nature of the stationary point of $f(t)$ at $t = a$. This is the result known as the Second Derivative Test that you saw in Section 1. To illustrate the usefulness of Taylor polynomials, let us examine the case when $f''(a) = 0$ a little further. (In this case, the Second Derivative Test is of no help.)

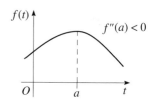

Figure 2.3

Example 2.2

Suppose that you are told that $f'(a) = f''(a) = 0$, but $f'''(a) \neq 0$, for a function $f(t)$. If $f(t)$ is approximated by its third-order Taylor polynomial $p_3(t)$, what does $p_3(t)$ tell you about the stationary point of $f(t)$ at $t = a$?

Solution

We have

$$f(t) \simeq p_3(t) = f(a) + \tfrac{1}{3!}f'''(a)(t - a)^3,$$

so

$$f(t) - f(a) \simeq \tfrac{1}{3!}f'''(a)(t - a)^3.$$

When a Taylor polynomial is used to approximate a function, we refer to the Taylor polynomial as a Taylor approximation to the function.

This will change sign as t passes through a (whatever the sign of $f'''(a)$). It follows that the stationary point is neither a local maximum nor a local minimum; such a point is a point of inflection. ■

You should take particular notice of the reasoning in Example 2.2, because we shall apply a similar process in discussing functions of two variables. It is the sign of $f(t) - f(a)$ near $t = a$ that determines the nature of the stationary point at $t = a$.

If we are concerned with the local behaviour of $f(t)$ near $t = a$, then we are interested in the behaviour of $f(t) - f(a)$ when $t - a$ is small (and certainly less than 1). If $t - a$ is small, then $(t - a)^2$ is even smaller, while higher powers of $t - a$ are smaller still. When, for example, we use the second-order Taylor polynomial as an approximation to $f(t)$, we are effectively ignoring terms involving $(t - a)^3$, $(t - a)^4$, ... This is another idea that extends to functions of two variables.

2.2 Higher-order partial derivatives

In the next subsection we shall extend the concept of Taylor polynomials to functions of two variables, but first we must develop the concept of partial derivatives a little further.

You saw in Section 1 that we can differentiate a function of two variables $f(x, y)$ partially with respect to x and partially with respect to y, to obtain the partial derivatives $\partial f / \partial x$ and $\partial f / \partial y$. For example, if $f(x, y) = \sin(xy)$, then $\partial f / \partial x = y \cos(xy)$ and $\partial f / \partial y = x \cos(xy)$. The partial derivatives are themselves functions of two variables, so it is possible to calculate their partial derivatives. In the case of the function $f(x, y) = \sin(xy)$, we may differentiate $\partial f / \partial x$ partially with respect to x and obtain

$$\frac{\partial}{\partial x} \left(\frac{\partial f}{\partial x} \right) = \frac{\partial}{\partial x} (y \cos(xy)) = -y^2 \sin(xy). \tag{2.3}$$

Each of $\partial f / \partial x$ and $\partial f / \partial y$ can be partially differentiated with respect to either variable, so, for this particular function $f(x, y)$, we have, in addition to Equation (2.3),

$$\frac{\partial}{\partial y} \left(\frac{\partial f}{\partial x} \right) = \frac{\partial}{\partial y} (y \cos(xy)) = \cos(xy) - xy \sin(xy),$$

$$\frac{\partial}{\partial x} \left(\frac{\partial f}{\partial y} \right) = \frac{\partial}{\partial x} (x \cos(xy)) = \cos(xy) - xy \sin(xy),$$

$$\frac{\partial}{\partial y} \left(\frac{\partial f}{\partial y} \right) = \frac{\partial}{\partial y} (x \cos(xy)) = -x^2 \sin(xy).$$

Definition

The **second-order partial derivatives** (or **second partial derivatives**) of a function $f(x, y)$ are

$$\frac{\partial^2 f}{\partial x^2} = \frac{\partial}{\partial x} \left(\frac{\partial f}{\partial x} \right), \quad \frac{\partial^2 f}{\partial y^2} = \frac{\partial}{\partial y} \left(\frac{\partial f}{\partial y} \right),$$

$$\frac{\partial^2 f}{\partial x \partial y} = \frac{\partial}{\partial x} \left(\frac{\partial f}{\partial y} \right), \quad \frac{\partial^2 f}{\partial y \partial x} = \frac{\partial}{\partial y} \left(\frac{\partial f}{\partial x} \right).$$

They are often abbreviated as f_{xx}, f_{yy}, f_{xy} and f_{yx}, respectively.

Both notations are in common use, and we shall use them interchangeably.

We can extend the ideas here to obtain higher-order partial derivatives of any order. For example, we can obtain third-order partial derivatives by partially differentiating the second-order partial derivatives.

Example 2.3

Determine the second-order partial derivatives of the function

$$f(x, y) = e^x \cos y + x^2 - y + 1.$$

Solution

We have

$$\frac{\partial f}{\partial x} = e^x \cos y + 2x, \quad \frac{\partial f}{\partial y} = -e^x \sin y - 1,$$

so

$$\frac{\partial^2 f}{\partial x^2} = e^x \cos y + 2, \quad \frac{\partial^2 f}{\partial x \partial y} = -e^x \sin y,$$

$$\frac{\partial^2 f}{\partial y \partial x} = -e^x \sin y, \quad \frac{\partial^2 f}{\partial y^2} = -e^x \cos y. \quad \blacksquare$$

Exercise 2.3 ────────────────────────────────

Given $f(x, y) = x \sin(xy)$, calculate f_{xx}, f_{yy}, f_{xy} and f_{yx}.

In both Example 2.3 and Exercise 2.3 (as well as in the work on $f(x, y) = \sin(xy)$ at the beginning of this subsection), you can see that

$$\frac{\partial^2 f}{\partial x \partial y} = \frac{\partial^2 f}{\partial y \partial x}, \tag{2.4}$$

that is, $f_{xy} = f_{yx}$. This is no accident; this result is always true, provided that the function $f(x, y)$ is sufficiently smooth for the second-order partial derivatives to exist and to be continuous.

Theorem 2.1   Mixed Derivative Theorem

For any function $f(x, y)$ that is sufficiently smooth for the second-order partial derivatives to exist and to be continuous,

$$\frac{\partial^2 f}{\partial x \partial y} = \frac{\partial^2 f}{\partial y \partial x}.$$

This can be written as $f_{xy} = f_{yx}$.

We assume throughout the remainder of this unit that the functions we deal with are smooth enough for the Mixed Derivative Theorem to apply.

Exercise 2.4 ────────────────────────────────

Given $f(x, y) = e^{2x+3y}$, calculate $f_x(0, 0)$, $f_y(0, 0)$, $f_{xx}(0, 0)$, $f_{yy}(0, 0)$, $f_{xy}(0, 0)$ and $f_{yx}(0, 0)$.

The ideas in this subsection can be extended to functions of more than two variables, though we do not do so here.

2.3   Functions of two variables

In the case of a function f of one variable, say x, you saw in Subsection 2.1 that the nth-order Taylor polynomial agrees with f in value and in the values of the first n derivatives at the chosen point $x = a$. This property of agreement in function value and values of the derivatives is crucial in the definition of Taylor polynomials, and is the property that we generalize to more than one variable.

Consider, for example, the function

$$f(x, y) = e^{x+2y}.$$

If we wish to find a first-order polynomial $p(x, y)$ that approximates $f(x, y)$ near $(0, 0)$, then it seems that we must ensure that p agrees with f in value and in the values of the first partial derivatives at $(0, 0)$. That is, we need to find a first-order polynomial

$$p(x, y) = \alpha + \beta x + \gamma y, \tag{2.5}$$

where α, β and γ are constants, with the properties that

$$p(0, 0) = f(0, 0), \quad p_x(0, 0) = f_x(0, 0), \quad p_y(0, 0) = f_y(0, 0).$$

In our example, $f_x(x, y) = e^{x+2y}$ and $f_y(x, y) = 2e^{x+2y}$, so

$$f(0, 0) = 1, \quad f_x(0, 0) = 1, \quad f_y(0, 0) = 2.$$

A first-order (linear) polynomial in one variable has the form $f(x) = c + mx$, where c and m are constants. A first-order polynomial in two variables has linear terms in both variables, so is of the form $f(x, y) = c + mx + ny$, where c, m and n are constants.

Thus, in defining p, we need to choose the coefficients α, β and γ so that

$$p(0,0) = 1, \quad p_x(0,0) = 1, \quad p_y(0,0) = 2.$$

From Equation (2.5), $p(0,0) = \alpha$, so we need $\alpha = 1$. Also, differentiating Equation (2.5), we obtain

$$p_x(x,y) = \beta, \quad p_y(x,y) = \gamma.$$

In particular,

$$p_x(0,0) = \beta, \quad p_y(0,0) = \gamma.$$

So we need $\beta = 1$ and $\gamma = 2$. The required Taylor polynomial is therefore

$$p(x,y) = 1 + x + 2y.$$

More generally, whatever the function $f(x,y)$ may be (provided that we can find its first partial derivatives), we can make $p(x,y) = \alpha + \beta x + \gamma y$ agree with $f(x,y)$ at $(0,0)$ by setting $\alpha = f(0,0)$. Also, we can make the first partial derivatives agree at $(0,0)$ by setting $\beta = f_x(0,0)$ and $\gamma = f_y(0,0)$.

Definition

For a function $f(x,y)$ that is sufficiently smooth near $(x,y) = (0,0)$, the **first-order Taylor approximation** (or **tangent approximation**) **to $f(x,y)$ near $(0,0)$** is

$$p_1(x,y) = f(0,0) + f_x(0,0)x + f_y(0,0)y.$$

---

*Exercise 2.5

Given $f(x,y) = e^{3x-y}$, find the tangent approximation to $f(x,y)$ near $(0,0)$.

As in the case of functions of one variable, we obtain a more accurate approximation than the tangent approximation if we use a second-order polynomial that agrees with the function not only in the above respects, but also in the values of the second partial derivatives at $(0,0)$.

A general second-order polynomial in x and y takes the form

$$q(x,y) = \alpha + \beta x + \gamma y + Ax^2 + Bxy + Cy^2. \tag{2.6}$$

In order to fit the value of $q(x,y)$ and its first and second partial derivatives at $(0,0)$ to those of a function $f(x,y)$, it is necessary to determine the partial derivatives of q. You are asked to do this in Exercise 2.6.

For the moment, we continue to consider approximations near $(0,0)$, though we shall generalize shortly.

*Exercise 2.6

For $q(x,y)$ as described in Equation (2.6):

(a) find the functions q_x, q_y, q_{xx}, q_{xy} and q_{yy};

(b) evaluate $q(x,y)$ and its first and second partial derivatives at $(0,0)$.

From the result of Exercise 2.6, it follows that in order to approximate $f(x,y)$ near $(0,0)$ by $q(x,y)$ in Equation (2.6), we must set

$$\alpha = f(0,0), \quad \beta = f_x(0,0), \quad \gamma = f_y(0,0),$$
$$A = \tfrac{1}{2}f_{xx}(0,0), \quad B = f_{xy}(0,0), \quad C = \tfrac{1}{2}f_{yy}(0,0).$$

> **Definition**
>
> For a function $f(x, y)$ that is sufficiently smooth near $(x, y) = (0, 0)$, the **second-order Taylor approximation** (or **quadratic approximation**) to $f(x, y)$ **near** $(0, 0)$ is
>
> $$p_2(x, y) = f(0, 0) + f_x(0, 0)x + f_y(0, 0)y$$
> $$+ \tfrac{1}{2}\left(f_{xx}(0, 0)x^2 + 2f_{xy}(0, 0)xy + f_{yy}(0, 0)y^2\right). \qquad (2.7)$$

If we take only the *linear* terms in Equation (2.7), we obtain the first-order Taylor polynomial. This is the equation of the *tangent plane* at $(0, 0)$.

Exercise 2.7

Verify that $z = g(x, y) = f(0, 0) + f_x(0, 0)x + f_y(0, 0)y$ is the equation of a plane through $(0, 0, f(0, 0))$. Show that the plane has the same gradient as the surface $z = f(x, y)$ at $(0, 0, f(0, 0))$.

It is also possible to obtain similar approximations for $f(x, y)$ near an arbitrary point (a, b). In this case, x is replaced by $x - a$, y is replaced by $y - b$, and the function f and its partial derivatives are evaluated at (a, b).

> **Definitions**
>
> For a function $f(x, y)$ that is sufficiently smooth near $(x, y) = (a, b)$, the **first-order Taylor polynomial for** $f(x, y)$ **about** (a, b) (or **tangent approximation to** $f(x, y)$ **near** (a, b)) is
>
> $$p_1(x, y) = f(a, b) + f_x(a, b)(x - a) + f_y(a, b)(y - b).$$
>
> The **tangent plane** to the surface $z = f(x, y)$ at $(a, b, f(a, b))$ is given by $z = p_1(x, y)$.
>
> For a function $f(x, y)$ that is sufficiently smooth near $(x, y) = (a, b)$, the **second-order Taylor polynomial for** $f(x, y)$ **about** (a, b) (or **quadratic approximation to** $f(x, y)$ **near** (a, b)) is
>
> $$p_2(x, y) = f(a, b) + f_x(a, b)(x - a) + f_y(a, b)(y - b)$$
> $$+ \tfrac{1}{2}\left(f_{xx}(a, b)(x - a)^2 + 2f_{xy}(a, b)(x - a)(y - b)\right.$$
> $$\left. + f_{yy}(a, b)(y - b)^2\right). \qquad (2.8)$$

Example 2.4

Determine the Taylor polynomials of degrees 1 and 2 about $(2, 1)$ for the function

$$f(x, y) = x^3 + xy - 2y^2.$$

Solution

Differentiating the function partially with respect to x and partially with respect to y gives

$$f_x = 3x^2 + y, \quad f_y = x - 4y.$$

Differentiating partially again gives

$$f_{xx} = 6x, \quad f_{xy} = 1, \quad f_{yy} = -4.$$

It follows that

$$f(2,1) = 8, \quad f_x(2,1) = 13, \quad f_y(2,1) = -2,$$
$$f_{xx}(2,1) = 12, \quad f_{xy}(2,1) = 1, \quad f_{yy}(2,1) = -4,$$

and therefore

$$p_1(x,y) = 8 + 13(x-2) - 2(y-1),$$
$$p_2(x,y) = 8 + 13(x-2) - 2(y-1)$$
$$+ 6(x-2)^2 + (x-2)(y-1) - 2(y-1)^2. \quad \blacksquare$$

Exercise 2.8 _____

Use the results of Exercise 2.4 to write down the second-order Taylor polynomial for $f(x,y) = e^{2x+3y}$ about $(0,0)$.

_____

We could extend the arguments of this subsection to define Taylor polynomials of order higher than two, or even to functions of more than two variables, but we do not do so here.

End-of-section Exercises

Exercise 2.9 _____

In Exercise 1.2 we discussed the potential energy U of the mechanical system shown in Figure 1.2, and you saw that $U(\theta, \phi) = -mga(\cos\theta + \cos\phi)$. Find the second-order Taylor polynomial for $U(\theta, \phi)$ about $(0,0)$.

Exercise 2.10 _____

Determine the second-order Taylor polynomial about $(0,0)$ for the function $f(x,y) = e^{xy} + (x+y)^2$.

Exercise 2.11 _____

Determine the second partial derivatives of $f(x,y) = (x^2 + 2y^2 - 3xy)^3$. Evaluate these partial derivatives at $(1,-1)$.

Exercise 2.12 _____

(a) Determine the Taylor polynomials of degrees 1 and 2 about $(0,0)$ for the function $f(x,y) = (2 + x + 2y)^3$. Compare your answers to the expression obtained by expanding $(2 + x + 2y)^3$.

(b) Determine the Taylor polynomials of degrees 1 and 2 about $(1,-1)$ for the function $f(x,y) = (2 + x + 2y)^3$.

(c) Putting $X = x - 1$ and $Y = y + 1$ (so that $X = 0$ when $x = 1$, and $Y = 0$ when $y = -1$), we have

$$f(x,y) = (2 + x + 2y)^3 = \left(2 + (X+1) + 2(Y-1)\right)^3$$
$$= (1 + X + 2Y)^3.$$

Write down the Taylor polynomials of degrees 1 and 2 about $(0,0)$ for the function $F(X,Y) = (1 + X + 2Y)^3$.

_____

3 Classification of stationary points

The main purpose of this section is to extend to functions of two variables the Second Derivative Test that was discussed in Section 1. If $f(x, y)$ is sufficiently smooth that the first and second partial derivatives are defined, and if $f_x(a, b) = f_y(a, b) = 0$ at some point (a, b), then there is a distinct possibility that $f(x, y)$ has a local maximum or a local minimum at (a, b).

In the case of a function of one variable, the sign of the second derivative at a stationary point is enough to distinguish whether that point is a local maximum or a local minimum (provided that the second derivative is not zero at that point). The situation is more complicated for functions of two variables (for a start, there are three second partial derivatives to consider), but, similarly, a knowledge of the values of these derivatives at a stationary point will often tell us whether it is a local maximum, a local minimum, or neither.

3.1 Extrema

In searching for the local maxima and local minima of a function of one variable, the first step is to locate the stationary points, i.e. the points where the derivative is zero. The same is true in the case of functions of two or more variables.

Definition

A **stationary point** of a function $f(x, y)$ is a point (a, b) in the domain of $f(x, y)$ at which $f_x(a, b) = f_y(a, b) = 0$.

The corresponding point $(a, b, f(a, b))$ on the surface S defined by $z = f(x, y)$ is a **stationary point** on S.

The definition of a stationary point can be extended to functions of three or more variables.

Example 3.1

Locate the stationary point(s) of the function $f(x, y) = 5 + (x - 1)^3 + y^2$.

Solution

Partially differentiating gives $f_x = 3(x - 1)^2$, which is zero when $x = 1$, and $f_y = 2y$, which is zero when $y = 0$. So $(1, 0)$ is the only stationary point (corresponding to the point $(1, 0, 5)$ on the surface). ∎

Generally, to find the stationary point(s), we need to solve a pair of simultaneous equations, as the following example shows.

Example 3.2

Locate the stationary point(s) of the function

$$f(x, y) = x^2 + y^2 + (x - 1)(y + 2).$$

Solution

Partially differentiating gives $f_x = 2x + y + 2$ and $f_y = 2y + x - 1$. To find the stationary points, we need to solve the pair of simultaneous equations

$$\begin{cases} 2x + y = -2, \\ x + 2y = 1. \end{cases}$$

We find that $x = -\frac{5}{3}$ and $y = \frac{4}{3}$. It follows that $(-\frac{5}{3}, \frac{4}{3})$ is the only stationary point. ∎

Exercise 3.1 ————————————————————

Locate the stationary point(s) of the function

$$f(x, y) = 3x^2 - 4xy + 2y^2 + 4x - 8y.$$

A word of warning! The simultaneous equations that must be solved in order to find stationary points are in general non-linear. For example, if

$$f(x, y) = e^{x+2y} + x^4y + xy^3,$$

then $f_x = e^{x+2y} + 4x^3y + y^3$ and $f_y = 2e^{x+2y} + x^4 + 3xy^2$, so we need to solve the pair of simultaneous equations

$$\begin{cases} e^{x+2y} + 4x^3y + y^3 = 0, \\ 2e^{x+2y} + x^4 + 3xy^2 = 0. \end{cases}$$

We shall not ask you to tackle problems as difficult as this by hand, but the next exercise involves a pair of non-linear equations that can be solved by factorization.

Exercise 3.2 ————————————————————

Locate the stationary points of the function $f(x, y) = xy(x + y - 3)$.

If a function f of n variables is smooth enough to have first partial derivatives everywhere on $\mathbb{R}^n$, then any local maxima or local minima that exist will occur at stationary points. For a function of one variable, we could apply the Second Derivative Test to the stationary points. We now generalize this to a method of classifying the stationary points of functions of several variables, using second partial derivatives.

The purpose of this section is to describe two ways of doing this. The first is particularly useful for functions of two variables, while the second can be used for functions of any number of variables. But, before going any further, we need definitions of 'local maximum' and 'local minimum' for functions of more than one variable. We shall state such definitions for functions of two variables; it is not difficult to see how to generalize these to several variables.

Definitions

A function $f(x, y)$, defined on a domain D, has a **local minimum** at (a, b) in D if, for all (x, y) in D sufficiently close to (a, b), we have $f(x, y) \geq f(a, b)$.

A function $f(x, y)$, defined on a domain D, has a **local maximum** at (a, b) in D if, for all (x, y) in D sufficiently close to (a, b), we have $f(x, y) \leq f(a, b)$.

A point that is either a local maximum or a local minimum is an **extremum** (and vice versa).

If the function $f(x, y)$ has an extremum at (a, b), then the section function $z = f(x, b)$ (a function of x only) must also have an extremum at $x = a$, so $(\partial f/\partial x)(a, b) = 0$. Similarly, $(\partial f/\partial y)(a, b) = 0$. It follows that every extremum of $f(x, y)$ is a stationary point of $f(x, y)$. However, not every stationary point is necessarily an extremum.

Definition

A stationary point of a function of two variables that is not an extremum is a **saddle point**.

The term saddle point originates from the shape of surfaces near some such points for functions of two variables. An example is provided by the shape of the hyperboloid shown in Figure 1.4(b) near a stationary point (in this case, the origin) — it looks like a rider's saddle. (A saddle drops *down* on either side of the rider, but rises *up* in front and behind.) For completeness, it is worth noting that there are more complicated possibilities for the shapes of surfaces near stationary points that are not extrema; all such points are referred to as saddle points, however.

Exercise 3.3 _____

In Exercise 1.2 you found that the potential energy U of the mechanical system shown in Figure 1.2 can be written as $U(\theta, \phi) = -mga(\cos\theta + \cos\phi)$. Show that $U(\theta, \phi)$ has a stationary point at $(0, 0)$, and that this point is a local minimum.

If we are looking for the extrema of a given function, then we know that we should look amongst the stationary points. However, not all cases are as straightforward as Exercise 3.3, and we shall need some general means of classifying them (much as we have for functions of one variable). You will see next that we can use the second-order Taylor polynomial to construct a useful test that will often distinguish between local maxima, local minima and saddle points.

Let $f(x, y)$ have a stationary point at (a, b). To ensure that $f(x, y)$ has a local minimum at (a, b), it is not enough to stipulate that each of the section functions $f(x, b)$ and $f(a, y)$ through (a, b) has a local minimum at that point. There may still be directions through (a, b) along which the value of $f(x, y)$ decreases as we move away from (a, b).

For example, consider the function $f(x, y) = x^2 + 6xy + 7y^2$, which possesses a stationary point at $(0, 0)$. The section functions through $(0, 0)$ are $f(x, 0) = x^2$ and $f(0, y) = 7y^2$, each of which has a local minimum at $(0, 0)$. But let us move along the parametrized curve (actually a straight line) given by $x(t) = 2t$, $y(t) = -t$. Then

$$f(x(t), y(t)) = (2t)^2 + 6(2t)(-t) + 7(-t)^2 = -t^2.$$

> $f_x = 2x + 6y$, so $f_x(0,0) = 0$.
> $f_y = 6x + 14y$, so $f_y(0,0) = 0$.

As we move along this line from $(0, 0)$, the value of $f(x(t), y(t))$ becomes negative. As $f(0, 0) = 0$, it follows that $(0, 0)$ cannot be a local minimum of f.

One way to understand the reason for this behaviour is to express the function as a difference of two squares:

$$f(x, y) = x^2 + 6xy + 7y^2 = 2(x + 2y)^2 - (x + y)^2.$$

> Strictly, as a difference of two squares this is
> $$(\sqrt{2}x + 2\sqrt{2}y)^2 - (x + y)^2.$$

Thus, no matter how close to the origin we look, we see some points where the function is positive and some where it is negative. In particular, in the direction along which $x + 2y = 0$, the expression on the right-hand side reduces to $-(x + y)^2$, which is negative except when $(x, y) = (0, 0)$. However, in the direction $x + y = 0$ the expression is $2(x + 2y)^2$, which is positive except when $(x, y) = (0, 0)$. Therefore $(0, 0)$ is a saddle point of $f(x, y)$.

In general, $f(x, y)$ may not be a function that can be manipulated as easily as the polynomial above. Nevertheless, the quadratic approximation to $f(x, y)$ about (a, b) *is* a polynomial, and you will see in the next subsection that its second-order terms can be manipulated in this way. Moreover, you will see that this is usually sufficient for us to be able to classify the stationary point at (a, b). The test that we shall derive, based on the quadratic approximation, is similar to the Second Derivative Test for functions of one variable.

Before going on to derive this test, it is worth recalling the logic behind the Second Derivative Test. The quadratic approximation to a function $f(x)$ of one variable about $x = a$ is given by

$$f(x) \simeq f(a) + f'(a)(x - a) + \tfrac{1}{2}f''(a)(x - a)^2.$$

If a is a stationary point, $f'(a) = 0$ and so $f(x) - f(a) \simeq \tfrac{1}{2}f''(a)(x - a)^2$. Therefore (provided that $f''(a) \neq 0$) the quadratic approximation will have a minimum or a maximum, depending on the sign of $f''(a)$. Close enough to a, the approximation will behave like the function itself, thus allowing us to conclude that the function has a local minimum or maximum. Thus the Second Derivative Test uses the second-order terms in the quadratic approximation to classify the stationary point.

3.2 $AC - B^2$ *criterion*

In considering a stationary point of a function $f(x, y)$, it will make the algebra easier if we take the stationary point to be at the origin, so that $f_x(0, 0) = 0$ and $f_y(0, 0) = 0$. It will also be useful to write

It will not be hard to generalize later.

$$A = f_{xx}(0, 0), \quad B = f_{xy}(0, 0) \left(= f_{yx}(0, 0)\right), \quad C = f_{yy}(0, 0).$$

The quadratic approximation to $f(x, y)$ is the second-order Taylor polynomial. Since we are assuming that the first derivatives are zero at $(0, 0)$, Equation (2.7) gives

$$f(x, y) \simeq f(0, 0) + \tfrac{1}{2}(Ax^2 + 2Bxy + Cy^2),$$

so

$$f(x, y) - f(0, 0) \simeq \tfrac{1}{2}(Ax^2 + 2Bxy + Cy^2). \tag{3.1}$$

As for functions of one variable, close to a point (a, b), the second-order Taylor polynomial for $f(x, y)$ about (a, b) behaves in the same way as $f(x, y)$ itself. This is a consequence of a theorem (similar to Taylor's Theorem) that we do not include in this course.

Thus we shall be able to classify the stationary point at $(0, 0)$ if we can determine the sign of the term $\tfrac{1}{2}(Ax^2 + 2Bxy + Cy^2)$. The multiplication by $\tfrac{1}{2}$ is not relevant to determining the sign; thus we shall concentrate on the term $Ax^2 + 2Bxy + Cy^2$ and, in particular, on expressing it as a sum of two squares. We consider three possible cases, depending on whether or not A and/or C is zero.

Case 1 $A \neq 0$

We can express $Ax^2 + 2Bxy + Cy^2$ as

$$Ax^2 + 2Bxy + Cy^2 = \frac{1}{A}\left((Ax + By)^2 + (AC - B^2)y^2\right).$$

Multiply out the right-hand side, and you will find that it gives the left-hand side.

Thus the sign of A and the sign of $AC - B^2$ between them tell us what kind of stationary point we have at the origin (provided that both are non-zero). If both are positive, we have a local minimum. If A is negative and $AC - B^2$ is positive, we have a local maximum. If $AC - B^2$ is negative, whatever the sign of A, the expression is a difference of two squares, so we have a saddle point.

If $AC - B^2 = 0$, we do not have enough information to classify the stationary point at the origin. Along the direction in which $Ax + By = 0$, the quadratic expression $Ax^2 + 2Bxy + Cy^2$ is zero. But terms as yet uncalculated in (say) x^3 or y^4 may be positive or negative, and we have to proceed to higher-order Taylor approximations in order to determine the nature of the stationary point. $\square$

Case 2 $A = 0,\ C \neq 0$

We can express $Ax^2 + 2Bxy + Cy^2$ as

$$Ax^2 + 2Bxy + Cy^2 = \frac{1}{C}\left((Bx + Cy)^2 - (Bx)^2\right).$$

Provided that $B \neq 0$, this is a difference of two squares, so we have a saddle point. (Since, for $A = 0$ and $B \neq 0$, $AC - B^2 < 0$, as in Case 1 we can say that the condition $AC - B^2 < 0$ leads to a saddle point.)

If $B = 0$ (and so $AC - B^2 = 0$), we do not have enough information to classify the stationary point at the origin. Along the direction in which $y = 0$, the quadratic expression $Ax^2 + 2Bxy + Cy^2$ is zero, so (as in Case 1) we have to proceed to higher-order Taylor approximations if we wish to determine the nature of the stationary point. $\square$

Case 3 $A = C = 0$

We can express $Ax^2 + 2Bxy + Cy^2$ as

$$Ax^2 + 2Bxy + Cy^2 = 2Bxy = \frac{B}{2}\left((x + y)^2 - (x - y)^2\right).$$

Again, provided that $B \neq 0$, we have a difference of two squares and there is a saddle point at the origin. (Again, the condition $B \neq 0$ implies that $AC - B^2 < 0$.)

If $B = 0$ (and so $AC - B^2 = 0$), we do not have enough information to classify the stationary point at the origin, since the quadratic expression $Ax^2 + 2Bxy + Cy^2$ is zero, so (as in Cases 1 and 2) we have to proceed to higher-order Taylor approximations in order to determine the nature of the stationary point. $\square$

All three cases can be generalized to the situation where the stationary point is not at the origin. When it is at (a, b), we evaluate the partial derivatives at (a, b) and replace Equation (3.1) by the quadratic approximation at (a, b):

$$f(x, y) - f(a, b) \simeq \tfrac{1}{2}\left(A(x - a)^2 + 2B(x - a)(y - b) + C(y - b)^2\right).$$

Setting $p = x - a$ and $q = y - b$, we now have the quadratic expression

$$Ap^2 + 2Bpq + Cq^2 \tag{3.2}$$

to analyse.

If this is always positive, we have a local minimum at (a, b).

If it is always negative, we have a local maximum at (a, b).

If it is sometimes positive and sometimes negative, we have a saddle point at (a, b).

The conditions on A, B and C for achieving these conclusions are exactly the same as in our analysis of the case of a stationary point at $(0, 0)$.

Test for classifying a stationary point

Given that the (sufficiently smooth) function $f(x, y)$ has a stationary point at (a, b), let

$$A = f_{xx}(a, b), \quad B = f_{xy}(a, b)(= f_{yx}(a, b)), \quad C = f_{yy}(a, b).$$

(a) If $AC - B^2 > 0$, there is:
  (i) a local minimum at (a, b) if $A > 0$;
  (ii) a local maximum at (a, b) if $A < 0$.

(b) If $AC - B^2 < 0$, there is a saddle point at (a, b).

(c) If $AC - B^2 = 0$, the test is unable to classify the stationary point.

Example 3.3

Locate and classify the stationary point of the function $f(x, y) = e^{-(x^2+y^2)}$.

Solution

Partially differentiating gives $f_x = -2xe^{-(x^2+y^2)}$ and $f_y = -2ye^{-(x^2+y^2)}$. Since $f_x = 0$ only when $x = 0$, and $f_y = 0$ only when $y = 0$, the stationary point is at $(0, 0)$.

Since $f_{xx} = -2e^{-(x^2+y^2)} + 4x^2 e^{-(x^2+y^2)}$, we have $A = f_{xx}(0, 0) = -2$. Also, $f_{yy} = -2e^{-(x^2+y^2)} + 4y^2 e^{-(x^2+y^2)}$, therefore $C = f_{yy}(0, 0) = -2$. Finally, $f_{xy} = 4xye^{-(x^2+y^2)}$, therefore $B = f_{xy}(0, 0) = 0$.

So we see that $AC - B^2 = 4 > 0$, and since $A = -2 < 0$, the stationary point is a local maximum. ∎

Exercise 3.4 ———————————————————

Locate and classify the stationary point of the function

$$f(x, y) = 2x^2 - xy - 3y^2 - 3x + 7y.$$

Exercise 3.5 ———————————————————

Locate and classify the four stationary points of the function

$$f(x, y) = x^3 - 12x - y^3 + 3y.$$

3.3 Classifying stationary points using eigenvalues

In Subsection 3.2 you saw that the critical factor in classifying a stationary point (a, b) of a function of two independent variables is the expression

$$Ap^2 + 2Bpq + Cq^2, \tag{3.2}$$

where A, B and C are the second derivatives $f_{xx}(a, b)$, $f_{xy}(a, b)$ and $f_{yy}(a, b)$, respectively, and $p = x - a$ and $q = y - b$.

In this subsection you will see how to use eigenvalues to classify a stationary point. In order to use eigenvalues, we need to think in terms of matrices. In particular, since $B = f_{xy}(a, b) = f_{yx}(a, b)$, it seems that B may be expected to occur twice in a relevant matrix expression. Indeed, it turns out that the matrix we require is the symmetric matrix

$$\mathbf{M} = \begin{bmatrix} A & B \\ B & C \end{bmatrix}.$$

As $\mathbf{M}$ is real and symmetric, it has real eigenvalues and eigenvectors (see *Unit 10*).

Exercise 3.6

Verify that

$$[p \quad q] \, \mathbf{M} \begin{bmatrix} p \\ q \end{bmatrix} = Ap^2 + 2Bpq + Cq^2.$$

Assuming that x and y can take any values, so can p and q. So, for certain values of x and y, $[p \quad q]^T$ will be an eigenvector of $\mathbf{M}$, corresponding to a real eigenvalue λ. Then

$$\mathbf{M} \begin{bmatrix} p \\ q \end{bmatrix} = \lambda \begin{bmatrix} p \\ q \end{bmatrix} = \begin{bmatrix} \lambda p \\ \lambda q \end{bmatrix},$$

so

$$[p \quad q] \, \mathbf{M} \begin{bmatrix} p \\ q \end{bmatrix} = [p \quad q] \begin{bmatrix} \lambda p \\ \lambda q \end{bmatrix} = \lambda(p^2 + q^2).$$

That is, if $[p \quad q]^T$ is an eigenvector of $\mathbf{M}$ with eigenvalue λ, then expression (3.2) is given by

$$Ap^2 + 2Bpq + Cq^2 = \lambda(p^2 + q^2).$$

If $\mathbf{M}$ has a positive eigenvalue and a negative eigenvalue, then, for certain values of x and y, $[p \quad q]^T$ will be an eigenvector corresponding to the positive eigenvalue, and for certain other values of x and y, $[p \quad q]^T$ will be an eigenvector corresponding to the negative eigenvalue. Therefore, since $p^2 + q^2$ is always positive, the expression $Ap^2 + 2Bpq + Cq^2$ will sometimes be positive and sometimes negative, according to the sign of λ. Furthermore, since a scalar multiple of an eigenvector is still an eigenvector, corresponding to the same eigenvalue, we can take p and q as close to zero as we like, and hence x and y as close to a and b as we like. Therefore the stationary point will be a saddle point.

The definition of an eigenvector excludes $[p \quad q]^T = [0 \quad 0]^T$.

If both eigenvalues are positive, it seems reasonable to expect that the expression $Ap^2 + 2Bpq + Cq^2$ will always be positive (and similarly for the negative case). In fact, this is true, although we shall not prove this statement.

Eigenvalue test for classifying a stationary point

Given that the (sufficiently smooth) function $f(x, y)$ has a stationary point at (a, b), let

$$A = f_{xx}(a, b), \quad B = f_{xy}(a, b) \, (= f_{yx}(a, b)),$$

$$C = f_{yy}(a, b), \quad \mathbf{M} = \begin{bmatrix} A & B \\ B & C \end{bmatrix},$$

and let λ_1 and λ_2 be the real eigenvalues of $\mathbf{M}$.

(a) If λ_1 and λ_2 are both positive, then there is a local minimum at (a, b).

(b) If λ_1 and λ_2 are both negative, then there is a local maximum at (a, b).

(c) If λ_1 and λ_2 are non-zero and opposite in sign, then there is a saddle point at (a, b).

(d) If either, or both, of λ_1 or λ_2 is zero, then the test is inconclusive.

For example, if we apply this test to the function

$$f(x, y) = 2x^2 - xy - 3y^2 - 3x + 7y$$

We make use of several ideas from *Unit 10* here.

(discussed in Exercise 3.4), we have a stationary point at $(1, 1)$, and $A = 4$, $B = -1$ and $C = -6$. It follows that $\mathbf{M} = \begin{bmatrix} 4 & -1 \\ -1 & -6 \end{bmatrix}$, and the characteristic equation is $\lambda^2 + 2\lambda - 25 = 0$. The eigenvalues are therefore $\sqrt{26} - 1$ and $-(\sqrt{26} + 1)$. The eigenvalues are non-zero and of opposite sign, so the stationary point is a saddle point.

This test can be extended to functions of three or more variables. If f is a sufficiently smooth function of n variables, then a stationary point of f is a point $(a_1, a_2, \ldots, a_n)$ at which all the n first partial derivatives are zero. There will be n^2 second partial derivatives, and their values at $(a_1, a_2, \ldots, a_n)$ can be written in the form of an $n \times n$ matrix $\mathbf{M}$, the entry in the ith row and jth column being the value $\dfrac{\partial^2}{\partial x_i \partial x_j} f(a_1, \ldots, a_n)$. This is called the **Hessian matrix** of f at the point $(a_1, \ldots, a_n)$. Our assumption that f is sufficiently smooth implies that $\mathbf{M}$ will be a symmetric matrix, since the Mixed Derivative Theorem extends from the two-variable case to the several-variable case. Thus the eigenvalues of $\mathbf{M}$ will be real and lead to the following classification.

(a) If all the eigenvalues are positive, then there is a local minimum at $(a_1, \ldots, a_n)$.

(b) If all the eigenvalues are negative, then there is a local maximum at $(a_1, \ldots, a_n)$.

(c) If all the eigenvalues are non-zero but they are not all of the same sign, then there is a saddle point at $(a_1, \ldots, a_n)$.

(d) If one or more of the eigenvalues is zero, then the test is inconclusive.

In the case of more than two variables, the analogy of a saddle is not very helpful in visualizing a saddle point. However, it remains true that there are sections through a saddle point giving a section function with a local minimum, and others giving a section function with a local maximum.

Example 3.4

Find and classify the stationary point of the function

$$w(x, y, z) = 3y^2 + 3z^2 - 4xy - 2yz - 4zx.$$

Solution

We find the stationary point by solving the simultaneous equations

$$\begin{cases} w_x = -4y - 4z = 0, \\ w_y = 6y - 4x - 2z = 0, \\ w_z = 6z - 2y - 4x = 0. \end{cases}$$

The only solution is $x = y = z = 0$.

The second partial derivatives of $w(x, y, z)$ are constants:

$$w_{xx} = 0, \quad w_{yy} = 6, \quad w_{zz} = 6,$$
$$w_{xy} = w_{yx} = -4, \quad w_{yz} = w_{zy} = -2, \quad w_{zx} = w_{xz} = -4.$$

Thus the required 3×3 Hessian matrix is

$$\mathbf{M} = \begin{bmatrix} w_{xx} & w_{xy} & w_{xz} \\ w_{yx} & w_{yy} & w_{yz} \\ w_{zx} & w_{zy} & w_{zz} \end{bmatrix} = \begin{bmatrix} 0 & -4 & -4 \\ -4 & 6 & -2 \\ -4 & -2 & 6 \end{bmatrix}.$$

To find the eigenvalues of $\mathbf{M}$, we find the values of λ that satisfy the characteristic equation $\det(\mathbf{M} - \lambda\mathbf{I}) = 0$. The solutions of the equation $\det(\mathbf{M} - \lambda\mathbf{I}) = -(\lambda - 8)^2(\lambda + 4) = 0$ are $\lambda_1 = -4$, $\lambda_2 = 8$ and $\lambda_3 = 8$. Our test then tells us immediately that there is a saddle point at the origin. ∎

Exercise 3.7

Find and classify the stationary point of the function

$$w(x, y, z) = 3x^2 + 3y^2 + 4z^2 - 2xy - 2yz - 2xz,$$

given that the characteristic equation of the matrix $\begin{bmatrix} 6 & -2 & -2 \\ -2 & 6 & -2 \\ -2 & -2 & 8 \end{bmatrix}$
is $(8 - \lambda)\left((6 - \lambda)^2 - 12\right) = 0$.

The functions in Exercises 3.7 and 3.8 recur in Activity 4.2, where you are asked to use the computer algebra package for the course to locate and classify the stationary points.

Exercise 3.8

Classify the stationary point at the origin of the function

$$w(x, y, z) = x^2 + 2y^2 + z^2 + 2\sqrt{3}xz,$$

given that the characteristic equation for the relevant Hessian matrix has $4 - \lambda$ as a factor.

Least squares approximation revisited

In Subsection 3.2 of *Unit 9*, you were introduced to the technique of finding the 'best' straight line through a set of data points that is subject to experimental error. The example used there consisted of four measurements that appeared (within the limits of experimental error) to satisfy a linear relationship. We sought an expression of the form $y = a_0 + a_1 x$ that best described the observed data, which were as shown in Table 3.1.

Table 3.1

x	1	2	3	4
y	0.9	2.1	2.9	4.1

We denoted by d_i the vertical distance of each point from the 'best' straight line, so that

$$d_i = (a_0 + a_1 x_i) - y_i \quad (i = 1, 2, 3, 4). \tag{3.3}$$

We sought the straight line that minimized the sum of the squares of these deviations. We then wrote Equations (3.3) in vector form, as

$$\mathbf{d} = \mathbf{X}\mathbf{a} - \mathbf{y}, \tag{3.4}$$

where

$$\mathbf{d} = [d_1 \quad d_2 \quad d_3 \quad d_4]^T, \quad \mathbf{X} = \begin{bmatrix} 1 & 1 & 1 & 1 \\ 1 & 2 & 3 & 4 \end{bmatrix}^T,$$

$$\mathbf{a} = [a_0 \quad a_1]^T \quad \text{and} \quad \mathbf{y} = [0.9 \quad 2.1 \quad 2.9 \quad 4.1]^T.$$

The sum of the squares of the deviations is $\mathbf{d}^T\mathbf{d}$, and the transpose of Equation (3.4) is

$$\mathbf{d}^T = \mathbf{a}^T\mathbf{X}^T - \mathbf{y}^T, \tag{3.5}$$

so Equations (3.4) and (3.5) yield

$$\mathbf{d}^T\mathbf{d} = \mathbf{a}^T\mathbf{X}^T\mathbf{X}\mathbf{a} - 2\mathbf{a}^T\mathbf{X}^T\mathbf{y} + \mathbf{y}^T\mathbf{y}. \tag{3.6}$$

In *Unit 9* it was stated that the vector $\mathbf{a}$ that minimizes this expression satisfies

$$(\mathbf{X}^T\mathbf{X})\mathbf{a} = \mathbf{X}^T\mathbf{y}. \tag{3.7}$$

It was also stated that the explanation of this would be postponed until *Unit 12*, so the time has come! Let us write the known quantities as

$$\mathbf{X}^T\mathbf{X} = \begin{bmatrix} S & T \\ T & U \end{bmatrix}, \quad \mathbf{X}^T\mathbf{y} = \begin{bmatrix} v \\ w \end{bmatrix}, \quad \mathbf{y}^T\mathbf{y} = z.$$

Calculating $\mathbf{X}^T\mathbf{X}$ for the data above gives $S = 4$, $T = 10$ and $U = 30$.

Let us also put $a_0 = x$ and $a_1 = y$. Then, by Equation (3.6), $\mathbf{d}^T\mathbf{d}$ is a function of x and y, namely

$$\mathbf{d}^T\mathbf{d} = f(x, y) = Sx^2 + 2Txy + Uy^2 - 2vx - 2wy + z. \tag{3.8}$$

Exercise 3.9

Assuming that $\mathbf{X}^T\mathbf{X}$ is invertible, show that the only stationary point of the function $f(x,y)$ defined in Equation (3.8) is at the point whose coordinates satisfy Equation (3.7).

Therefore, provided that $\mathbf{X}^T\mathbf{X}$ is invertible, the sum of the squares of the deviations $\mathbf{d}^T\mathbf{d}$ will have just one stationary point. It turns out that the eigenvalues of $\mathbf{X}^T\mathbf{X}$ are always both positive, so it is a local minimum. The values of a_0 and a_1 that produce this minimum will thus be the parameters of the 'best' straight line through the data points.

The matrix $\mathbf{X}^T\mathbf{X}$ is invertible provided that the second column of $\mathbf{X}$ contains at least two distinct entries. We do not prove this here.

This gives a justification for Procedure 3.2 (least squares straight line) of *Unit 9*.

End-of-section Exercises

Exercise 3.10

Find and classify the stationary points of the following functions.

(a) $f(x,y) = \sqrt{1 - x^2 + y^2}$ (b) $T(x,y) = \cos x + \cos y$

Exercise 3.11

Find and classify the stationary point of the function $f(x,y) = \sqrt{1 - x^2 - y^2}$.

4 Computer activities

The computer algebra package for the course allows you to locate and classify stationary points.

Use your computer to complete the following activities.

Activity 4.1

Locate and classify the stationary points of the following functions of two variables.

(a) $f(x,y) = 2x^2 - xy - 3y^2 - 3x + 7y$

(b) $f(x,y) = x^3 - 12x - y^3 + 3y$

(c) $f(x,y) = \sqrt{1 - x^2 + y^2}$

See Exercise 3.4.

See Exercise 3.5.

See Exercise 3.10.

Activity 4.2

Locate and classify the stationary points of the following functions of three variables.

(a) $f(x,y,z) = x^2 + y^2 - z^2 + 2xyz + 4z$

(b) $f(x,y,z) = 3x^2 + 3y^2 + 4z^2 - 2xy - 2yz - 2xz$

(c) $f(x,y,z) = x^2 + 2y^2 + z^2 + 2\sqrt{3}xz$

See Exercise 3.7.

See Exercise 3.8.

Outcomes

After studying this unit you should be able to:

- calculate first and second partial derivatives of a function of several variables;
- understand the use of a surface to represent a function of two variables;
- construct the equation of the tangent plane at a given point on a surface;
- calculate the Taylor polynomials of degree n for a function of one variable;
- calculate the first-order and second-order Taylor polynomials for a function of two variables;
- locate the stationary points of a function of two (or more) variables by solving a system of two (or more) simultaneous equations;
- classify the stationary points of a function of two variables by using the $AC - B^2$ test;
- classify the stationary points of a function of two (or more) variables by examining the signs of the eigenvalues of an appropriate matrix;
- use the computer algebra package for the course to find and analyse stationary points of a function of more than one variable.

Solutions to the exercises

Section 1

1.1 (a) $f(2,3) = 12 - 54 = -42$

(b) $f(3,2) = 27 - 16 = 11$

(c) $f(a,b) = 3a^2 - 2b^3$

(d) $f(b,a) = 3b^2 - 2a^3$

(e) $f(2a,b) = 3(2a)^2 - 2b^3 = 12a^2 - 2b^3$

(f) $f(a-b,0) = 3(a-b)^2$

(g) $f(x,2) = 3x^2 - 16$

(h) $f(y,x) = 3y^2 - 2x^3$

1.2 The potential energy U of a particle of mass m placed at height h (relative to a datum O) is given by $U(h) = mgh$ (where g is the acceleration due to gravity). Now A is $a\cos\theta$ below O, and B is $a\cos\phi$ below A; so B is $a(\cos\theta + \cos\phi)$ below O. Thus, in this case, we have

$$U(\theta,\phi) = -mga(\cos\theta + \cos\phi).$$

The least possible value of U occurs when $\cos\theta$ and $\cos\phi$ take their greatest values, and this happens when $\theta = \phi = 0$. So the least value of U is $U(0,0) = -2mga$, and it occurs when the system is hanging vertically.

1.3 The section function of $F(x,y) = 100e^{-(x^2+y^2)}$ with y fixed at 0 is $F(x,0) = 100e^{-x^2}$. It follows that

$$\frac{d}{dx}(F(x,0)) = -200xe^{-x^2}.$$

This derivative is zero when $x = 0$, so $F(x,0)$ has a stationary point at $x = 0$.

Differentiating again with respect to x, we obtain

$$\frac{d^2}{dx^2}(F(x,0)) = -200\frac{d}{dx}(xe^{-x^2})$$
$$= -200(1 - 2x^2)e^{-x^2}.$$

This derivative is -200 when $x = 0$. It follows that the section function has a local maximum at $x = 0$.

1.4 $\dfrac{\partial f}{\partial x} = 2x\sin(xy) + (x^2 + y^3)y\cos(xy),$

$\dfrac{\partial f}{\partial y} = 3y^2\sin(xy) + (x^2 + y^3)x\cos(xy).$

1.5 $u_\theta = \cos\theta + \phi\sec^2\theta$ and $u_\phi = \tan\theta$.

1.6 (a) Treating y and t as constants, and differentiating with respect to x,

$$f_x = 2y^3t^4x + 2y + 8t^2x.$$

Treating x and t as constants, and differentiating with respect to y,

$$f_y = 3x^2t^4y^2 + 2x + 1.$$

Treating x and y as constants, and differentiating with respect to t,

$$f_t = 4x^2y^3t^3 + 8x^2t.$$

(b) We have $\dfrac{\partial z}{\partial x} = 2(1 + x)$ and $\dfrac{\partial z}{\partial y} = 3(1 + y)^2$.

Sketches of the section functions $z(x,0) = (1 + x)^2 + 1$ and $z(0,y) = 1 + (1 + y)^3$ are shown in the following figure.

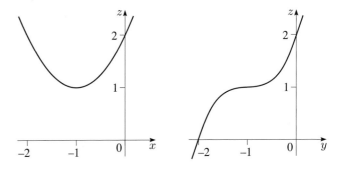

We obtain $(\partial z/\partial x)(0,0) = 2$, which represents the slope of the left-hand graph above where $x = 0$. Also, we obtain $(\partial z/\partial y)(0,0) = 3$, which represents the slope of the right-hand graph above where $y = 0$.

1.7 We obtain $\dfrac{\partial z}{\partial x} = 2(1 + x)$ and $\dfrac{\partial z}{\partial y} = 3(1 + y)^2$. So we have

$$\frac{\partial z}{\partial x}(0,2) = 2, \quad \frac{\partial z}{\partial y}(0,2) = 27.$$

So

$$\delta z \simeq 2\delta x + 27\delta y.$$

1.8 We have $\dfrac{\partial z}{\partial x} = \cos x$, $\dfrac{\partial z}{\partial y} = 3\sin y$, $\dfrac{dx}{dt} = 2t$ and $\dfrac{dy}{dt} = 2$. Thus

$$\frac{dz}{dt} = \frac{\partial z}{\partial x}\frac{dx}{dt} + \frac{\partial z}{\partial y}\frac{dy}{dt}$$
$$= 2t\cos x + 6\sin y$$
$$= 2t\cos(t^2) + 6\sin(2t).$$

1.9 (a) We have

$$\nabla f(x,y) = (4xy + 3y^3)\mathbf{i} + (2x^2 + 9xy^2)\mathbf{j}.$$

(b) $\nabla f(2,1) = 11\mathbf{i} + 26\mathbf{j}$, so the slope at $(2,1,14)$ in the direction $\frac{3}{5}\mathbf{i} + \frac{4}{5}\mathbf{j}$ is

$$(11\mathbf{i} + 26\mathbf{j}) \cdot \left(\tfrac{3}{5}\mathbf{i} + \tfrac{4}{5}\mathbf{j}\right) = \tfrac{137}{5}.$$

1.10 We need to evaluate the partial derivatives at $x = 2$ and $y = 1$. Since $\partial z/\partial x = x$ and $\partial z/\partial y = 2\sqrt{3}y$, Equation (1.12) becomes $dz/dt = 2\cos\alpha + 2\sqrt{3}\sin\alpha$. We see that the slope dz/dt is a function of α only, but to make the argument clear we shall replace the slope dz/dt by $s(\alpha)$, so that $s(\alpha) = 2\cos\alpha + 2\sqrt{3}\sin\alpha$. The exercise requires us to find the maximum value of $s(\alpha)$ for varying values of α.

The stationary points of $s(\alpha)$ occur when $ds/d\alpha = -2\sin\alpha + 2\sqrt{3}\cos\alpha = 0$, which gives $\tan\alpha = \sqrt{3}$. This equation has two solutions in the interval $0 \le \alpha < 2\pi$, at $\alpha = \frac{\pi}{3}$ and $\alpha = \frac{4\pi}{3}$. Using the Second Derivative Test, we see that $\alpha = \frac{\pi}{3}$ corresponds to a maximum value of $s(\alpha)$ (while $\alpha = \frac{4\pi}{3}$ gives a minimum value). It follows that the greatest slope at the point $(2, 1, 2 + \sqrt{3})$ is

$$2\cos\tfrac{\pi}{3} + 2\sqrt{3}\sin\tfrac{\pi}{3} = 1 + (2\sqrt{3})\tfrac{\sqrt{3}}{2} = 4.$$

The direction of the greatest slope of $z = f(x, y)$ at $(2, 1, 2 + \sqrt{3})$ is at an angle of $\frac{\pi}{3}$ measured anticlockwise from the positive x-axis.

Now $\nabla f(2, 1) = 2\mathbf{i} + 2\sqrt{3}\mathbf{j}$, so the angle θ between $\nabla f(2, 1)$ and the positive x-axis (measured anticlockwise) is also given by $\tan\theta = \sqrt{3}$. So, since both components of $\nabla f(2, 1)$ are positive, $\theta = \frac{\pi}{3}$. Thus the direction of greatest slope is the same as the direction of $\nabla f(2, 1)$.

1.11 We have $\dfrac{\partial z}{\partial x} = y\cos x$, $\dfrac{\partial z}{\partial y} = \sin x$, $\dfrac{dx}{dt} = e^t$ and $\dfrac{dy}{dt} = 2t$, so

$$\begin{aligned}
\frac{dz}{dt} &= \frac{\partial z}{\partial x}\frac{dx}{dt} + \frac{\partial z}{\partial y}\frac{dy}{dt} \\
&= (y\cos x)e^t + (\sin x)2t \\
&= t^2\cos(e^t)e^t + \sin(e^t)2t \\
&= t\left(te^t\cos(e^t) + 2\sin(e^t)\right).
\end{aligned}$$

Thus $z'(0) = 0$.

1.12 **(a)** We have $f_x = 3(x + 2y)^2 - 4(2x - y)$ and $f_y = 6(x + 2y)^2 + 2(2x - y)$, so

$$\begin{aligned}
\nabla f(x, y) = {}& \left(3(x + 2y)^2 - 4(2x - y)\right)\mathbf{i} \\
& + \left(6(x + 2y)^2 + 2(2x - y)\right)\mathbf{j}.
\end{aligned}$$

(b) The vector $\mathbf{i} + \mathbf{j}$ has length $\sqrt{2}$, so $\hat{\mathbf{d}} = \frac{1}{\sqrt{2}}(\mathbf{i} + \mathbf{j})$ is a unit vector in the required direction. At the point $(1, 0, -3)$, we have

$$\nabla f \cdot \hat{\mathbf{d}} = (-5\mathbf{i} + 10\mathbf{j}) \cdot \tfrac{1}{\sqrt{2}}(\mathbf{i} + \mathbf{j}) = \tfrac{5}{\sqrt{2}}.$$

Section 2

2.1 $p_1(0) = 0$ and $\sin 0 = 0$, thus $p_1(0) = \sin 0$. $p_1'(x) = 1$, so $p_1'(0) = 1$, and $\sin' x = \cos x$, so $\sin' 0 = 1$, thus $p_1'(0) = \sin' 0$. $p_1''(x) = 0$, so $p''(0) = 0$, and $\sin'' x = -\sin x$, so $\sin'' 0 = 0$, thus $p_1''(0) = \sin'' 0$.

$p_2(0) = 1 - 0 = 1$ and $\cos 0 = 1$, thus $p_2(0) = \cos 0$. $p_2'(x) = -x$, so $p_2'(0) = 0$, and $\cos' x = -\sin x$, so $\cos' 0 = 0$, thus $p_2'(0) = \cos' 0$. $p_2''(x) = -1$, so $p_2''(0) = -1$, and $\cos'' x = -\cos x$, so $\cos'' 0 = -1$, thus $p_2''(0) = \cos'' 0$. $p_2'''(x) = 0$, so $p_2'''(0) = 0$, and $\cos''' x = \sin x$, so $\cos''' 0 = 0$, thus $p_2'''(0) = \cos''' 0$.

2.2 From Example 2.1, we have $p_0(x) = 1$, $p_1(x) = 1 + 2x$ and $p_2(x) = 1 + 2x + 2x^2$. Thus $p_0(0.1) = 1$, $p_1(0.1) = 1.2$ and $p_2(0.1) = 1.22$. Also, $f(0.1) = e^{0.2} = 1.221\,40$, to 5 d.p.. Thus

$$p_0(0.1) = f(0.1) \text{ to the nearest integer,}$$
$$p_1(0.1) = f(0.1) \text{ to 1 d.p.,}$$
$$p_2(0.1) = f(0.1) \text{ to 2 d.p..}$$

2.3 $f_x = \sin(xy) + xy\cos(xy)$ and $f_y = x^2\cos(xy)$, so

$$\begin{aligned}
f_{xx} &= y\cos(xy) + y\cos(xy) - xy^2\sin(xy) \\
&= 2y\cos(xy) - xy^2\sin(xy), \\
f_{yy} &= -x^3\sin(xy), \\
f_{xy} &= 2x\cos(xy) - x^2 y\sin(xy), \\
f_{yx} &= x\cos(xy) + x\cos(xy) - x^2 y\sin(xy) \\
&= 2x\cos(xy) - x^2 y\sin(xy).
\end{aligned}$$

2.4 $f_x = 2e^{2x+3y}$ and $f_y = 3e^{2x+3y}$, so

$$f_{xx} = 4e^{2x+3y}, \quad f_{xy} = f_{yx} = 6e^{2x+3y},$$
$$f_{yy} = 9e^{2x+3y}.$$

Then

$$\begin{aligned}
f_x(0, 0) &= 2, \quad f_y(0, 0) = 3, \\
f_{xx}(0, 0) &= 4, \quad f_{yy}(0, 0) = 9, \\
f_{xy}(0, 0) &= f_{yx}(0, 0) = 6.
\end{aligned}$$

2.5 $f_x = 3e^{3x-y}$ and $f_y = -e^{3x-y}$, so

$$f(0, 0) = 1, \quad f_x(0, 0) = 3, \quad f_y(0, 0) = -1.$$

Thus the tangent approximation near $(0, 0)$ is

$$\begin{aligned}
p_1(x, y) &= f(0, 0) + f_x(0, 0)x + f_y(0, 0)y \\
&= 1 + 3x - y.
\end{aligned}$$

2.6 (a) $q_x = \beta + 2Ax + By$, $q_y = \gamma + Bx + 2Cy$, $q_{xx} = 2A$, $q_{xy} = B$ and $q_{yy} = 2C$.

(b) $q(0,0) = \alpha$, $q_x(0,0) = \beta$, $q_y(0,0) = \gamma$, $q_{xx}(0,0) = 2A$, $q_{xy}(0,0) = B$ and $q_{yy}(0,0) = 2C$.

2.7 $f(0,0)$, $f_x(0,0)$ and $f_y(0,0)$ are constants, so the equation is that of a plane. Since $g(0,0) = f(0,0)$, the plane goes through $(0,0,f(0,0))$.

Now $g_x(x,y) = f_x(0,0)$ and $g_y(x,y) = f_y(0,0)$, so $g_x(0,0) = f_x(0,0)$ and $g_y(0,0) = f_y(0,0)$.

Thus, at $(0,0)$, the plane has gradient

$$\nabla g(0,0) = g_x(0,0)\mathbf{i} + g_y(0,0)\mathbf{j}$$
$$= f_x(0,0)\mathbf{i} + f_y(0,0)\mathbf{j}$$
$$= \nabla f(0,0),$$

which is the gradient of $z = f(x,y)$ at $(0,0)$.

2.8 We have $f(0,0) = 1$,

$$f_x(0,0) = 2, \quad f_y(0,0) = 3,$$
$$f_{xx}(0,0) = 4, \quad f_{yy}(0,0) = 9,$$
$$f_{xy}(0,0) = 6.$$

Substituting these values into Equation (2.7), we obtain

$$p_2(x,y) = 1 + 2x + 3y + \tfrac{1}{2}(4x^2 + 12xy + 9y^2)$$
$$= 1 + 2x + 3y + 2x^2 + 6xy + \tfrac{9}{2}y^2.$$

2.9 We have $U(0,0) = -2mga$ and

$$\frac{\partial U}{\partial \theta} = mga\sin\theta, \quad \frac{\partial U}{\partial \phi} = mga\sin\phi,$$

so

$$\frac{\partial U}{\partial \theta}(0,0) = \frac{\partial U}{\partial \phi}(0,0) = 0.$$

We also see that

$$\frac{\partial^2 U}{\partial \theta^2} = mga\cos\theta, \quad \frac{\partial^2 U}{\partial \phi^2} = mga\cos\phi,$$

so

$$\frac{\partial^2 U}{\partial \theta^2}(0,0) = \frac{\partial^2 U}{\partial \phi^2}(0,0) = mga, \quad \frac{\partial^2 U}{\partial \theta \partial \phi} = 0.$$

It follows from Equation (2.7) that the second-order Taylor polynomial about $(0,0)$ is

$$p_2(\theta,\phi) = -2mga + \tfrac{1}{2}mga(\theta^2 + \phi^2).$$

2.10 $f_x = ye^{xy} + 2(x+y)$ and $f_y = xe^{xy} + 2(x+y)$, so

$$f_{xx} = y^2 e^{xy} + 2, \quad f_{xy} = e^{xy} + xye^{xy} + 2,$$
$$f_{yy} = x^2 e^{xy} + 2.$$

Therefore

$$f(0,0) = 1,$$
$$f_x(0,0) = f_y(0,0) = 0,$$
$$f_{xx}(0,0) = 2, \quad f_{xy}(0,0) = 3, \quad f_{yy}(0,0) = 2.$$

Thus, from Equation (2.7), the second-order Taylor polynomial about $(0,0)$ is

$$p_2(x,y) = 1 + \tfrac{1}{2}(2x^2 + 2(3xy) + 2y^2)$$
$$= 1 + x^2 + 3xy + y^2.$$

2.11 $f_x(x,y) = 3(x^2 + 2y^2 - 3xy)^2(2x - 3y)$ and $f_y(x,y) = 3(x^2 + 2y^2 - 3xy)^2(4y - 3x)$, so

$$f_{xx}(x,y) = 6(x^2 + 2y^2 - 3xy)(2x - 3y)^2 + 6(x^2 + 2y^2 - 3xy)^2,$$

$$f_{xy}(x,y) = 6(x^2 + 2y^2 - 3xy)(2x - 3y)(4y - 3x) - 9(x^2 + 2y^2 - 3xy)^2,$$

$$f_{yy}(x,y) = 6(x^2 + 2y^2 - 3xy)(4y - 3x)^2 + 12(x^2 + 2y^2 - 3xy)^2.$$

If $x = 1$ and $y = -1$, then

$$f_{xx}(1,-1) = 6(1+2+3)(2+3)^2 + 6(1+2+3)^2$$
$$= 1116,$$

$$f_{yy}(1,-1) = 6(1+2+3)(-4-3)^2 + 12(1+2+3)^2$$
$$= 2196.$$

Similarly, $f_{xy}(1,-1) = -1584$.

2.12 (a) $f_x = 3(2 + x + 2y)^2$ and $f_y = 6(2 + x + 2y)^2$, so

$$f_{xx} = 6(2 + x + 2y), \quad f_{xy} = 12(2 + x + 2y),$$
$$f_{yy} = 24(2 + x + 2y).$$

It follows that

$$f(0,0) = 8,$$
$$f_x(0,0) = 12, \quad f_y(0,0) = 24,$$
$$f_{xx}(0,0) = 12, \quad f_{xy}(0,0) = 24, \quad f_{yy}(0,0) = 48.$$

Therefore

$$p_1(x,y) = f(0,0) + f_x(0,0)x + f_y(0,0)y$$
$$= 8 + 12x + 24y,$$

$$p_2(x,y) = f(0,0) + f_x(0,0)x + f_y(0,0)y$$
$$+ \tfrac{1}{2}\left(f_{xx}(0,0)x^2 + 2f_{xy}(0,0)xy + f_{yy}(0,0)y^2\right)$$
$$= 8 + 12x + 24y + 6x^2 + 24xy + 24y^2.$$

Expanding the bracket in the expression for f, we obtain

$$f(x,y) = 8 + 12x + 24y + 6x^2 + 24xy + 24y^2 + x^3 + 6x^2y + 12xy^2 + 8y^3.$$

Notice that the function $f(x,y)$ is itself a polynomial of degree three and that the Taylor polynomial of second degree about $(0,0)$ consists of the terms of f of degree less than three.

(b) $f(1,-1) = 1$, $f_x(1,-1) = 3$, $f_y(1,-1) = 6$, $f_{xx}(1,-1) = 6$, $f_{xy}(1,-1) = 12$ and $f_{yy}(1,-1) = 24$.

It follows that

$$p_1(x,y) = f(1,-1) + f_x(1,-1)(x-1)$$
$$+ f_y(1,-1)(y+1)$$
$$= 1 + 3(x-1) + 6(y+1),$$

$$p_2(x,y) = f(1,-1) + f_x(1,-1)(x-1)$$
$$+ f_y(1,-1)(y+1)$$
$$+ \tfrac{1}{2}\left(f_{xx}(1,-1)(x-1)^2\right.$$
$$+ 2f_{xy}(1,-1)(x-1)(y+1)$$
$$\left.+ f_{yy}(1,-1)(y+1)^2\right)$$
$$= 1 + 3(x-1) + 6(y+1) + 3(x-1)^2$$
$$+ 12(x-1)(y+1) + 12(y+1)^2.$$

(c) $F_X = 3(1 + X + 2Y)^2$ and $F_Y = 6(1 + X + 2Y)^2$, so

$$F_{XX} = 6(1 + X + 2Y), \quad F_{XY} = 12(1 + X + 2Y),$$
$$F_{YY} = 24(1 + X + 2Y).$$

It follows that

$$F(0,0) = 1,$$
$$F_X(0,0) = 3, \quad F_Y(0,0) = 6,$$
$$F_{XX}(0,0) = 6, \quad F_{XY}(0,0) = 12, \quad F_{YY}(0,0) = 24.$$

Therefore

$$p_1(X,Y) = 1 + 3X + 6Y,$$
$$p_2(X,Y) = 1 + 3X + 6Y + 3X^2 + 12XY + 12Y^2.$$

(By substituting $X = x - 1$ and $Y = y + 1$, these polynomials are the same as those you obtained in part (b). Finding the Taylor polynomials for f near $(1, -1)$ is equivalent to making a suitable change of variables and then calculating the Taylor polynomials near $(0,0)$. This often leads to simpler arithmetic, because evaluations of the partial derivatives at $(0,0)$ are often particularly easy. You can then change variables back again to obtain the polynomial in terms of the original variables.)

Section 3

3.1 $f_x(x,y) = 6x - 4y + 4$ and $f_y(x,y) = -4x + 4y - 8$, so there is one stationary point, at the solution of the simultaneous equations

$$\begin{cases} 6x - 4y = -4, \\ -4x + 4y = 8, \end{cases}$$

which is $x = 2$, $y = 4$. Thus the only stationary point is at $(2, 4)$.

3.2 $f_x = 2xy + y^2 - 3y = y(2x + y - 3)$ and $f_y = 2xy + x^2 - 3x = x(2y + x - 3)$, so, to find the stationary points, we have to solve the simultaneous equations

$$\begin{cases} y(2x + y - 3) = 0, & \text{(S.1)} \\ x(2y + x - 3) = 0. & \text{(S.2)} \end{cases}$$

From (S.1), we have two cases.

If $y = 0$, then (S.2) becomes $x(x - 3) = 0$; thus $x = 0$ or $x = 3$, so we have found the two solutions $(0,0)$ and $(3,0)$.

If $2x + y - 3 = 0$, i.e. $y = 3 - 2x$, then (S.2) becomes $x(3 - 3x) = 0$, and we have $x = 0$ or $x = 1$. Substituting these values for x into $y = 3 - 2x$ gives $y = 3$ when $x = 0$ and $y = 1$ when $x = 1$. Thus we have two more solutions, $(0,3)$ and $(1,1)$.

So we have four stationary points: $(0,0)$, $(3,0)$, $(0,3)$ and $(1,1)$.

3.3 We have $U_\theta = mga \sin\theta$ and $U_\phi = mga \sin\phi$, so $U_\theta(0,0) = U_\phi(0,0) = 0$, which shows that $(0,0)$ is a stationary point. Also, $U(0,0) = -2mga$ and, near $(0,0)$, $0 < \cos\theta \leq 1$ and $0 < \cos\phi \leq 1$, so $U(\theta,\phi) \geq -2mga$, and it follows that this point is a local minimum.

3.4 $f_x = 4x - y - 3$ and $f_y = -x - 6y + 7$, so to find the stationary point, we need to solve the simultaneous equations

$$\begin{cases} 4x - y - 3 = 0, \\ -x - 6y + 7 = 0. \end{cases}$$

The solution is $x = 1$, $y = 1$, so the stationary point is at $(1,1)$. Also, $f_{xx}(1,1) = 4$, $f_{xy}(1,1) = -1$ and $f_{yy}(1,1) = -6$, so $AC - B^2 = -25$; therefore the stationary point is a saddle point.

3.5 $f_x = 3x^2 - 12$ and $f_y = -3y^2 + 3$, so the stationary points are at the points (x,y) where $x^2 = 4$ and $y^2 = 1$, namely $(2,1)$, $(2,-1)$, $(-2,1)$, $(-2,-1)$. Also, $f_{xx} = 6x$, $f_{xy} = 0$ and $f_{yy} = -6y$. Thus, at $(2,1)$ and $(-2,-1)$, we have $AC - B^2 = -36xy = -72$, and these are saddle points. At $(2,-1)$ and $(-2,1)$, we have $AC - B^2 = -36xy = 72$. Since $A > 0$ at $(2,-1)$, this is a local minimum; since $A < 0$ at $(-2,1)$, this is a local maximum.

3.6 $\mathbf{M}\begin{bmatrix} p \\ q \end{bmatrix} = \begin{bmatrix} A & B \\ B & C \end{bmatrix}\begin{bmatrix} p \\ q \end{bmatrix} = \begin{bmatrix} Ap + Bq \\ Bp + Cq \end{bmatrix}$, so

$$\begin{aligned}[p \ q]\mathbf{M}\begin{bmatrix} p \\ q \end{bmatrix} &= [p \ q]\begin{bmatrix} Ap + Bq \\ Bp + Cq \end{bmatrix} \\ &= p(Ap + Bq) + q(Bp + Cq) \\ &= Ap^2 + 2Bpq + Cq^2.\end{aligned}$$

3.7 First we find the stationary point by solving the simultaneous equations

$$\begin{cases} w_x = 6x - 2y - 2z = 0, \\ w_y = 6y - 2x - 2z = 0, \\ w_z = 8z - 2y - 2x = 0. \end{cases}$$

The only solution is $x = y = z = 0$, so the stationary point is at $(0,0,0)$.

Now $w_{xx} = 6$, $w_{yy} = 6$, $w_{zz} = 8$, $w_{xy} = -2$, $w_{xz} = -2$ and $w_{yz} = -2$, so the Hessian matrix is

$$\begin{bmatrix} w_{xx} & w_{xy} & w_{xz} \\ w_{yx} & w_{yy} & w_{yz} \\ w_{zx} & w_{zy} & w_{zz} \end{bmatrix} = \begin{bmatrix} 6 & -2 & -2 \\ -2 & 6 & -2 \\ -2 & -2 & 8 \end{bmatrix}.$$

The given characteristic equation of this matrix is

$$\begin{aligned}0 &= (8 - \lambda)\left((6 - \lambda)^2 - 12\right) \\ &= (8 - \lambda)(6 - \lambda + 2\sqrt{3})(6 - \lambda - 2\sqrt{3}),\end{aligned}$$

so the eigenvalues are 8, $6 - 2\sqrt{3}$ and $6 + 2\sqrt{3}$. These are all positive, thus there is a local minimum at the origin.

3.8 We have
$$w_x = 2x + 2\sqrt{3}z, \quad w_y = 4y, \quad w_z = 2z + 2\sqrt{3}x,$$
$$w_{xx} = 2, \quad w_{yy} = 4, \quad w_{zz} = 2,$$
$$w_{xy} = 0, \quad w_{xz} = 2\sqrt{3}, \quad w_{yz} = 0.$$
So the Hessian matrix is
$$\begin{bmatrix} 2 & 0 & 2\sqrt{3} \\ 0 & 4 & 0 \\ 2\sqrt{3} & 0 & 2 \end{bmatrix}.$$

The characteristic equation is $(4-\lambda)(\lambda^2 - 4\lambda - 8) = 0$, giving the eigenvalues 4, $2 - 2\sqrt{3}$ and $2 + 2\sqrt{3}$. Two of these are positive and one is negative; thus the stationary point is a saddle point.

3.9 Partially differentiating, $f_x = 2Sx + 2Ty - 2v$ and $f_y = 2Tx + 2Uy - 2w$. Thus, at any stationary point, $2Sx + 2Ty = 2v$ and $2Tx + 2Uy = 2w$, i.e. $Sx + Ty = v$ and $Tx + Uy = w$, or, as a matrix equation,
$$\begin{bmatrix} S & T \\ T & U \end{bmatrix} \begin{bmatrix} x \\ y \end{bmatrix} = \begin{bmatrix} v \\ w \end{bmatrix}. \tag{S.3}$$

Since $\begin{bmatrix} S & T \\ T & U \end{bmatrix} = \mathbf{X}^T\mathbf{X}$, $\begin{bmatrix} x \\ y \end{bmatrix} = \mathbf{a}$ and $\begin{bmatrix} v \\ w \end{bmatrix} = \mathbf{X}^T\mathbf{y}$,
(S.3) is identical to Equation (3.7). Provided that $\mathbf{X}^T\mathbf{X}$ is invertible, (S.3) has a unique solution, so there is only one stationary point.

3.10 (a) Partially differentiating,
$$f_x = -x(1 - x^2 + y^2)^{-1/2},$$
$$f_y = y(1 - x^2 + y^2)^{-1/2},$$
so the only stationary point is at $(0,0)$. We also have
$$f_{xx} = -(1 - x^2 + y^2)^{-1/2} - x^2(1 - x^2 + y^2)^{-3/2},$$
so $A = f_{xx}(0,0) = -1$. Since
$$f_{xy} = xy(1 - x^2 + y^2)^{-3/2},$$
we have $B = f_{xy}(0,0) = 0$. Also,
$$f_{yy} = (1 - x^2 + y^2)^{-1/2} - y^2(1 - x^2 + y^2)^{-3/2},$$
so $C = f_{yy}(0,0) = 1$.
So $AC - B^2 = -1 < 0$, and there is a saddle point at the origin.

(b) $T_x = -\sin x$ and $T_y = -\sin y$, so the stationary points occur when $\sin x = 0$ and $\sin y = 0$, i.e. at the points $(n\pi, m\pi)$ where n and m are integers. We also see that $T_{xx} = -\cos x$, $T_{xy} = 0$ and $T_{yy} = -\cos y$, so at the stationary point $(n\pi, m\pi)$ we have $A = -\cos n\pi$, $B = 0$ and $C = -\cos m\pi$. There are three cases to consider.

If m and n are both even, then $AC - B^2 = 1 > 0$ and $A = -1 < 0$, so there is a local maximum at $(n\pi, m\pi)$.

If m and n are both odd, then $AC - B^2 = 1 > 0$ and $A = 1 > 0$, so there is a local minimum at $(n\pi, m\pi)$.

Otherwise, $AC - B^2 = -1 < 0$ and there is a saddle point at $(n\pi, m\pi)$.

3.11 Partially differentiating,
$$f_x = -x(1 - x^2 - y^2)^{-1/2},$$
$$f_y = -y(1 - x^2 - y^2)^{-1/2},$$
so the only stationary point is at the origin. We have
$$f_{xx} = -(1 - x^2 - y^2)^{-1/2} - x^2(1 - x^2 - y^2)^{-3/2},$$
$$f_{xy} = -xy(1 - x^2 - y^2)^{-3/2},$$
$$f_{yy} = -(1 - x^2 - y^2)^{-1/2} - y^2(1 - x^2 - y^2)^{-3/2},$$
so $A = f_{xx}(0,0) = -1$, $B = f_{xy}(0,0) = 0$ and $C = f_{yy}(0,0) = -1$.

Since $AC - B^2 = 1 > 0$ and $A = -1 < 0$, there is a local maximum at $(0,0)$.

Index

non-invertible   22, 24, 27, 70
non-singular   22
order of   18
power of   21
product   20
singular   22
size of   18
square   18, 21, 22, 27
sum   19
symmetric   21, 69
transpose   21
triangular   22, 68
upper triangular   11, 22, 31
zero   18
Mixed Derivative Theorem   162
modified inverse iteration   86, 87
multiplication
matrix   20
scalar   19
multiplier   12

negative of a matrix   19
non-invertible matrix   22, 24, 27, 70
non-trivial linear combination   17
norm of a vector   39
nth-order Taylor polynomial   159

order of a matrix   18
overdetermined system of equations   37

paraboloid   145
parallelepiped (volume of)   28, 32
parallelogram (area of)   26, 28
parametrized curve   155
partial derivative   151
particular integral   121, 122, 125, 127
particular solution   108
pivot   12
plane, equation of   144
point of inflection   147
polynomial interpolation   34, 36
power of a matrix   21
principle of superposition   108, 121
product of matrices   20

quadratic approximation   164

real eigenvalue   67
repeated eigenvalue   67
repeated real eigenvalue   115
right-hand-side vector   10
row operation   11
row vector   18

saddle point   168
scalar multiplication of a matrix   19
scalar triple product   32
scaling a vector   83
Second Derivative Test   147
second partial derivative   161
second-order homogeneous linear system   128, 130
second-order partial derivative   161
second-order Taylor approximation   164
second-order Taylor polynomial   164
section function   145, 147
simple harmonic motion   131
simultaneous linear equations   7
size of a matrix   18
slope of a function of two variables   157
slope of a surface   157
square matrix   18, 21, 22, 27
stationary point   147, 166
classification of   147, 171, 172
surface   144
symmetric matrix   21, 69
system of linear equations   6

tangent approximation   163, 164
tangent line   148
tangent plane   149, 164
Taylor polynomial
first-order   164
nth-order   159
of degree n 159
second-order   164
Taylor's Theorem   160, 169
trace of a matrix   65
transformation of the plane   25
transition matrix   56
transpose of a matrix   21
triangle (area of)   33
triangular matrix   22, 68

upper triangular form   8
upper triangular matrix   11, 22, 31

vector   6
column   6, 18
norm of   39
row   18
volume of a parallelepiped   28, 32

well-conditioned   39, 42

zero matrix   18